D0422606

METADYNE STATICS

TECHNOLOGY PRESS BOOKS

THE MATHEMATICS OF CIRCUIT ANALYSIS
Extensions to the Mathematical Training of Electrical Engineers
By E. A. Guillemin

MAGNETIC CIRCUITS AND TRANSFORMERS
A First Course for Power and Communication Engineers
By Members of the Electrical Engineering Staff, M.I.T.

APPLIED ELECTRONICS
A First Course in Electronics, Electron Tubes, and Associated Circuits
By Members of the Electrical Engineering Staff, M.I.T.

ELECTRIC CIRCUITS
A First Course in Circuit Analysis for Electrical Engineers
By Members of the Electrical Engineering Staff, M.I.T.

METADYNE STATICS
By Joseph Maximus Pestarini

THE PREFABRICATION OF HOUSES
By Burnham Kelly

METHODS OF OPERATIONS RESEARCH
By Philip M. Morse and George E. Kimball

PRESSURES ON WAGE DECISIONS
A Case Study in the Shoe Industry
By George P. Shultz

THE DOLLAR SHORTAGE
By Charles P. Kindleberger

TRANSMISSION OF NERVE IMPULSES AT NEUROEFFECTOR JUNCTIONS AND PERIPHERAL
SYNAPSES
By Arturo Rosenblueth

MID-CENTURY
The Social Implications of Scientific Progress
By John Burchard

AN INDEX OF NOMOGRAMS
Compiled and edited by Douglas P. Adams

EXTRAPOLATION, INTERPOLATION, AND SMOOTHING OF STATIONARY TIME SERIES
with Engineering Applications
By Norbert Wiener

CYBERNETICS
Or Control and Communication in the Animal and the Machine
By Norbert Wiener

Q.E.D., M.I.T. IN WORLD WAR II
By John Burchard

INDEX FOSSILS OF NORTH AMERICA
By H. W. Shimer and R. R. Shrock

THE MOVEMENT OF FACTORY WORKERS
By C. A. Myers and W. R. Maclaurin

WAVELENGTH TABLES
Measured and compiled under the direction of G. L. Harrison

P. Boucherot
64 Bould Auguste Blanqui, Paris (13º)
15 Juillet 1937

Monsieur:

L'Alsthom m'a envoyé ces jours-ci son bulletin, où j'ai vu les belles réalisations que vous avez faites de la métadyne, ce dont je vous félicite avec pleine sincérité.

Je connaissais vos travaux théoriques sur ce sujet puisque, en particulier, je fus du Jury Montefiore à qui vous les soumites. Mais je déplorais, il y a peu de temps encore, devant mes élèves, que cela ne sorte pas du laboratoire. C'est fait maintenant, et je m'en réjouis: Voici enfin que l'on s'engage dans cette voie, que je préconise depuis plus de trente ans, de l'emploi de transformations de distributions à V constante en distributions à I constante, pour les appareils de manutention à courant continu. C'est vraiment du nouveau. Et cela, je le dis encore très sincèrement, par un procédé supérieur à ceux que j'ai imaginés dans ce but, il y a longtemps, si vous avez réussi à vaincre les difficultés de la commutation.

Bien à vous
signé: Boucherot

M. Pestarini à Turin

P. BOUCHEROT
64 Bould Auguste Blanqui
PARIS (13ᵉ)

15 Juillet 1937

Monsieur,

L'extrême n'a aucun à fourni son bulletin. On l'a vu de telles réalisations que vous avez faits, de la metadyne, et dont je vous félicite avec pleine sincérité.

Je connaissais vos travaux théoriques une seul point, en particulier, je fus du jury mondiale à qui vous les soumetz. Mais je déferai, il y a fort longtemps encore beaucoup des choses, que cela n'a sorti pas de laboratoire. C'et fait maintenant, et je m'en réjoui.

Voici enfin que l'on s'engage dans cette voie, j'ai je prévoirai depuis plus de 30 ans, de l'emploi de transformateurs à distribution. Vous aurez en distribution à distribution. I contribute font les graviés et maintenance. Couvent continu.

C'est vraiment le nouveau. Et est-il, je le vous en ais très sincèrement! je m'en prouve supérieur à eux que j'ai imaginé dans ce but, il y a longtemps, si vous avez retouri à maintient de différente Silu commentation.

Prière à vous

Boucherot

Me Pestarini – Turin.

METADYNE STATICS,

Joseph Maximus Pestarini

LECTURER, MASSACHUSETTS INSTITUTE OF
TECHNOLOGY AND COLUMBIA UNIVERSITY

LIBRARY
MISSISSIPPI STATE COLLEGE

122934

PUBLISHED JOINTLY BY

The Technology Press of

Massachusetts Institute of Technology

AND

John Wiley & Sons, Inc., New York

Chapman & Hall, Ltd., London

621.3132
P439m

Copyright, 1952
BY
The Massachusetts Institute of Technology

All Rights Reserved

*This book or any part thereof must not
be reproduced in any form without
the written permission of the publisher.*

Library of Congress Catalog Card Number: 52–7400

PRINTED IN THE UNITED STATES OF AMERICA

PAULO BOUCHEROT

Dedicatum

7/31/53 Jenkins S. 53

FOREWORD

The reader who is familiar with Dr. Pestarini's papers in the *Revue Générale de l'Électricité* of 1930 will welcome this pioneering volume in which he treats in detail basic concepts concerning the metadyne. The reader who comes to this book without that earlier acquaintance will find it novel, both in point of view and in subject matter. To the field of direct-current machines, which was already well established at the turn of the century and which remained largely conservative for decades thereafter, Dr. Pestarini brought invigorating new scholarliness, generality, and invention that have led to the casting of such machines in quite new and powerful roles. Much of the history and cause of that development is implicit in the discussion of principles contained in this volume. In the preface, the author recounts major steps in the evolution of the metadyne yet does not permit himself to appraise its place in the scheme of engineering.

Certain of these generalized direct-current machines, or metadynes, may, without too great liberty, be called electromechanical vacuum tubes. This concept carries major implications, for it is worthy of note that many versions of the generalized metadyne have already an established function throughout the whole range of sophisticated, high-performance, automatic control systems.

Metadyne machines are usually used in systems of machines, rather than individually, as is conventional machinery. These systems of machines can be designed to absorb power under a prescribed relationship between torque and speed, as well as response time. They are applied to electric locomotives, rolling mills, cranes, etc. They are designed from a *synthesis standpoint* with the necessary characteristics built into the component machines. This procedure is in contrast to the conventional method of employing machines that have inherent characteristics and that have to be closely regulated by feedback techniques to secure the desired behavior. Dr. Pestarini's approach to the analysis and design problem of these machines is so general, permitting arbitrary distribution of windings and brushes around the machine, that an almost unlimited range of characteristics relating speed, voltages, torque, and currents can be achieved.

Many of these metadyne machine systems employ "constant current" or utilize generators or rotating transformers having nearly constant, but drooping, current characteristics. A wide variety of machines is available as components for these systems, and their characteristics can be modified by feeding into their multiple fields signals from other parts of the machine system. When these machines are thus employed, other beneficial and useful characteristics arise, such as ease of regenerative braking, limited short-circuit currents in direct-current systems (constant current), and reduced machine size for prescribed horsepower outputs compared to conventional direct-current machinery.

The present volume has grown out of presentation of the subject to graduate students at the Massachusetts Institute of Technology, Columbia University, and the University of Rome. Its treatment of the static aspects of metadynes, lucid and thoroughgoing, provides a sound foundation for an anticipated subsequent discussion of the dynamics which are all-important to control systems. In the rigor of its reasoning, the classic clarity of its style, and the direct utility of its analysis, *Metadyne Statics* embodies the skills of a writer who is both practicing design engineer and academic scholar and teacher, obviously at home both in the shop and on the university lecture podium. It may confidently be expected to prove a stimulating influence in broadening the applications of electric rotating machinery.

Harold L. Hazen

PREFACE

In analyzing the operation of commutation in electric machines provided with a commutator, I studied some years ago a group of inventions that resulted in several new machines. Making a methodical investigation of these devices, I recognized that they formed a new group of electric machines, which I classified and named "metadynes."

Paul Girault, known for his contribution to the theory of commutation, saw the manuscript record of this investigation and urged that it be sent to the Montefiore International Contest, which is held every three years in Liége, Belgium. The manuscript was awarded the Montefiore prize in 1928. A. E. Blondel, P. M. J. Boucherot, and P. A. M. Janet immediately encouraged tests, which were sponsored by A. Detoeuf, P. Charpentier, and A. Pihier of the French Thomson Houston. These proved the correctness of the theoretical predictions contained in the manuscript and opened a new field of electrical applications.

In April of 1931, the *Bulletin de l'Institut Montefiore*, Liége, summarized the manuscript. It was published in full by the *Revue Générale de l'Électricité*, Paris, France, March 8 and 15, August 16 and 23, November 22 and 29, and December 6, 1930. At the end of the final installment, the first tests were also mentioned.

Since that time, a great many metadynes have been constructed, particularly in France, England, Italy, and the United States, and important metadyne plants are now in operation. Almost all these plants were originally designed by the author, collaborating with selected designers of each country. A large number of patents were granted. The exceptional experience thus obtained prompted revision and expansion of the initial manuscript for the Savoyan Academy (Torino, Accademia della Scienze, 1939), but this work was left unfinished.

A graduate course on metadynes was instituted first at the Institute Galileo Ferraris of the University of Torino in 1938 and at the Massachusetts Institute of Technology in 1948, where Professor Harold L. Hazen, head of the Department of Electrical Engineering, encouraged the drafting of this book.

The Montefiore manuscript established several facts about the new class of machines that it described. These machines have many common properties distinguishing them from other classes of rotating electric machines; they can comprise the direct-current dynamos as a degenerate case; and, although the number of members of the metadyne family is rather large, many characteristics of operation are common to all of them, so that general theorems may be found applying to all metadynes. Some of the steady-state characteristics of metadynes are similar to the characteristics of direct-current dynamo machines; others are similar to the characteristics of alternating-current apparatus. When metadynes are acted upon by rapid transient currents, their operation may be compared to the operation of electronic tubes.

Fundamental discussion of metadynes thus naturally occupies two main areas. The steady-state characteristics, which may be referred to as "metadyne statics," are presented in the present volume. The transient characteristics of the machines when they are subjected to rapidly varying currents may be referred to as "metadyne dynamics."

A third area, furthermore, is opened by the following contrast between metadynes and other electric machinery: In most electric machines the steady-state operation may be substantially characterized as a constant-voltage or a constant-current operation, and these machines, therefore, are generally coupled electrically in a very simple arrangement, say in parallel or in series with one another. In many metadynes, however, the steady-state operation is characterized by a more elaborate function between voltages and currents. Since the parameters of this function between voltages and currents are often very easily controlled, the metadynes have great flexibility of operation, and a large number of arrangements of the machines with each other is possible. It is apparent, in addition, that some metadynes may be particularly suited for control and for particular cyclical performances, but in these cases a close investigation of the stability of operation becomes necessary. Therefore, control arrangements and cyclical operation, as well as combinations of metadynes, are a third center of possible discussion.

To be fruitful, even the best ideas need supporters who are not motivated by desire for personal advantage. I wish to express gratitude to those who have helped and to take the liberty of mentioning some of them: A. E. Blondel and P. M. J. Boucherot, who pointed out the importance of the Montefiore manuscript; G. H. Fletcher, who enthusiastically supported practical applications; Admiral J. Pizzuti, who first introduced metadynes into the Italian Navy; E. Rosenberg, who, at the national meeting of electrical engineers in London in 1936, predicted a promising future; Philip Alger, who sponsored the metadyne in America; and Giovanni Giorgi, who has repeatedly endorsed the author's work. Thanks and acknowledgment are extended to the staff members of the Department of Electrical Engineering at the Massachusetts Institute of Technology and the members of the Electrical Engineering Department at Columbia University for their endorsement; and to the many faithful engineers with whom I shared my enthusiasm in designing the first metadyne.

In the preparation of the present work, I have had valuable assistance from A. L. Pike, Assistant, and Miss Ednah Blanchard, secretary, in the Department of Electrical Engineering at Massachusetts Institute of Technology, for which I express my gratitude.

JOSEPH MAXIMUS PESTARINI

Cambridge, Massachusetts
August, 1952

CONTENTS

PART

I

GENERAL RULES VALID
FOR ALL METADYNES

1 · Introduction

1. CONSIDERATIONS CONCERNING ARMATURE WINDINGS

For the sake of simplicity the armature is supposed rotating in the center of a fixed member; thus the fixed member will usually be called the stator. This designation is useful for the metadyne, owing to the fact that, in general, the armature also acts as the inductor, creating the field necessary for correct operation.

Consider an observer traveling circumferentially around the air gap of a rotating electric machine. In making just one circumference he would observe that the electric and magnetic elements constituting the machine repeat their form, sizes, mutual location, interaction, and connections n times; that is, he might say that the machine has n cycles. Such an observation will be used here as a definition, and the number of cycles will hereafter be represented by the symbol &.

In the conventional dynamo, alternator, and asynchronous motor and in many other well-known electric machines, the number of cycles & is equal to the number of pairs of magnetic poles. The terminology of poles would be confusing with a metadyne, however, and this reason led the author to make use of the notion of cycles as defined above.

Let us first separately consider an armature with no stator. Strictly speaking, all the known armature windings have as many cycles as armature teeth, but their action varies when the number of cycles of the magnetic field in which they rotate varies. For instance, consider the action of various armature windings in a magnetic field with a sinusoidal distribution of magnetic induction showing $\&_m$ cycles.

A Pacinotti's armature winding (ring winding) works with a magnetic field of any number of cycles; at a given speed, with a given maximum magnetic induction along the air gap, and with a given number of peripheral conductors N, it is always possible to obtain the maximum available voltage by using two brushes forming an angle $\pi/\&_m$ between them. The value of this maximum available voltage is

$$\frac{1}{\&_m} \cdot e_0$$

where e_0 is the maximum voltage obtained between two diametrically opposite brushes with a one-cycle field.

3

A drum mesh winding having a pitch y_2 on the commutator side, and a pitch y_1 on the opposite side, satisfying the relation

$$y_1 - y_2 = \pm 2$$

gives its maximum possible voltage, say e_a, when $\&_m = \&_a$, the value of $\&_a$ being equal to the nearest whole number to N/y_1, and the two brushes including an angle $\pi/\&_m$ between them. When $\&_a$ increases above or decreases below $\&_m$, the maximum value of the magnetic induction being kept constant, the maximum obtainable voltage decreases, the angle between the two brushes being $\pi/\&_a$, until it reaches its minimum value of zero, whenever either $\&_a$ or $\&_m$ becomes an integer multiple of the other. Therefore, the number of cycles of the mesh armature winding considered here is $\&_a$ as defined above.

For a single drum wave winding characterized by pitches y_1 and y_2 satisfying the condition

$$\&_a(y_1 + y_2) = N \pm 2$$

the maximum possible voltage is obtained for $\&_m = \&_a$. For $\&_m = (2k + 1)\&_a$, k being an integer, this voltage is

$$e_a \cdot \frac{1}{2k + 1}$$

and for all other values this voltage vanishes identically. Therefore, the value of $\&_a$ determined above may be considered as the number of cycles of the corresponding drum mesh winding and drum single wave winding.

The first armature winding mentioned above, the Pacinotti's winding, may be called "flexible"; the second, the mesh winding, "semiflexible"; and the third, the single drum wave winding, may be termed "rigid." Since the angular location and angular width of the magnetic poles vary in a metadyne, a larger variety of types of metadynes may be expected when flexible armature windings are used.

Similar deductions follow from the consideration of compound armature windings such as series-parallel wave windings and windings composed of a number, say m, mesh turns followed by an equal or a different number, say n, of wave turns, followed again by m mesh turns, and so on. Hereafter, for the sake of conciseness, only mesh windings will be considered, normally, as it is easy to transfer the results to the other types of windings. Detailed investigation of the various kinds of windings will not be undertaken here, for it properly belongs with a careful study of commutation itself.

The determination of the number of cycles $\&_s$ on a stator having polar segments, considered separately without an armature, is obvious. For the complete assembly of rotor and stator, the number of cycles of the whole arrangement depends on the construction of both the stator and the rotor; and this number may be different from the number of cycles of the stator and from the number of cycles characteristic of the armature winding considered separately, the complete number of cycles being the maximum common divisor. Hereafter, reference will be made only to the number of cycles of the assembled machine, comprising stator and rotor; this number will be indicated by $\&$ without index.

2. ISOTROPIC AND ANISOTROPIC MACHINES

For the purpose of the study undertaken here, it is useful to distinguish the magnetically isotropic machines from the anisotropic ones. A machine is magnetically isotropic when it shows the same magnetic permeance for any radial direction; otherwise it is anisotropic.

Iron saturation does not matter, provided that it is the same for any radial direction. A machine that is isotropic when the iron is not saturated becomes anisotropic when saturation occurs if the state of saturation varies with the direction of the radius considered.

An anisotropic magnetic circuit of a machine may be considered to be the superposition of an isotropic one and an anisotropic one having in any radial direction a permeance equal to the difference of the permeances of the actual machine and of the assumed isotropic one. Sometimes this resolution may be helpful.

3. CONSIDERATIONS CONCERNING AN ARMATURE CARRYING A CURRENT SUPPLIED BY TWO BRUSHES

The armature is considered here separately without stator. The winding considered here is a drum winding in its simplest form, and the number of cycles of the assembly, armature, and surrounding field is therefore equal to unity:

$$\& = 1$$

In this case the number of cycles, $\&_a$, given to the winding is always one for a dynamo, and then y_1 is generally very near to $N/2$; but with a metadyne it may sometimes be useful to give to $\&_a$ a value different from $\&$, for instance $2\&$ or $3\&$. The drum winding is said to have approximately a "diametrical pitch" in the former example and a "fractional pitch" in the latter example.

A fractional pitch will be considered here for the sake of generality, and it will be defined by the angle α included between conductors separated from one another by a pitch y_1. For each brush there are two commutation radii or axes, i.e., two radii passing through the peripheral conductors short-circuited by the brush. The commutation axis corresponding to the external layer of the winding is called the external commutating axis, the other the internal. In the figures, the commutation axes are shown by solid lines, and the brush is conventionally shown along the external commutation axis; thus for two brushes there are four commutation axes.

Let the brushes be at any angular position and the machine be isotropic; the example in Fig. 1 shows an armature rotating in air, and this implies an isotropic machine. Let the rotation be in the clockwise direction, and let angles be measured in this same sense; finally, let the winding be right-handed. Hereafter, these assumptions will always be valid unless the contrary is explicitly stated.

Suppose that a current I passes through the armature, entering through a brush a and leaving through a brush b; then the current is divided into two unequal parts and flows through the armature as shown by the dots and crosses in Fig. 1; two active layers of ampere-turns are then created, one layer covering the segment included between the two external commutation axes, and the other layer lying across the angle between the two internal commutation axes. All other segments give inactive layers of ampere-turns because the external conductors carry a current equal in magnitude but opposite in direction to the current flowing in the corresponding internal conductors.

The active layers are symmetrically disposed with respect to the bisector of the angle formed by the external commutating axis of one brush and the internal commutating axis of the other brush. The same bisector is an axis of symmetry of the magnetic field generated by the two active layers of ampere-turns. This magnetic field is fixed with respect to the brushes and it is fixed in space if the brushes are stationary.

Figure 2 shows schematically the magnetic field created by the armature ampere-turns when the winding pitch is diametrical. Here the field has two axes of symmetry, the two bisectors of the commutating axes forming two diameters, each diameter formed from the two commutating axes of a brush.

Assume that the brushes are stationary and the armature is rotating, and consider first a diametrical winding pitch. That no electromotive force will be induced between the brushes is easy to check considering the symmetry of the active layers and the magnetic flux with respect to the same two axes, the two bisectors.

Now assume that the winding pitch is fractional and the two brushes are diametrically opposite; the magnetic field and the two active layers are still symmetrical to both bisectors of the two diameters formed by

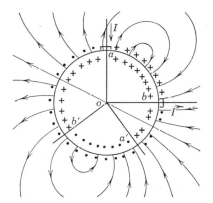

Fig. 1. Isotropic armature with fractional pitch; brush angle is $\pi/2$.

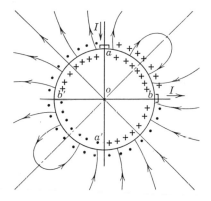

Fig. 2. Isotropic armature with diametrical pitch; brush angle is $\pi/2$.

the four commutating axes, the two commutating axes corresponding to the same layer being located on a diameter; therefore, no electromotive force is induced between the two brushes.

For the most general case of a fractional pitch and any angular position of the brushes, the magnetic field and the active layers show only one axis of symmetry and the net electromotive force along one active layer is not generally zero. The proof is evident from a simple inspection of Fig. 1, showing the distribution of ampere-turns along the periphery of the armature for the general case; Fig. 3 shows the distribution for a particular case of fractional pitch having two brushes not diametrically opposite. But the voltage between the two brushes is the sum of the electromotive forces of both the internal and the external layers; therefore, because of the symmetry of the active layers and of the flux with respect to the single axis mentioned above, the voltage induced between the two brushes is zero.

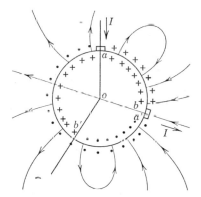

Fig. 3. Isotropic armature with fractional pitch; brush angle = pitch angle.

Examination of the case of an armature surrounded by a homogeneous magnetic ring, the machine remaining isotropic, leads to the same conclusion. Hence the following theorem:

I. THEOREM. *In an isotropic machine having an armature associated with a commutator, with a drum winding of any pitch, having no active stator windings, and having two brushes at any angular position to supply a current to the armature, no electromotive force is induced between the two brushes by the magnetic field created by the armature ampere-turns.*

This theorem holds for any of the windings mentioned in Section 1. In general, though, this theorem is not valid for an anisotropic machine. Nevertheless, it is still true if the anisotropic machine has an axis of symmetry along the bisectors mentioned above, as may be easily shown by following a procedure identical to that above.

Henceforth, for the sake of simplicity, the armature winding pitch will always be assumed to be diametrical unless explicitly indicated otherwise.

4. DEFINITION OF THE METADYNE

Generally, the first theorem does not hold for three or more brushes per cycle on the commutator. Then electromotive forces almost always appear between the brushes, even for an isotropic machine comprising only an armature rotating in free space; the armature winding may be considered to be divided by the brushes into many segments which act inductively upon one another, which results in important new electric properties. Thus, the following definition:

A metadyne is a machine provided with an armature having a commutator upon which bear at least three brushes per cycle of the machine, commutation being independent of the main windings of the stator or any eventual magnetic member acting upon the armature. The windings of commutating poles are hereafter considered auxiliary windings and not main windings; and the commutating poles may often be called auxiliary poles according to convention.

In the event that the condition regarding commutation, as described above, is not satisfied, the machine is called a pseudometadyne. This definition will stand completely justified by the remainder of the first part of this volume.

2 · Canonical Currents

The general case of two brushes per cycle having been examined in the previous chapter, the use of any number of brushes per cycle will be considered here. Then, more currents than a single one may exist, and a number of questions arise regarding their distribution, their action, the magnetic field they create, and the induced electromotive forces. These questions have been solved in a simple way by an elementary analytical device which the author called the device of "canonical currents"; this chapter deals with these virtual currents.

1. DISTRIBUTION OF CURRENTS IN AN ARMATURE

Suppose that the commutator of an armature has any number, say m, of brushes, indicated by small letters having alphabetic sequence for a clockwise tracing direction. Let $I_a, I_b, \cdots, I_m$ be the currents entering the armature through brushes $a, b, \cdots, m$, respectively; let i_{cd} be the current flowing in the armature from brush c to brush d through the clockwise branch of the armature winding. It is then possible to indicate the armature winding by a circle and the brushes by blocks as shown in Fig. 4, the blocks being placed at the same angular position as the external commutating axis.

The following fundamental relations are satisfied:

$$\sum_{h=a}^{m} I_h = 0 \qquad (1)$$

$$
\begin{aligned}
I_a &= i_{ab} - i_{ma}\\
I_b &= i_{bc} - i_{ab}\\
&\cdots\cdots\cdots\\
&\cdots\cdots\cdots\\
I_m &= i_{ma} - i_{lm}
\end{aligned}
\qquad (2)
$$

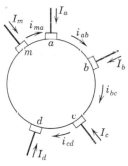

Fig. 4. General armature current distribution.

The armature is assumed to be revolving in a magnetic field, and therefore an electromotive force will be induced in each peripheral conductor. Let E_{bc} be the electromotive force induced in segment bc of the armature winding going from brush b to brush c and following the clockwise branch of the armature.

9

To the previous relations, the following is added:

$$\sum_{g=a}^{m} E_{g(g+1)} = \sum_{g=a}^{m} r_{g(g+1)} i_{g(g+1)} \tag{3}$$

where $r_{g(g+1)}$ is the resistance of the clockwise branch of the armature joining brush g to brush $(g+1)$, and where $m+1 \equiv a$. The first member of the last equation set is zero; hence, Equation 3 may be written as follows:

$$0 = \sum_{g=a}^{m} r_{g(g+1)} i_{g(g+1)} \tag{4}$$

Of the m Equations 2, only $m - 1$ are independent, as is evident upon adding them term by term and taking Equation 1 into account. Retention of $m - 1$ equations from system 2 after elimination of the first equation, for instance, and the use of set 3 lead to a system that uniquely defines the currents i_{bc} when the currents I_h are given. The determinant D of the coefficients is

$$D = \begin{vmatrix} -1 & +1 & 0 & \cdots & 0 & 0 \\ 0 & -1 & +1 & \cdots & 0 & 0 \\ \cdot & \cdot & \cdot & \cdots & \cdot & \cdot \\ \cdot & \cdot & \cdot & \cdots & \cdot & \cdot \\ 0 & 0 & 0 & \cdots & -1 & +1 \\ r_{ab} & r_{bc} & r_{cd} & \cdots & r_{lm} & r_{ma} \end{vmatrix}$$

If the second column is replaced by its sum with the first one, then the third by its sum with the new second column, and so on, the determinant becomes

$$D = \begin{vmatrix} -1 & 0 & 0 & \cdots & 0 & 0 \\ 0 & -1 & 0 & \cdots & 0 & 0 \\ \cdot & \cdot & \cdot & \cdots & \cdot & \cdot \\ \cdot & \cdot & \cdot & \cdots & \cdot & \cdot \\ 0 & 0 & 0 & \cdots & -1 & 0 \\ \alpha & \beta & \gamma & \cdots & \lambda & \mu \end{vmatrix} = (-1)^{m-1} \mu \neq 0$$

where $\alpha = r_{ab}; \beta = r_{ab} + r_{bc}; \gamma = r_{ab} + r_{bc} + r_{cd}; \cdots \mu = r_{ab} + r_{bc} + r_{cd} + \cdots + r_{ma}$.

Conversely, Equations 2 uniquely define the currents, I_b, of the brushes when the currents, i_{cd}, of the armature winding are given. Note that this result is independent of the induced voltage and therefore independent of the speed and the distribution of the magnetic field. Thus the following theorem is obtained:

II. THEOREM. *The system of currents in the armature winding and the system of brush currents are uniquely determined from one another, independently of the induced voltage in the armature.*

The system of brush currents necessarily satisfies Equation 1, but it may be resolved into many, say η, groups, each of which also satisfies the given equation. Let these groups of currents be designated by the superscripts α, β, $\cdots$, η and consider the winding currents, corresponding to each of the groups; for each group of currents, relations similar to Equations 1, 2, 3, and 4 are valid:

$$\sum_{h=a}^{m} I_h^\gamma = 0$$

$$I_g^\gamma = i_{gh}^\gamma - i_{fg}^\gamma \qquad g = a, b, \cdots, m$$

$$0 = \sum_{g,h=a}^{m} E_{gh}^\gamma = \sum_{g,h=a}^{m} r_{gh} i_{gh}^\gamma$$

for $\gamma = \alpha, \beta, \cdots, \eta$.

It follows that Theorem II holds for each group. Further, because of the assumption made, the following relations are fulfilled:

$$I_h - \sum_{\gamma=\alpha}^{\eta} I_h^\gamma$$

and, as the armature winding currents are uniquely determined, there is necessarily

$$i_{gh} = \sum_{\gamma=\alpha}^{\eta} i_{gh}^\gamma$$

whence the following corollary is obtained:

III. COROLLARY. *From a system of brush currents satisfying the fundamental Equation 1 there is derived one and only one system of armature winding currents, independently of other eventual armature winding currents due to other systems of brush currents satisfying the same fundamental equation.*

2. DEFINITION OF CANONICAL CURRENTS

The calculation of the armature winding currents for a metadyne provided with a large number of brushes per cycle is more laborious than for a dynamo. This question and others are simplified by the use of "canonical currents."

A canonical current is a current entering the armature by one brush and leaving it by another. This is not generally the case with the brush currents for more than two brushes per cycle. For a given system of brush currents satisfying Equation 1, the question arises whether it is possible to determine an equivalent system of canonical currents.

Let I_{gh} be a canonical current entering the armature through brush g and leaving it through brush h. For the equivalence of the two systems of currents, the following equations must be satisfied:

$$I_h = \sum_g I_{hg} - \sum_k I_{kh} \qquad h = a, b, \cdots, m \tag{5}$$

Adding Equations 5 term by term and taking into account Equation 1 yields the identity $0 = 0$. Thus in Equations 5 only $m - 1$ equations are linearly independent. Yet there are $m(m - 1)/2$ combinations of the m brushes taken two at a time; further, $m(m - 1) > 2(m - 1)$ for $m > 2$. Thus it is obvious that there is an infinite number of systems of canonical currents equivalent to the given system of brush currents, provided that there are at least three brushes per cycle.

Choose, for example, the following $m - 1$ canonical currents: $I_{ab}, I_{bc}, \cdots, I_{lm}$ and set $I_{ma} = 0$. Then the system of Equations 5 yields the following equivalent system of canonical currents:

$$I_{ab} = I_a$$

$$I_{bc} = I_a + I_b$$
$$\cdots\cdots\cdots\cdots\cdots\cdots\cdots$$
$$I_{gh} = I_a + I_b + \cdots + I_g \tag{6}$$
$$\cdots\cdots\cdots\cdots\cdots\cdots\cdots$$
$$I_{lm} = -I_m$$

If the following $m - 1$ canonical currents are chosen, $I_{am}, I_{bm}, \cdots, I_{lm}$, then system 5 yields

$$I_{am} = I_a$$

$$I_{bm} = I_b \tag{7}$$
$$\cdots\cdots\cdots$$
$$I_{lm} = I_l$$

and, as a consequence, $I_{am} + I_{bm} + \cdots + I_{lm} = -I_m$.

Take the following system of $m - 1$ canonical currents: $I_{h(h+\alpha)}$ for $h = a, b, \cdots, l$ with $I_{(m-\alpha+1)a} = 0$, α being an integer chosen so that

m will not be a multiple of α. The values of the canonical currents are then obtained from system 5 as follows:

$$I_{a(a+\alpha)} = I_a$$

$$I_{(a+\alpha)(a+2\alpha)} = I_a + I_{a+\alpha}$$

$$\dots\dots\dots\dots\dots\dots\dots\dots\dots$$

(8)

From a given equivalent canonical system, as given by Equations 6 and 8, an infinite number of others may be obtained by adding a constant current to each canonical current of the given system, including the canonical current set equal to zero.

3. VOID SYSTEM OF CURRENTS

Some systems of canonical currents having special properties may be convenient for the solution of problems met in practice; among these systems are the "void systems." A system giving no ampere-turns whatever along the periphery of the armature is called "a void system of brush currents."

Consider Fig. 1, where a current, say I_{ab}, enters the armature winding through brush a and leaves it through brush b. Add two other brushes, c and d, located along the internal commutation axes oa' and ob' of brushes a and b, and assume a current I_{cd} entering the armature winding through brush c and leaving it through brush d.

Suppose that $I_{cd} = I_{ab}$; then the two armature winding currents due exclusively to the current I_{cd} have exactly the same values as the two armature winding currents due exclusively to the current I_{ab}, according to Corollary III; therefore, at any point on the periphery of the armature the ampere-turns are zero, and the system of canonical currents I_{ab} and I_{cd} considered here gives a void system.

From a single canonical current the process can be extended to a system of canonical currents, and from this stage to a normal system of brush currents; in this manner the following rule is justified:

IV. RULE. *If to a normal (that is, satisfying Equation 1) system of brush currents, for example, I_a, I_b, $\cdots$, another normal system of brush currents, for example, I'_a, I'_b, $\cdots$, is added, where oa', ob', $\cdots$ are the axes of commutation of the internal layer corresponding to the brushes a, b, $\cdots$, a void system of brush currents is obtained.*

4. CALCULATION OF THE ARMATURE WINDING
CURRENTS BY MEANS OF THE CANONICAL CURRENTS

Consider a single canonical current, say I_{ab}, for instance that in Fig. 1, and apply the results obtained in Section 1; then the corresponding armature winding currents i_{ab} and i_{ba} may be expressed as follows:

$$i_{ab} = I_{ab} \frac{2\pi - \gamma}{2\pi}$$

$$i_{ba} = -I_{ab} \frac{\gamma}{2\pi}$$

(9)

where γ is the angle between commutation axes oa and ob.

Now consider a normal system of brush currents. After it has been resolved into an equivalent system of canonical currents and Corollary III has been applied, formulas 9 may be applied to each canonical current separately; this procedure yields the following rule:

V. RULE. *To obtain the armature winding currents corresponding to a given system of brush currents, resolve the latter into an equivalent system of canonical currents; find the two armature winding currents separately corresponding to each canonical current, and add the currents so obtained for each segment of the armature winding.*

5. CALCULATION OF THE AMPERE-TURNS ALONG THE PERIPHERY OF THE ARMATURE

This constitutes another fundamental problem frequently met in practice. If the armature winding currents are known, the distribution of ampere-turns on the armature may be found immediately. But if an equivalent system of canonical currents is known, the knowledge of the armature winding currents is no longer necessary for the calculation of the ampere-turns.

Consider Fig. 1 again and the canonical current I_{ab}; let i_{ab} and i_{ba} be the actual armature winding currents derived from formulas 9. Further, consider a current i_0 of any value flowing through the whole armature winding and always in the same direction; it will give no ampere-turns at all, the ampere-turns of the external layer being just canceled by the ampere-turns of the internal layer.

Thus the superposition of the current i_0 on the currents i_{ab} and i_{ba} does not modify the distribution of ampere-turns on the armature; this superposition means the addition of i_0 to the currents i_{ab} and i_{ba}. With various values of i_0, any value of the currents $i_{ab} + i_0$ and $i_{ba} + i_0$ may be obtained with the sole condition that their difference is always equal to the canonical current I_{ab}. For instance,

$$i_{ab} + i_0 = -i_{ba} - i_0 = \tfrac{1}{2} I_{ab}$$

will give equal currents in the two branches of the armature winding; or an alternative arrangement is

$$i_{ab} + i_0 = I_{ab}$$

$$i_{ba} + i_0 = 0$$

This means that the whole canonical current traverses one branch only, and this result may be stated in the following way:

VI. THEOREM. *The distribution of the ampere-turns along the periphery of the armature may be obtained from any system of canonical currents equivalent to the given system of brush currents, even if the subdivision of each canonical current in the two branches of the armature winding is made on the basis of Kirchhoff's first law only, independently of the second law.*

After the distribution of the ampere-turns has been determined, it is relatively easy to calculate the magnetic induction at any point of the air gap.

3 · Electromotive Force Induced in an Isotropic Metadyne

This chapter deals with the electromotive forces induced between the brushes of the rotating armature; valuable assistance will be obtained by the use of canonical currents. Two cases are examined: first the case of an isotropic machine with windings only on the armature, and second the general case that does not restrict windings to the armature alone; a striking differentiation of the metadyne from the dynamo results.

1. ELECTROMOTIVE FORCES INDUCED BY THE MAGNETIC FIELD CREATED BY THE ARMATURE AMPERE-TURNS

The magnetic field created by the armature ampere-turns is due to the simultaneous action of all the canonical currents. If the reluctance of the machine is independent of the currents flowing, the resultant magnetic field is simply the superposition of the component magnetic fields created by each canonical current. Practically, this occurs when the iron is not at all saturated. When the iron is saturated, the resultant field is no longer the superposition of the component fields, unless the iron saturation is the same along any radial direction; isotropic saturation often does occur in practice. In this section, the reluctance of the magnetic circuit of the machine will be assumed constant, independent of the currents that create the flux. It is always possible for a skilled designer to choose parameters for his equations so as to take into account the iron saturation corresponding to the actual values of currents and then to apply the superposition principle without appreciable error.

Let the electromotive force induced by the resultant flux between brushes a and b be represented by E_{ab}, its positive sense being in the clockwise direction from brush a to brush b. Let the electromotive force induced between the same brushes by the component flux due to a single canonical current, I_{gh}, be represented by E_{ab}^{gh}. Then, because the reluctance is constant,

$$E_{ab} = \sum_{gh} E_{ab}^{gh} \tag{10}$$

the sum being extended on all pairs of superscripts gh corresponding to the various canonical currents forming a system equivalent to the system of brush currents.

There are as many Equations 10 as there are permutations in m letters taken two at a time, i.e., $m(m - 1)$ equations, but only $m - 1$ among them are independent; the remaining equations are linear combinations of the first ones. In fact, only $m - 1$ differences of potential between the brushes may be selected arbitrarily; all the others are then defined. Further, the $m - 1$ voltages must be conveniently chosen.

For example, the following groups are made up of independent voltages:

$$E_{gm} \qquad g = a, b, \cdots, l \tag{11}$$

$$E_{ab}, E_{bc}, \cdots, E_{lm} \tag{12}$$

$$E_{a(a+\alpha)}, E_{(a+\alpha)(a+2\alpha)}, \cdots, E_{[a+(m-2)\alpha][a+(m-1)\alpha]} \tag{13}$$

where α is an integer such that m is not a multiple of α.

Constant reluctance also makes possible the following relations:

$$\frac{1}{n} E_{ab}^{gh} = K_{ab}^{gh} I_{gh} \tag{14}$$

where n is the rotational speed of the machine expressed in revolutions per second and where K_{ab}^{gh} is a constant.

There are as many Equations 14 as the product of the number of permutations of m letters two at a time by the number of the canonical currents. As the canonical currents are at most $m(m - 1)/2$, the number of possible Equations 14 is $\frac{1}{2}m^2(m - 1)^2$. This is also the number of the constants K_{ab}^{gh}, and they would form a square matrix. For a definite special case, this matrix may be reduced to a smaller number of terms; then it is generally a rectangular matrix.

If Equations 10 and 14 are combined, the following ones are obtained:

$$\frac{1}{n} E_{ab} = \sum_{gh} K_{ab}^{gh} I_{gh} \tag{15}$$

from which only $m - 1$ are independent, forming a group called the "fundamental group of metadyne equations."

The corresponding matrix of the coefficients K_{ab}^{gh} is a square one having $(m - 1)^2$ members, if the number of the canonical currents is the minimum possible, $m - 1$.

2. RELATIONS BETWEEN THE COEFFICIENTS K_{ab}^{gh}

The determination of the matrix of the coefficients K_{ab}^{gh} is basic for calculations on a metadyne; any rule yielding a relation between these coefficients to allow the determination of a number of them from the remainder is valuable. Here the simplest of these relations are investigated. From

$$E_{ab}^{cd} = -E_{ba}^{cd}$$

$$E_{ab}^{cd} = -E_{ab}^{dc}$$

it follows that

$$K_{ag}^{ch} = -K_{ga}^{ch}$$

$$K_{ag}^{ch} = -K_{ag}^{hc} \tag{16}$$

Further derivation from Theorem I yields

$$K_{gh}^{gh} = 0 \tag{17}$$

whatever the letters a, b, c, d, g, h may be.

It is readily understood that, if the two letters of the compound index are two consecutive letters of the alphabet, they are often interpreted as corresponding to two objects immediately following one another. In general, however, they correspond to two objects of indifferent sequence.

Consider three brushes, a, b, c, following one another as Fig. 5 shows, and a canonical current, I_{ac}. Hence

$$E_{ac}^{ac} = E_{ab}^{ac} + E_{bc}^{ac}$$

Application of Theorem I three times gives

$$E_{ac}^{ac} = 0$$

$$E_{ab}^{ac} = E_{ab}^{bc}$$

$$E_{bc}^{ac} = E_{bc}^{ab}$$

and, as a consequence, therefore

$$E_{ab}^{bc} = -E_{bc}^{ab}$$

and, correspondingly,

$$K_{ab}^{bc} = -K_{bc}^{ab} \tag{18}$$

Now consider four brushes, a, b, g, h, as shown in Fig. 6, and two canonical currents, I_{ab} and I_{gh}, of equal intensity. By means of Theorem I, the following relations are derived:

$$E_{gh} = E_{gh}^{ab}$$

$$E_{ab} = E_{ab}^{gh}$$

Now assume another canonical current, I_{bg}, of the same magnitude as the two previous ones; the three currents are equivalent to a single canonical current, I_{ah}, of the same magnitude. Indicate the new electromotive forces by a primed letter; that is,

$$E'_{ah} = 0 = E'_{ab} + E'_{bg} + E'_{gh}$$

whence is derived

$$0 = (K_{ab}^{bg} + K_{ab}^{gh}) + (K_{bg}^{ab} + K_{bg}^{gh}) + (K_{gh}^{ab} + K_{gh}^{bg})$$

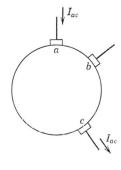 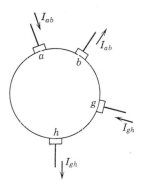

Fig. 5. A three-brush armature with one canonical current.

Fig. 6. A four-brush armature with two ca-nonical currents.

Upon application of relation 18 to the second member of this last expression, there is finally obtained

$$K_{ab}^{gh} = -K_{gh}^{ab} \tag{19}$$

This relation may be stated as follows:

VII. THEOREM. *The electromotive force induced between a pair of brushes by the canonical current flowing between any other pair of brushes is equal, but of opposite sign, to the electromotive force induced between the brushes of the second pair by a canonical current of equal intensity flowing through the brushes of the first pair.*

The coefficient K_{ab}^{gh} has the dimensions of a coefficient of self-inductance or mutual inductance and is numerically equal to the voltage for one revolution per second induced between brushes a and b by the magnetic field created by the unit canonical current flowing through brushes g and h.

The results contained in formulas 16, 17, 18, and 19 may be summarized by the following rule:

VIII. RULE. *The coefficient K_{ab}^{gh} changes sign when a permutation occurs, either of the two letters of either index, the upper or the lower, or of the indices themselves. Consequently, if the indices are equal, the coefficient vanishes.*

If the reluctance is a function of the currents, Rule VIII still holds, provided that the values of the coefficient K take account of the actual reluctance due to the simultaneous action of all the currents.

The square matrix of the coefficients K_{ab}^{gh} is therefore a skew-symmetric matrix, and all the members of its diagonal of symmetry are zero.

3. DISCUSSION OF THE FUNDAMENTAL EQUATIONS OF A METADYNE WITHOUT STATOR WINDINGS

So far the armature has been supposed to be rotating and the brushes to be fixed in space, but the results and the formulas obtained depend only on the relative motion between armature and brushes; the armature may be fixed while the brushes are rotating, or both may rotate with respect to a fixed reference—in opposite directions or even in the same direction with different values of speed. Hereafter, for the sake of simplicity, the armature will always be assumed to be rotating and the brushes to be fixed in space, unless the contrary is explicitly specified.

With reference to Fig. 1, it has been shown in Section 4 of Chapter 1 that, if the armature, bearing two brushes by which a current is passed through the armature windings, rotates in free space, no electromotive force will be induced between the two brushes, and the armature behaves as a passive resistance.

Let current I_{ab} flow through the armature and add a third brush, say c, as Fig. 7 shows. An electromotive force will appear between this brush and either of the other two brushes, a and b, for the general case of any angular position of c with respect to the original brushes. It is easy to ascertain this fact by moving brush c from commutating axis ob in the clockwise direction: the voltage increases at starting and becomes maximum (when brush c reaches the direction oh), then decreases again; when brush c reaches commutating axis oa, the voltage is zero. Further, it increases with reversed sign to a negative maximum (reached at the direction ok) and then decreases to zero when brush c has accomplished a complete revolution. There will be one maximum and one minimum, or more than two extreme values, depending on the relations between the angular winding pitch α and the angular distance θ between the two original brushes. Conversely, if only the current I_{bc} flows through the armature, an electromotive force varying with the position of the movable brush c will appear between the original fixed brushes.

Instead of one new brush, two new movable brushes may be considered; then similar results are obtained. In particular, it should be noted that, with the current I_{ab} alone flowing in the armature, the induced voltage between brushes located at a' and b' is zero. In Section 3 of Chapter 2, such brushes were shown to correspond to a void system of currents. In general, if the number of brushes is greater than 2, $(m > 2)$, the currents flowing through a segment of the armature will induce an electromotive force, generally not zero, between any pair of brushes.

Thus in a metadyne, the various segments of the armature winding defined by the commutating axes of the brushes act inductively on each other when the armature rotates in free space, and this action will be greatly increased if the armature is surrounded by a homogeneous magnetic ring with only a small air gap. Although an inductor or field winding is necessary in a conventional dynamo

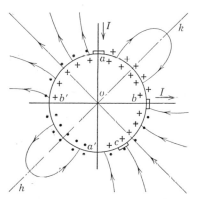

Fig. 7. An unsymmetrical location of the third brush.

for creating an action upon the rotating armature different from that of a passive resistance, in a metadyne no field windings are necessary. This is a first striking difference.

Consider Equation 15; if $m - 1$ brush currents, say the currents I_a, I_b, $\cdots$, I_m, are substituted for the canonical ones with the aid of Equations 5, the following relations will be obtained:

$$\frac{1}{n} E_{bd} = \sum_{g=a}^{m-1} K_{bd}^g I_g \tag{20}$$

There are as many Equations 20 as there are permutations of m letters two at a time. But only $m - 1$ of these may be independent equations, and this set constitutes a fundamental group of metadyne equations. The constants K_{bd}^g having only three indices are evidently linear combinations of the constants K_{bd}^{gk} with four indices; and as the calculation of the latter set has been shown, the process of calculating the former is at once evident.

Form 20 of the fundamental equations is very useful; for a current I_g entering brush g, the equations give the voltage that this current induces between any pair of brushes without requiring the knowledge of the distribution of the given brush current within the armature. A fundamental group of metadyne Equations 20 may generally be put in another form, which shows the brush currents as functions of the induced voltages by solving Equation 20 for the brush currents:

$$I_g = \frac{1}{n} \sum_{bd} E_{bd} \Lambda_g^{bd} \qquad g = a, b, \cdots, m-1 \qquad (21)$$

where the sum is extended to the $m-1$ combinations relative to the chosen $m-1$ independent voltages.

If the determinant of the coefficients of system 20 vanishes, set 21 cannot be obtained. Then the metadyne is called a "nonreactive metadyne." This singular case is examined in a later chapter.

In general, the matrix of the coefficients Λ_g^{bd} may be obtained by multiplying the matrix of coefficients K_{bd}^g by a matrix of coefficients the determinant of which is generally not zero; and conversely. Thus the determinant of both matrices of K_{bd}^g and Λ_g^{bd} are simultaneously zero or different from zero. Equations 21 show that, if an induced voltage between two given brushes is specified, the corresponding components of each of the brush currents are defined.

From a group of $m-1$ independent Equations 15 with $m-1$ independent canonical currents, one may generally derive in an analogous way a group of the following form:

$$I_{gh} = \frac{1}{n} \sum_{bd} \Lambda_{gh}^{bd} E_{bd} \qquad (22)$$

The matrices of K_{gh}^{bd} and Λ_{bd}^{gh} are also obtained from one another by a matrix multiplication and have their determinant simultaneously either zero or not zero.

Consider a group of fundamental equations chosen among Equations 15 so as to have $m-1$ canonical currents having the same pair of indices as the chosen independent voltages. It has been shown that this is always possible; take, for example, the voltages and canonical currents

$$E_{ab}, E_{bc}, E_{cd}, \cdots, E_{kl}$$

$$I_{ab}, I_{bc}, I_{cd}, \cdots, I_{kl}$$

For this fundamental group there are $(m-1)^2$ coefficients K_{ab}^{gh}.

Multiply both members of each equation of this group, having the general form

$$E_{bc} = \sum_{gh} K_{bc}^{gh} I_{gh} \qquad (23)$$

by the corresponding canonical current, I_{bc}, and add term by term. It follows that

$$\sum_{bc} E_{bc}I_{bc} = \sum_{bc}\sum_{gh} K_{bc}^{gh}I_{gh}I_{bc} \tag{24}$$

Among the $(m-1)^2$ coefficients appearing in the second member of the last equation there are $m-1$ of the form K_{gh}^{gh}. These vanish identically, as Equation 17 shows. The remainder $(m-1)^2 - (m-1) = (m-1)(m-2)$ may be subdivided into $(m-1)(m-2)/2$ pairs of the following form:

$$K_{bc}^{gh} \qquad K_{gh}^{bc}$$

Since the sum of each such pair is zero, according to Equation 19, and since each is multiplied by the same product of currents $I_{bc}I_{gh}$, their partial sum is also zero. There are necessarily $(m-1)(m-2)/2$ such pairs. Thus the second member of Equation 24 has been reduced to single vanishing terms and to vanishing partial sums of two terms; therefore, the whole sum is zero. The second terms of Equation 24 form a skew-symmetric matrix of $(m-1)^2$ terms, all the elements of the diagonal of symmetry being zero.

On the other hand, the first member of Equation 24 is evidently equal to the total power, P, generated in the revolving armature. Thus Equation 24 reduces to

$$P = 0$$

which means that the revolving armature supplies no power. But it has been shown that voltages E_{bd} and currents I_{bd} are generally different from zero, and therefore their single products will also be nonzero. It follows then that the products figuring in the first member of Equation 24 are partly positive and partly negative; these just balance one another to give a zero sum. Hence the following theorem:

IX. THEOREM. *An isotropic metadyne without stator or with a stator having no current in its windings operates as a transformer, transforming the input currents into output currents generally different from the former; the algebraic sum of input and output power is zero if the losses are neglected.*

Ohmic drops have not been considered.

This theorem points to another substantial difference between the dynamo and the metadyne: the metadyne is able to transform currents even without a stator, a property unknown for a dynamo. It is because of this main property that the machine derived its name from the Greek μετά-δύναμισ, in which the preposition μετά expresses the transformation. In the following description, attention will be directed to such transformations of electric energy for the purpose of finding useful applications.

4. FUNDAMENTAL EQUATIONS OF THE METADYNE WITH STATOR WINDINGS

In Section 1, the induced electromotive forces between brushes were derived from equations valid for an armature rotating without a stator or with a stator with no currents in its windings, the whole machine being isotropic. In this chapter the action of stator windings will also be considered.

In the usual dynamo, the stator windings have only one well-known position in relation to the brushes of the armature, the magnetic axes

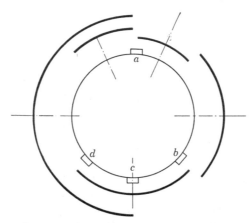

Fig. 8.   Stator windings placed at various angular positions.

of the windings being substantially normal to the commutating axis and therefore substantially normal to the axis joining the two brushes assumed to be located along the external commutating axis. Further, their width is always the same, corresponding to the whole width of the magnetic poles.

In a metadyne, both the radial location of the magnetic axis of the stator winding and its angular width may vary for obtaining various useful results. The discussion about the choice of the orientation of the magnetic axis and the width of the stator windings will be undertaken when their general effect is examined. Figure 8 shows schematically various stator windings with different angular orientation of their magnetic axis and with different widths.

The connections of the stator windings on a dynamo are of three kinds: series connection with the two armature brushes, shunt connection across the two brushes, and finally connections to an independent source of power. In a metadyne these three kinds are no longer unique; in fact, the series connection may be made with various brushes because, generally speaking, the brushes collect different currents; with m brushes there are m different currents among which only $m - 1$ are, usually, independent. Although the shunt connection may be made between any pair of brushes, each pair of brushes generally supplies a different voltage, and so there are $m(m - 1)/2$ different ways to make a shunt connection. Among them, nevertheless, only $m - 1$ are independent, or as many ways as there are independent voltages. Thus the variety of stator winding arrangements is very wide for a metadyne as compared with a dynamo.

Hereafter, the currents flowing through the stator windings will be distinguished by a Greek-letter index. They create a flux that induces an electromotive force between the brushes; this may be expressed in a way similar to that above for the electromotive force induced by armature currents.

Thus the fundamental Equations 15 may be completed as follows:

$$\frac{1}{n} E_{gh} = \sum_{bd} K_{gh}^{bd} I_{bd} + \sum_{\gamma=\alpha}^{\nu} K_{gh}^{\gamma} I_{\gamma} \tag{25}$$

The first sum is extended over all pairs of Roman letters characterizing the canonical currents of the chosen equivalent system, and the second sum is extended to all Greek letters characterizing the stator currents. Finally, there are as many equations as there are permutations of m letters two at a time. Among these equations, only $m - 1$ may be independent and will then form a group of fundamental equations of the metadyne with currents in the stator windings.

With the aid of Equations 5, the canonical currents I_{bd} may be replaced by the brush currents in Equations 25; and the latter equations assume the following form:

$$\frac{1}{n} E_{gh} = \sum_{c=a}^{m-1} K_{gh}^{c} I_c + \sum_{\gamma=\alpha}^{\nu} K_{gh}^{\gamma} I_{\gamma} \tag{26}$$

Among these equations we may choose the $m - 1$ having the following indices for the first member: $am, bm, cm, \cdots, lm$. They are all independent from one another. Let all brush currents appear in the second member except I_m; multiply each member of these equations by $I_a, I_b, \cdots, I_l$, respectively, and add them term by term; the following relation is obtained:

$$\sum_{c=a}^{l} E_{cm} I_c = n \sum_{c=a}^{l} \sum_{g=a}^{l} K_{cm}^{g} I_g I_c + n \sum_{c=a}^{l} \sum_{\gamma=\alpha}^{\nu} K_{cm}^{\gamma} I_{\gamma} I_c \tag{27}$$

The first member is the total output of the machine (with omission of the losses), as is stated in the following theorem:

X. THEOREM. *If an electric network is fed by a direct-current or an alternating-current system, by means of n terminals, the total power supplied to the network equals the algebraic sum of the indications of n − 1 wattmeters; the potential circuits are connected across two terminals, one of which is common for all wattmeters, say the nth terminal, and the other is one among the other n − 1 terminals; the current circuit of each wattmeter carries the current flowing through the terminal corresponding to the special connection point of its potential circuit, i.e., the currents I_a, I_b, $\cdots$, I_{n-1}, respectively.*

A proof of this theorem is given in the *Bulletin de L'Association Internationale des Électriciens*, Paris, March 1914, and a complete set of theorems regarding the behavior of real and complex power in a network is given in *Elettromeccanica.**

Here is a simple demonstration of this theorem. Let i_a, i_b, $\cdots$, i_n be the instantaneous values of the currents feeding the electric network under consideration; let p_a, p_b, $\cdots$, p_n be the instantaneous potentials of the n feeding points. Let p_0 be the potential of an arbitrarily chosen point.

Consider a system of canonical currents equivalent to the system of currents i_a, i_b, $\cdots$, i_n; such a system of canonical currents is possible because $i_a + i_b + \cdots + i_n = 0$. Let i_{gk}, i_{bh} be two canonical currents of the system, and let their number be q.

The instantaneous power that these currents convey to the network is

$$\sum_{(q)} i_{gk}(p_g - p_k)$$

where the sum has q members similar to the one written above. We may resolve this sum into components as follows:

$$\sum_{(q)} i_{gk}(p_g - p_k) = \sum_{(q)} [i_{gk}(p_g - p_0) + i_{kg}(p_k - p_0)]$$

$$= \sum_{g=a}^{n} i_g(p_g - p_0)$$

Substitution of p_n for p_0 yields the expression corresponding to the theorem, since the last member of the sum vanishes.

The theorem is applied to the first term of Equation 26 by choosing as the common terminal for all wattmeters brush m, and as the other

* J. M. Pestarini, *Elettromeccanica*, Volume I, Chapter I, Part 6, Edizioni Italiane, Rome, 1946.

terminal one of the other brushes. Thus Equation 27 may be written as follows:

$$P = n \sum_{c=a}^{l} \sum_{g=a}^{l} K_{cm}^g I_g I_c + n \sum_{c=a}^{l} \sum_{\gamma=\alpha}^{\nu} K_{cm}^\gamma I_\gamma I_c \qquad (28)$$

Upon substitution of the canonical currents I_{ab}, I_{bc}, $\cdots$, I_{lm} for the brush currents appearing in the first double sum of the second member of Equation 28, this double sum is reduced to the second member of Equation 24, since the power supplied by the metadyne has only one value. Thus the first sum of the second member of Equation 28 is zero, and the remainder is

$$P = n \sum_{c=a}^{l} \sum_{\gamma=\alpha}^{\nu} K_{cm}^\gamma I_\gamma I_c \qquad (29)$$

The second member of Equation 29 is generally not zero, and this means that a torque now appears on the shaft, given by

$$T = \frac{-1}{2\pi} \sum_{c=a}^{l} \sum_{\gamma=\alpha}^{\nu} K_{cm}^\gamma I_\gamma I_c \qquad (30)$$

T being generally different from zero. Formula 30 shows that the electromagnetic torque of the metadyne may be considered a resultant of a number of component torques each of which is due to the action of an armature current upon a stator current.

If $T > 0$ the metadyne operates as a generator because the algebraic sum of the power supplied by it is positive. Then either of two different cases may occur: either the sum of the absolute values of each term appearing in the first member of Equation 27 equals the absolute value of the whole sum

$$\sum_c \left| E_{cm} I_c \right| = \left| \sum_c E_{om} I_c \right| \qquad (31)$$

(then the metadyne operates exclusively as a generator and it is said to be a generator metadyne—and sometimes briefly a metagenerator); or the first member of the last equation is greater than its second member

$$\sum_c \left| E_{cm} I_c \right| > \left| \sum_c E_{cm} I_c \right| \qquad (32)$$

(then the metadyne operates as a generator and as a transformer simultaneously).

If $T < 0$ the metadyne operates as a motor. And if Equation 31 holds, the machine is a motor metadyne (and sometimes briefly a metamotor). In the event that the inequality 32 is satisfied, the metadyne operates as a motor and as a transformer simultaneously. Equation 31 and the inequality 32 may be considered when the electric sources supplying the metadyne with power provide the voltages E_{am}, E_{bm}, $\cdots$, $E_{(m-1)m}$ and create the currents I_a, I_b, $\cdots$, I_{m-1}, respectively; otherwise, if the sources supply the power P_a, P_b, $\cdots$, P_q, respectively, then the identity of the sign of all the values P_a, P_b, $\cdots$, P_q may be taken as the criterion, or, alternatively, the existence of some values of power having a positive sign and of others having a negative sign may be used.

Finally, if $T = 0$ the machine has no torque and the metadyne transforms electric energy exclusively into electric energy of different form. Then it is called a transformer metadyne (and sometimes metatransformer).

The enumeration of the various cases renders obvious a striking new difference between a metadyne and a dynamo. A dynamo may be considered a special degenerate type of metadyne, degenerate because it has lost two of the main characteristics of the metadyne: to operate without any stator, and to transform electric power into electric power of another kind.

4 · Main Characteristics of an Isotropic Metadyne: The Case of Absolutely Constant Speed

In this chapter an investigation of the simplest metadynes is made along the main lines of their operating characteristics; this procedure allows the use of graphical diagrams. A comparison with conventional dynamos is given.

1. CLASSIFICATION OF THE STATOR WINDINGS

A stator winding of the metadyne may carry a brush current, and then it is called a "series winding"; or it may be supplied by the voltage existing between two brushes, and then it is called a "shunt winding"; or it may be fed by a source outside the metadyne, and then it is called an "independent winding" or "variator winding."

From the point of view of their dynamic action during rapid transient phenomena, the series stator windings behave very differently from one another; and they are named according to their dynamic action. This action may vary with variation in the particular metadyne circuit under consideration. In fact, when a brush current enters the armature winding, it divides so that a portion enters the clockwise branch and the remainder enters the counterclockwise branch. Following one of these portions, say the clockwise, we find that it meets various brushes, and it may stop at any of them, then, from such a brush onward, it follows an external circuit; and, before this circuit closes, the current may pass through the armature again.

Thus many different closed circuits may be traced to include the stator winding under consideration here. Choose a circuit carrying a brush current; the stator winding is then called:

Stabilizing winding, with respect to the closed circuit being considered, if the flux created by the brush current flowing through the contemplated stator winding induces an electromotive force in the given circuit in a direction opposite to the brush current.

Stimulating winding, with respect to the given closed circuit, if the flux created by the brush current flowing through the contemplated stator winding induces an electromotive force in the given circuit in the same direction as the brush current.

29

Compensating winding, with respect to the closed circuit considered here, if the brush current flowing through the armature along this closed circuit and passing through the contemplated stator winding creates a flux, due to the ampere-turns of the stator winding, and further, if this flux, which will be referred to as the stator flux, has a component in a direction opposite to that flux, which will be referred to as the rotor flux, created by the ampere-turns established by the same current passing through the armature in the circuit defined above.

Hypocompensating winding, with respect to the closed circuit under consideration, if the component of stator flux defined above is directed in opposition to and is smaller than the rotor flux defined above.

Hypercompensating winding, with respect to the closed circuit under consideration, if the component of stator flux is directed in opposition to and is larger than the rotor flux.

Amplifying winding, with respect to the closed circuit under consideration, if the component of stator flux has the same direction as the rotor flux.

The stator windings may have their conductors either concentrated in a small number of stator slots or uniformly distributed along the air gap like the rotor windings. If the ampere-turns of a compensating stator winding are equal to the ampere-turns of the corresponding armature winding of the closed circuit considered here, and if both groups of ampere-turns are distributed along the air gap in the same manner, then the compensating winding is called a "normal total compensating winding."

These definitions are necessarily laborious in their exact expression, but frequently, in practice, the differentiation is immediately apparent. Sometimes a further classification of the compensating windings is advantageous. The usefulness of the following scheme will become apparent after more advanced study of the metadyne.

Apart from the particular closed circuit considered above, the position of a pair of additional brushes is defined and the voltage between them is specified. Let E_r be the voltage induced between these brushes by the rotor flux defined above, and let E_s be the voltage induced by the stator flux defined for the closed circuit. If $E_r + E_s = 0$, the compensating winding is called a "voltage total compensating winding" with respect to the specified pair of brushes. If E_s has a smaller absolute value than E_r and the signs are opposite, the compensating winding is called a "voltage hypocompensating winding" with respect to the designated pair of brushes. If E_s has a larger absolute value than E_r and the signs are opposite, the compensating winding is called a "voltage hypercompensating winding."

In a metadyne the ampere-turns act and react in a way very similar to that in alternating-current machines, and the classification made in this section allows for a simple and exact description of a given arrangement.

2. GENERAL INFORMATION ON CHARACTERISTICS

Any characteristic relationship may be expressed analytically, but it is made readily intelligible if it is illustrated by a diagram. The simplest diagram is the one that deals with only two variables and may be drawn on paper.

Equations 25 or Equations 26 substantially summarize the characteristics of the metadynes as they have been considered so far.

Some of the stator currents are the brush currents; some other stator winding currents, say I_θ, are shunt-connected across two brushes, say brushes b and h, and therefore they are a linear function of the voltage E_{bh}:

$$I_\theta = \frac{E_{bh}}{R_\theta} = \frac{E_{dh} - E_{db}}{R_\theta} \qquad d = a, b, c, \cdots, m \qquad (33)$$

where R_θ is the resistance of the winding under consideration. The following relation recalls the identity of some stator currents with some brush currents:

$$I_\lambda = I_o \qquad (34)$$

The remaining stator windings are assumed to be fed by sources other than the armature of the metadyne. Let their currents be the following ones:

$$I_\alpha, I_\beta, I_\gamma, \cdots, I_\eta \qquad (35)$$

Thus the first η indices of the ν stator currents are reserved for the stator currents supplied by sources outside of the metadyne. These currents will hereafter be referred to as "independent currents."

Choose $l = m - 1$ fundamental Equations 26 to form a group of independent equations; for instance, choose

$$am, bm, cm, \cdots, lm$$

as indices for the voltages and choose

$$I_a, I_b, I_c, \cdots, I_l$$

as brush currents. Substitute the brush currents for the currents with a Greek index in Equations 26 in the case of the series stator windings; replace the currents in the shunt stator windings by their expression 33 as a function of the voltages, and collect terms algebraically for the equations of the group. The general equation of the group will then be

$$-\frac{1}{n}E_{hm} + \sum_{k=a}^{l} A_{hm}^{k}E_{km} + \sum_{k=a}^{l} B_{hm}^{k}I_{k} + \sum_{\gamma=\alpha}^{\eta} K_{hm}^{\gamma}I_{\gamma} = 0 \qquad (36)$$

where A_{hm}^{k} and B_{hm}^{k} are constants easily derived from the values of K_{hm}^{b}, K_{hm}^{c}, and R_{θ}.

Group 36 establishes $m - 1$ relations between the $2m - 1$ variables, which are:

$$E_{am}, E_{bm}, \cdots, E_{lm}$$

$$I_a, I_b, \cdots, I_l$$

$$n$$

Thus the equations of group 36 determine one of these variables as a function of $2m - 1 - (m - 1) = m$ others, the stator currents I_α, I_β, $\cdots$, I_η being considered as parameters. These equations are all of the second degree, and generally their solution is not readily evolved; the higher the number m of brushes, the more difficult the problem.

For an exhaustive graphical representation of the metadyne characteristics, it is necessary to consider a space of $2m - 1$ dimensions, as many as there are variables. In this space, Equations 36 determine a geometrical variety, say $W_{(2m-1)}^{(m)}$, of $2m - 1 - (m - 1) = m$ dimensions, representing the characteristic of the metadyne under examination. A variety referred to a space of q dimensions, having p dimensions, and determined by r independent equations between the q coordinates is indicated by the symbol $W_{(q)}^{(p)}$, where $q = p + r$. The variety $W_{(2m-1)}^{(m)}$ is called the "global characteristic."

In order to visualize this variety, one may cut it with other varieties, arbitrarily chosen, so that the section is a curve which is a variety having only one dimension. To do this, the arbitrary variety must have x dimensions, where x is determined by the following condition:

$$2m - 1 - (m - 1 + x) = 1$$

giving $x = m - 1$. Thus the arbitrary variety must have $x = m - 1$ dimensions. This means that $x = m - 1$ other arbitrary conditions independent of one another must be imposed.

If a plane curve is to be traced on a flat sheet of paper, it is sufficient (but not necessary) that the conditions imposed be represented by linear equations. Each of these equations defines a variety which may be called a hyperplane and may be indicated by $W_{(q)}^{(q-2)}$. The simplest of these are $m - 1$ equations giving as constant $m - 1$ different variables.

Each of these equations defines a hyperplane, normal to the coordinate axis relative to the variable made constant.

Consider a dynamo with $m = 2$; the variables are $2m - 1 = 3$, the voltage E between the two brushes, the current I, and the speed n. The currents of the independent field windings are parameters. The group of fundamental Equations 36 is reduced to a single equation. For the general characteristic, a three-dimensional space is necessary $(2m - 1 = 3)$. Since the characteristic is represented by a variety of $m = 2$ dimensions, this variety $W_{(3)}^{(2)}$ is then a surface. In order to obtain curves as sections

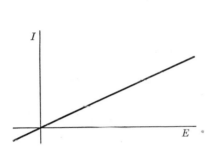

Fig. 9.   Characteristic of a series dynamo at constant speed.

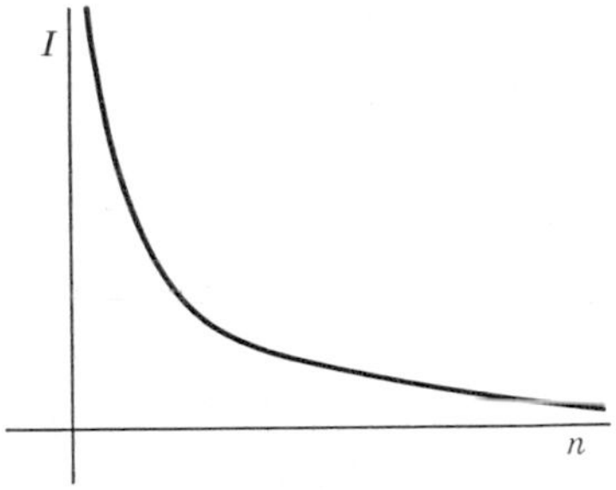

Fig. 10.   Characteristic of a series dynamo at constant voltage.

of this surface $W_{(3)}^{(2)}$, the space must be cut by an arbitrary variety of $m = 2$ dimensions; this means that $x = m - 1 - 1$ arbitrary condition must be imposed. In order to obtain a plane curve it is sufficient to let this condition be linear, and the simplest condition is to make one variable constant at an arbitrarily chosen value, that is, to cut the surface $W_{(3)}^{(2)}$ by a plane normal to the axis of the variable made constant. In this way the well-known dynamo characteristics are obtained.

Take, for example, a series-excited dynamo. The fundamental equation is

$$\frac{1}{n} E = KI \qquad (37)$$

If n is made constant, the characteristic obtained is a straight line, $E = nKI$, crossing the origin of the coordinate axes, as shown in Fig. 9. A similar characteristic is obtained by making I constant.

If E is made constant, the well-known equilateral hyperbola is obtained (see Fig. 10), the power * of which is proportional to the value given to E. The surface $W_{(3)}^{(2)}$ is then a ruled surface, three sections of which are indicated by the straight lines ab and bc and by the hyperbola

* If $xy = k$ is the equation of the hyperbola, k is the power of the hyperbola.

dbe and *fgh* of Fig. 11. When the plane normal to the axis of E approaches the origin, the hyperbola degenerates into two straight lines, the axis of I and the axis of n.

It is important to note that a given point of surface $W_{(3)}^{(2)}$, representing the global characteristic of the series dynamo, actually corresponds to a real operating condition of the machine, provided that the external circuit of the machine is represented by the proper parameters. If R is the total resistance of the circuit of the series dynamo, then

$$E = IR \tag{38}$$

where the value of the parameter R must be the proper one for each point of the global characteristic $W_{(3)}^{(2)}$.

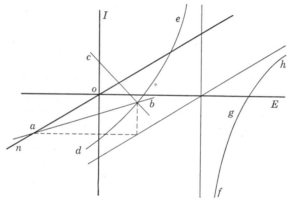

Fig. 11.   Traces of the ruled surface representing the global characteristic of a series dynamo.

Consider the opposite procedure; assume that the parameter R remains constant at the arbitrarily chosen value, and then determine the values of the other variables, E, I, n. If Equations 38 and 37 are combined,

$$E\left(\frac{1}{n} - \frac{K}{R}\right) = 0 \tag{39}$$

which can be solved for $E \neq 0$ only if

$$R = Kn \tag{40}$$

The section of surface $W_{(3)}^{(2)}$, representing the global characteristic of the series dynamo, with the plane

$$n = \frac{R}{K} \tag{41}$$

is a straight line as has been seen, a straight-line generatrix of the global characteristic, the ruled surface $W_{(3)}^{(2)}$. Therefore, the values of E and I corresponding to this operating point are infinite. At this point, operation is almost certainly unstable; the values of the resistance R and the speed n defined by Equation 40 are called the critical resistance and critical speed, respectively.

Now consider a shunt dynamo; the fundamental equation is

$$\frac{1}{n} E = AE$$

which may be written

$$E \left(\frac{1}{n} - A \right) = 0$$

This equation shows that only two possibilities exist: either $E = 0$, and then the machine does not operate at all; or $nA = 1$, which is the "building-up" condition that defines the "critical speed" of the dynamo, and then E may have any value. The current I does not appear in the fundamental equation, and therefore it may have any value. In this case the global characteristic is represented by a plane normal to the axis of the speed n.

As for the series dynamo, the only type of operation possible for the shunt dynamo is obtained under conditions of instability. (The stability of operation of these machines in actual applications results from a secondary phenomenon due to iron saturation not considered here.)

If the parameter A is modified continuously, the global characteristic will be represented by the volume generated by the plane $n = 1/A$ moving along the axis of speed.

For independent excitation, $(1/n)E = K^{\alpha}I_{\alpha}$, where I_{α} is a parameter; with n constant, a straight line parallel to the I axis is obtained, and the current I may have any value while on the plane of n. The corresponding global characteristic, the surface $W_{(3)}^{(2)}$, is a cylindrical one parallel to the axis of I. See Fig. 12.

Consider a compound-wound characteristic; the fundamental equation is

$$\frac{1}{n} E = AE + BI$$

For constant n the characteristic is a straight line through the origin of the coordinates as represented by Fig. 9; for E constant, a hyperbola is obtained with one of its asymptotes on the I axis, and the other parallel to the n axis, as Fig. 13 shows; with I constant, a similar characteristic is obtained. If the building-up condition is fulfilled, ($nA = 1$), then E may have any value while I is zero.

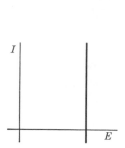

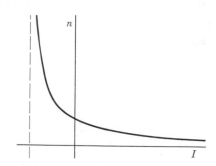

Fig. 12. Characteris-
tic for a separately ex-
cited dynamo.

Fig. 13. Characteristic for a compound
dynamo.

Finally, consider all types of excitation operating simultaneously; the fundamental equation is

$$\frac{1}{n} E = AE + BI + I_\alpha K^\alpha$$

With n constant, the characteristic is again a straight line but not passing through the origin of the coordinates, as Fig. 14 shows. This straight

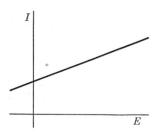

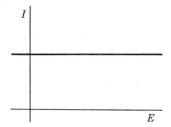

Fig. 14. Constant-speed
characteristic of a triply excited dynamo.

Fig. 15. Critical-speed characteristic of a triply excited dynamo.

line may be given any position and inclination; if it is to be horizontal ($I =$ constant, see Fig. 15), the critical condition must be satisfied: $(1/n) - A = 0$; this yields the well-known Craemer constant-current dynamo. With E or I constant, hyperbolas are obtained similar to those previously found.

3. A METADYNE ROTATING AT ABSOLUTELY CONSTANT SPEED

Great simplification is obtained by considering the rotational speed n to be a constant. This simplification can be justified if a metadyne operates as a generator driven by an engine at constant speed; or if the metadyne operates as a motor driving special machines, for instance, an alternator connected to a large network having constant frequency; or, finally, the simplification may be justified if the metadyne operates as a transformer, because this application generally requires the transformation of the largest possible energy with a given size of machine, the machine rotating constantly at its maximum safe speed.

The equations then become linear, and their solution is obvious. Nevertheless, to obtain a given variable as a function of only one other so that the characteristics may be represented on paper, $m - 1$ other linear arbitrary conditions may be imposed. The simplest linear conditions are those that fix $m - 1$ variables as constant.

First consider the simple case of a metadyne armature rotating in free space or in an isotropic stator without windings. Then the last sum appearing in Equations 26 vanishes, and the group of Equations 36 is simplified as follows:

$$\frac{1}{n} E_{hm} = \sum_{k=a}^{l} K_{hm}^{k} I_{k} \qquad h = a, b, \cdots, l \tag{42}$$

If all variables x_h,

$$x_h \quad \text{where } h \neq b, h \neq g \tag{43}$$

except two, say the variables x_b and x_g, whatever these may be (currents I_k or voltages E_{bd}), are eliminated between the $m - 1$ equations and the $m - 1$ homogeneous arbitrary linear conditions, the following linear relation results:

$$A x_b + B x_g + C = 0 \tag{44}$$

If, then, $A \neq 0$, $B \neq 0$, the characteristic is an inclined straight line that does or does not pass through the origin if C is equal to or different from zero, respectively. If $A = 0$ and $B \neq 0$ and $C \neq 0$, then x_g has a constant value:

$$x_g = -\frac{C}{B} \tag{45}$$

whatever x_b may be. Finally, if $A = 0$, $B = 0$, and $C \neq 0$, there is instability. The constants A, B, and C are easily calculated from the constants K_{hm}^{k} of the metadyne armature and the constant values of the arbitrary conditions.

The conditions to be fulfilled for obtaining the interesting case in which x_g has the constant value given in Equation 45, independently of x_b, may thus be generally met by modifying either the constants K_{hm}^k or the arbitrarily defined constant values given in Equation 43. Particularly useful is the case in which the coefficient A is made zero with the aid of the coefficients K_{hm}^k, that is, by a suitable choice of the angular position of the brushes on the commutator independently of the arbitrary values given in Equation 43, because then the variable x_g (a brush current or a voltage between brushes) remains constant at a

Fig. 16. A family of characteristics obtained through variation of the parametric currents.

value independent of the variable x_b (another brush current or another voltage between brushes); and this value may arbitrarily be modified by varying the arbitrary constants of Equation 43 without moving the brushes from their position.

Now take the case of a metadyne with stator windings carrying current; the group of fundamental Equations 36 must be considered. When the process of elimination is applied in the same way as shown above for a metadyne without stator windings, Equation 44 is obtained again even when all the values of the variables of Equation 43 are taken equal to zero.

The resulting linear characteristic will now be a straight line generally occupying any desired position in the plane of the coordinates, not only when the brushes remain fixed in their position, but even if the values of the currents or voltages of Equation 43 are made zero. This result, which is important in practice, is obtained by varying the independent stator-winding currents I_α, I_β, $\cdots$, I_η. Thus the linear characteristic can be made to sweep the whole plan of the diagram while remaining parallel to itself by means of an appropriate variation of the parametric currents I_α, I_β, $\cdots$, I_η. See Fig. 16.

It has been shown in Section 2 that, for a dynamo with any type of excitation whatever, there are fundamentally three plane character-istics. But if the speed n is kept constant, only one characteristic is left.

For a metadyne with m brushes, under the same conditions, there are as many characteristics as there are combinations of the $m - 1$ inde-pendent voltages and the $m - 1$ independent currents taken two at a time: $(m - 1)(2m - 3)$. For $m = 4$ brushes, there are fifteen different characteristics.

The results of this section may be summarized as follows:

XI. THEOREM. *Among the 2(m − 1) variables—independent brush currents and voltages between two brushes, call them x_a, x_b, $\cdots$, $x_{2(m-1)}$— any one, say the variable x_g, is a linear function of all others, of the form*

$$x_g = \sum_{k \neq g} A_{gk} x_k + B_g \tag{46}$$

where the coefficients A_{gk} are defined by the geometrical characteristics of the machine: size of the machine, brush orientation, resistance of the stator windings, and the speed of rotation n; while the coefficients B_g are defined not only by the geometrical characteristics of the machine but also by the independent stator-winding currents I_α, I_β, I_γ, $\cdots$, I_η, supplied by ex-ternal sources.

By suitable choice of the independent stator windings carrying the independent currents I_α, I_β, $\cdots$, I_η, supplied by external sources, and a suitable simultaneous variation of these currents, it is generally possible to vary the variables x_a, x_b, $\cdots$, $x_{2(m-1)}$ within wide limits.

4. AN ELEMENTARY EXAMPLE OF APPLICATION

As a rudimentary example, consider a metadyne consisting of an armature having a winding with diametrical pitch surrounded by a magnetic ring leaving an air gap of constant length, the ring having no windings. The resulting torque is zero, and a small auxiliary motor is then sufficient to keep the armature rotating at a constant speed n.

The commutator carries four equidistant brushes, a, b, c, d, per cycle, as Fig. 17 shows. Brushes a and c are connected to an external source supplying direct current at constant voltage; brushes b and d are con-nected to the armatures of two motors $M1$ and $M2$ connected in series and independently excited. Neglect the ohmic drop.

Because of the external connections there are only two independent currents, say I_a and I_b. Further,

$$I_a + I_c = 0$$
$$I_b + I_d = 0$$

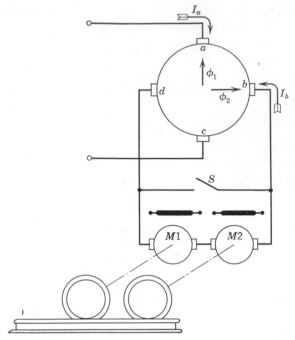

Fig. 17.　Elementary scheme of a locomotive controlled with a transformer metadyne.

Current I_a creates the flux ϕ_1, and current I_b creates the flux ϕ_2. Because of symmetry,

$$\frac{1}{n} E_{ca} = K I_b$$

$$\frac{1}{n} E_{bd} = K I_a$$

(47)

As a result of the symmetrical location of the brushes, there are two independent brush voltages. Consider E_{ca}, E_{bd}, and E_{ba}; it is easy to see that

$$E_{ba} = \tfrac{1}{2} E_{ca} + \tfrac{1}{2} E_{bd}$$

Therefore the number of variables may be limited to only five:

$$E_{ca},\ E_{bd},\ I_a,\ I_b,\ \text{and}\ n$$

(48)

Consider the voltage of the external source as an independent parameter, and assume that the speed at which the armature is driven by the auxiliary motor is constant. Then

$$E_{ca} = C$$

$$n = n_0$$

(49)

There are three variables, E_{bd}, I_a, and I_b, satisfying the two equations:

$$\frac{1}{n_0} C = KI_b$$

$$\frac{1}{n_0} E_{bd} = KI_a \tag{50}$$

The global characteristic referred to a space of three dimensions, E_{bd}, I_b, and I_a, is a variety $W_{(3)}^{(1)}$ having only one dimension. It is a straight line as indicated by the plain thin line of Fig. 18; the dotted lines are the partial characteristics. The dotted lines may be drawn on the same plane, as Fig. 19 shows.

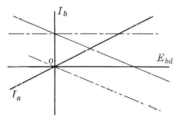

Fig. 18. Global characteristic for the elementary railway metadyne.

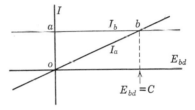

Fig. 19. Partial characteristics for the elementary railway metadyne.

Multiply the first of Equations 47 by I_a and the second by I_b, and subtract the second from the first. This operation will yield the total input to the metadyne divided by n:

$$\frac{1}{n} [E_{ca}I_a - E_{bd}I_b] = KI_bI_a - KI_aI_b = 0$$

according to Theorem IX.

From Equations 47 we obtain

$$I_b = \frac{E_{ca}}{nK}$$

$$I_a = \frac{E_{bd}}{E_{ca}} \tag{51}$$

Thus the metadyne operates as a transformer, converting direct current at constant voltage into direct current of constant magnitude.

Suppose that the switch S of Fig. 17 is closed; brushes b and d are short-circuited, but current I_b will remain at the same value. This current I_b may be compared to the magnetizing current of an alternating-current static transformer, the secondary winding of which is open, the primary being connected to a source of alternating current of constant voltage and constant frequency. Variation of the supply voltage produces a similar effect in both cases, and variation of the speed n of the metadyne is equivalent to variation of the frequency ω of the alternating current.

If switch S is opened, the secondary current I_b will flow into the armatures of the motors, always remaining at the same constant value. Suppose that the motors drive a locomotive. As long as no current is supplied to the field of the motors, the locomotive will remain at standstill; when the motors are excited, the locomotive will start and will accelerate at a constant rate because the torque of the motors will remain constant.

At starting, the line current I_a will be zero as Fig. 19 shows (copper and iron losses are neglected here). It will increase proportionally to the voltage E_{bd} and hence proportionally to the speed of the motors.

When the speed reaches a value for which $E_{bd} = C$, line current I_a will be equal to the constant current, I_b, supplied to the motors. This corresponds to point b of Fig. 19, the intersection of the two straight lines.

When the desired maximum speed is reached, the engineer reduces the excitation of the motors to such a low value as to cause the motors to develop a torque just sufficient to overcome the traction resistance.

When the train must decelerate by braking, the engineer simply reverses the direction of the excitation of the motors; deceleration will occur at a constant rate to complete standstill if desired. The line current will be reversed and the kinetic energy of the train will be transformed at constant voltage into electric energy returned to the line. The line current and therefore the regenerated power will be proportional to the speed of the train.

When at standstill, the engineer may either switch off the excitation of the motors, or close switch S, or shut off the metadyne from the line. This last operation can be done without rupturing an appreciable current because I_a will then be practically zero.

The value of current I_b may be modified either by modifying the value of the voltage of the supply or by modifying the speed n as the first Equation 51 indicates. Although the engineer in the locomotive cannot modify the line voltage, he can modify the speed of the small auxiliary motor driving the metadyne within wide limits.

Now let the speed n be variable, and consider the three variables E_{bd}, I_b, and n; the first Equation 47 shows that the characteristic as referred to these three axes will be a cylinder parallel to the axis of E_{bd} with an equilateral hyperbola for the normal section, as Fig. 20 shows.

Alternatively, consider the variables E_{bd}, I_a, and n; from the second Equation 47 it is easy to see that the characteristic as referred to these axes is a conoid generated by the straight line cab parallel to the plane

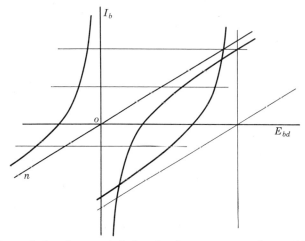

Fig. 20. A particular characteristic for the elementary metadyne, with speed as a variable.

$E_{bd}oI_a$, intersecting the axis on and the equilateral hyperbolas $gbhjl$ and $mcpq$ of equal power and opposite sign where $or = os$. The straight-line generatrix becomes parallel to the axis oE_{bd} for $n = \infty$ and coincides with the axis oI_a for $n = 0$. See Fig. 21.

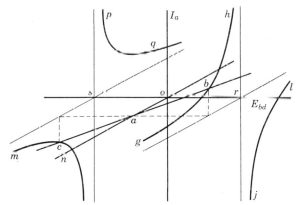

Fig. 21. Another characteristic for the elementary metadyne, with emphasis on the primary current.

Now consider all four variables E_{bd}, I_b, I_a, n; the global characteristic referred to a four-dimensional space will be a variety $W_{(4)}^{(2)}$ of two dimensions, which, when cut by a hyperplane that makes one of the four variables constant, will give one of the plane characteristics determined above.

Finally, suppose that the voltage E_{ca} also varies, and consider the five variables E_{ca}, E_{bd}, I_a, I_b, n; the global characteristic referred to a five-dimensional space will be a variety $W_{(5)}^{(3)}$ of three dimensions, which will give one of the plane characteristics determined above if it is cut by two hyperplanes that establish two of the five variables as constant.

5 · Principal Characteristics of an Isotropic Metadyne: The Case of Approximately Constant Speed Due to a Regulating Device

---

In the case to be examined, the metadyne assists in maintaining the speed approximately constant; some means used by the author to achieve this result are described; the shape of the characteristics obtained is discussed.

1. GENERAL DISCUSSION

If the shaft mechanically coupled to the metadyne has an angular speed (expressed by n revolutions per second) which is a function of the torque T,

$$n = \phi(T) \tag{52}$$

then the torque developed by the metadyne may be used to control the speed by some arbitrary relationship. In this chapter the only case examined is where n is held substantially constant. By "substantially constant" is meant that n may oscillate between two limits n_1 and n_2,

$$n_1 \leq n \leq n_2 \tag{53}$$

so close to one another that its variation may be neglected when considering the fundamental equations.

If the angular speed is to be kept constant, the resultant torque on the shaft must be zero, this resultant torque may be resolved into three components: the main electromagnetic torque T which is given by formula 30; torque T_l, corresponding to the losses in the metadyne; and torque T_a, developed by another machine coupled to the shaft of the metadyne.

In the case examined here, it is assumed that

$$T - T_l + T_a = 0 \tag{54}$$

In order to achieve this, one may use the action of one or more of the stator currents, $I_\alpha, I_\beta, \cdots, I_\eta$, sensitive to such small speed variations that the speed can be maintained between the limits n_1 and n_2 mentioned above. These currents are called "speed regulator currents" or, more concisely, "regulator currents," and the stator windings through which they pass are called "regulator windings."

The most natural device for creating a regulator current is a contact sensitive to centrifugal force opening its circuit at a speed n_a and closing it at a speed n_b, where

$$n_1 < n_a < n_b < n_2 \tag{55}$$

thus inserting or short-circuiting, at short intervals of time, a resistance in series with the regulator winding and therefore creating the regulator current, which may be designated by I_ρ.

To the group of fundamental equations, the following equation must then be added:

$$T - T_l + T_a = \frac{1}{2\pi} \sum_{c=a}^{m-1} \sum_{\gamma=\alpha}^{\nu} K_{cm}^{\gamma} I_\gamma I_c - T_l + T_a = 0 \tag{56}$$

where the positive sign corresponds to an accelerating torque. Equation 56 will hereafter be referred to as the "regulator equation" for constant speed. In Equation 56, the regulator current I_ρ is assumed to be one of the ν stator currents.

2. SIMPLE REGULATOR DYNAMO

Consider a series dynamo feeding the regulator winding as shown in Fig. 22. Suppose that the iron is not saturated; the current i created by the series dynamo satisfies the equation

$$nKi - L\frac{di}{dt} - Ri = 0 \tag{57}$$

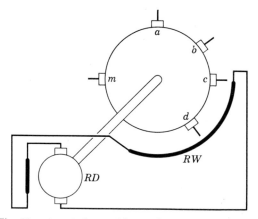

Fig. 22.   A metadyne with a series regulator dynamo.

where K is a constant, L the coefficient of self-inductance of the whole circuit, and R its resistance. The solution of Equation 57 is

$$i = i_0 \epsilon^{-\frac{R-nK}{L}t} \tag{58}$$

where i_0 is a small current due to the residual magnetism of the machine.

As long as $R > nK$, the current is zero or becomes zero rapidly; if, on the contrary, $R < nK$, the current increases quickly. Thus the value

$$n_0 = \frac{R}{K} \tag{59}$$

where K corresponds to the nonsaturated part of the magnetic characteristic, is a particular value called "critical speed."

For $n > n_0$ the current does not increase indefinitely but quickly reaches a definite constant value easily determined by the graphical construction shown by Fig. 23. The ratio E/n is plotted versus the

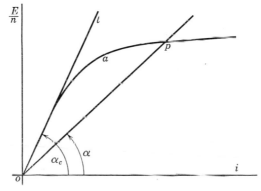

Fig. 23. Characteristic for the series regulator dynamo, showing the critical building-up angle.

current i; the slope of the tangent at the origin gives the value K considered in Equation 57. The steady current is then equal in value to the abscissa of the intersection p of the magnetic characteristic and the straight line op, the slope of which is equal to R/n.

Plotting the current i thus determined against n gives the curve n_0a, which possesses a high value of the derivative along its first segment. See Fig. 24. The machine will act as a good regulating device if the points having n_1 and n_2 as abscissas are chosen along the segment n_0a with a sufficient variation of the current i to cover all the range of the required torque created by the regulator current.

Now consider a shunt-excited dynamo connected to the regulator winding as shown in Fig. 25. Let I_0 and i be the armature and the field-winding currents, respectively; let L_1, L_0, L_2 be the coefficient of self-induction of the field winding, the armature winding, and the regulator

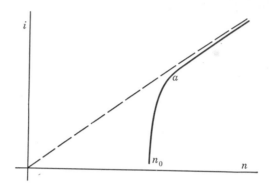

Fig. 24.   Regulator current as a function of speed.

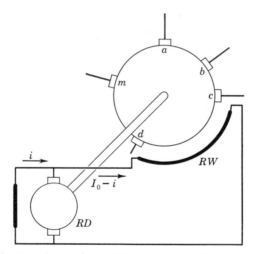

Fig. 25.   A metadyne with a shunt regulator dynamo.

winding; and R_1, R_0, R_2, their respective resistances. During the transient period, the equations are as follows:

$$nKi - L_1\frac{di}{dt} - R_1 i - L_0\frac{dI_0}{dt} - R_0 I_0 = 0$$

$$nKi - L_0\frac{dI_0}{dt} - R_0 I_0 - L_2\frac{d(I_0 - i)}{dt} - R_2(I_0 - i) = 0$$

(60)

Currents I_0 and i are the sum of two exponentials the exponents of which, say α_1 and α_2, are the roots of the following equation:

$$\begin{vmatrix} L_1\alpha + R_1 - nK & L_0\alpha + R_0 \\ L_2\alpha + R_2 + nK & -(L_0 + L_2)\alpha - R_0 - R_2 \end{vmatrix} = 0 \quad (61)$$

from which

$$\alpha = -\frac{1}{2} \frac{L_0(R_1 + R_2) + L_1(R_1 + R_0) + L_2(R_0 + R_1) - L_2 nK}{L_0L_1 + L_1L_2 + L_2L_0}$$

$$\pm \sqrt{(F)^2 + \frac{nKR_2 - R_0R_1 - R_1R_2 - R_2R_0}{L_0L_1 + L_1L_2 + L_2L_0}} \quad (62)$$

where the F in the parentheses under the radical is the fraction outside of the radical.

As $R_0 \ll R_2 \ll R_1$ and as nK has a value very near to R_1, no oscillations occur.

When the real parts of α_1 and α_2 are both negative, the currents are zero or become zero very quickly; if at least one of the roots α_1 and α_2 is positive, building-up takes place. Thus the critical speed n_0 is given, to a good approximation, by

$$n_0K = R_0 + R_1\left(1 + \frac{R_0}{R_2}\right) \quad (63)$$

For values of $n > n_0$ the currents increase quickly and reach a finite value because of saturation of the iron. To find this value, the characteristic of Fig. 23 is used again, the slope of the straight line op now being

$$\tan \alpha = \frac{R_0 + R_1\left(1 + \frac{R_0}{R_2}\right)}{n} \quad (64)$$

The current thus obtained is the field current i; the value of current I_0 is then defined from any equation derived from the Equations 60 through setting the derivatives equal to zero. Then, if $I_0 + i$ are plotted against speed n, a curve very similar to the one of Fig. 24 is obtained. Thus a shunt-excited dynamo may be used for a regulating device under the same limitations as a series-excited dynamo.

So far a unidirectional regulator current has been obtained, oscillating from a low value, practically zero, corresponding to n_1, to a maximum value corresponding to speed n_2. With the following alternative arrangement, this current may have both directions and oscillate from a minimum negative value, corresponding to n_1, through zero, to a maximum positive value, corresponding to n_2, the maximum and the minimum generally having nearly the same absolute value.

Consider the scheme of Fig. 26, where the shunt-excited dynamo is connected to a source of direct current with V volts at its terminals $T1$ and $T2$. The transient interval satisfies the same Equations 60 with the value V substituted for the zero of the second member of the second

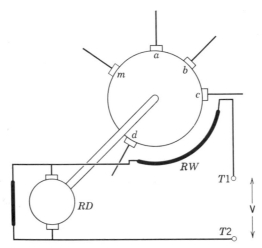

Fig. 26.   Connection to give both positive and negative values of regulator current.

equation.   Thus while the same variable part of the transient current will be obtained the steady-state current, I_ρ, will have approximately the following value:

$$I_\rho = \frac{V - E}{R_0 + R_2} = \frac{V - nKi}{R_0 + R_2} \tag{65}$$

and, as E is very nearly equal to V, small variations of n involve large variations of I_ρ with change of sign.

This variation is increased when the mean speed, n_m, is made equal to the critical one, n_0:

$$n_m = \frac{n_1 + n_2}{2} = n_0$$

The value of the derivative dI_ρ/dn may be increased by adding a series field winding approximately compensating for the ohmic drop, $(R_0 + R_2)I_\rho$, as Fig. 27 shows.   It is important to notice that the impressed voltage V is not required to remain constant, and it may vary without an appreciable modification of the derivative dI_ρ/dn, provided that its value remains on the straight part of the magnetic characteristic drawn for the speed $n_m = (n_1 + n_2)/2$.

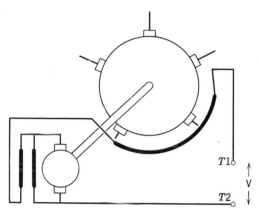

Fig. 27.   Compound regulator dynamo operating in conjunction with a separate voltage source.

3. REGULATOR AND BASE DYNAMO SET

The device considered here does not need any external auxiliary source of direct current.   Figure **28** shows its fundamental scheme.   Two shunt-excited dynamos are coupled to the metadyne shaft, the regulator dynamo, *RD*, having its critical speed n_0 equal to the mean speed of the metadyne, and the so-called "base dynamo," *BD*, having its critical speed s_0 at a definitely lower value: $s_0 < n_0$. The two dynamos are connected to one another, and the current circulating between them flows through the regulator winding, *RW*.

In the neighborhood of the speed n_0, the equations determining the circulating current, i.e., the regulator current, are the following:

$$nKi - L_1 \frac{di}{dt} - R_1 i - L_0 \frac{dI_0}{dt} - R_0 I_0 = 0$$

$$nKi - L_0 \frac{dI_0}{dt} - R_0 I_0 - L_2 \frac{d(I_0 - i)}{dt} - R_2(I_0 - i) = E_b$$

(66)

where the symbols have the same meaning as in Equations 60 and where E_b is the voltage induced by the base dynamo, which can be considered practically constant owing to the intense iron saturation in the base dynamo at that speed.   Thus the critical speed of the regulator dynamo is again a building-up speed that allows the creation of a regulator current varying very quickly with the speed n in the neighborhood of the critical speed, and this regulator current may vary from a negative value to a positive one passing through zero. Thus the same satisfactory result is obtained as that for the shunt regulator dynamo connected to an external source having good regulation. In this case also the derivative dI_ρ/dn may be increased by the addition of a series winding

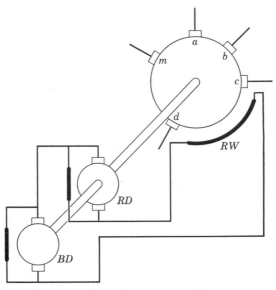

Fig. 28.   The base dynamo replaces the separate voltage source for the regulator dynamo.

on the field of the regulator dynamo for compensating the total ohmic drop. It is important to note that, whereas a conventional dynamo operates in a stable domain, the regulator dynamo operates in an unstable domain.

4. FUNDAMENTAL CHARACTERISTICS

With the use of a speed-regulating device acting through the regulator current, I_ρ, on the metadyne torque, Equation 56 must be added to the $m - 1$ fundamental ones of the group 42. Thus the global characteristic of the metadyne is now defined by m equations, and the number of variables has increased by one: the variable I_ρ. Therefore, the global characteristic will now be represented by a geometrical variety, $W_{(2m)}^{(m)}$, referred to a space having $2m - 1 + 1 = 2m$ dimensions, the variety thus having the same number of dimensions: $m = 2m - (m)$.

In order to obtain plane sections of the variety $W_{(2m)}^{(m)}$ in the simplest way, $m - 1$ variables will be kept constant; among the latter is the speed n according to the assumption previously made. Thus there will be $2m$ variables related by $m - 1 + 1 + (m - 1) = 2m - 1$ equations among which only one, Equation 56, is of the second degree, whereas all others are linear.

If in Equation 56 the stator currents flowing in the shunt-connected stator windings are replaced by their values given by Equations 33, and if all the $2m$ variables are eliminated except two which may generally be designated by x_b and x_g, representing any independent brush voltage, or any of the $m - 1$ independent brush currents, or regulator current I_ρ, an equation of second degree is obtained in the form

$$a_{11}x_b^2 + 2a_{12}x_bx_g + a_{22}x_g^2 + 2a_{13}x_b + 2a_{23}x_g + a_{33} = 0 \qquad (67)$$

where the constants a_{11}, a_{12}, $\cdots$, a_{23} are rational combinations of the constants K_{cg}^b, K_{cg}^γ and the arbitrary parameters I_α, $\cdots$, I_η which are the independent currents due to auxiliary external sources; and where a_{33} is a linear combination of the same constants and of the values T_l and T_a appearing in Equation 56.

Assume first that T_l and T_a are constant; then the nature of the curve representing Equation 67, a plane section of the geometrical variety $W_{(2m)}^{(m)}$, may readily be recognized by means of well-known relations.

Construct the two determinants

$$A = \begin{vmatrix} a_{11} & a_{12} & a_{13} \\ a_{12} & a_{22} & a_{23} \\ a_{13} & a_{23} & a_{33} \end{vmatrix} \qquad A_{33} = \begin{vmatrix} a_{11} & a_{12} \\ a_{12} & a_{22} \end{vmatrix}$$

If $A \neq 0$ and $A_{33} > 0$, Equation 67 is an ellipse

If $A \neq 0$ and $A_{33} = 0$, Equation 67 is a parabola

If $A \neq 0$ and $A_{33} < 0$, Equation 67 is a hyperbola

If $A = 0$, Equation 67 is a couple of straight lines

$$(68)$$

This result deserves notice, since the usual laws relating currents and electromotive forces in the absence of secondary phenomena, like iron saturation, are generally linear.

If one of the coefficients a_{11} or a_{22} is zero, no ellipse is possible; if, moreover, $a_{12} \neq 0$ and $A \neq 0$, the characteristic is a hyperbola; and, further, if $a_{22} = 0$, the hyperbola has its two asymptotes parallel to the coordinate axes as Fig. 29 shows. These hyperbolas are frequently met in practice. The branch of the curve lying in three quadrants is then particularly interesting for many practical applications because it may be resolved into two parts, one part giving substantially constant current for an unlimited range of electromotive force, and the other part giving substantially constant voltage for an unlimited range of current.

The "power" of the hyperbola is then given by the ratio a_{33}/a_{12}, which is a function of the parameters, of the independent currents $I_\alpha, \cdots, I_\eta$, and of the value of the torque T_a, which may also be considered as a parameter. Thus the power of the hyperbola may be modified by regulating one or more of these parameters. A family of characteristics, as indicated in Fig. 29, is then obtained by the very simple control of a comparatively small current supplied independently to some stator winding.

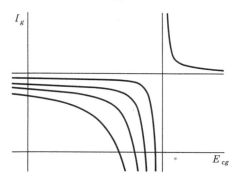

Fig. 29. Hyperbolic current-voltage characteristics extending over three quadrants.

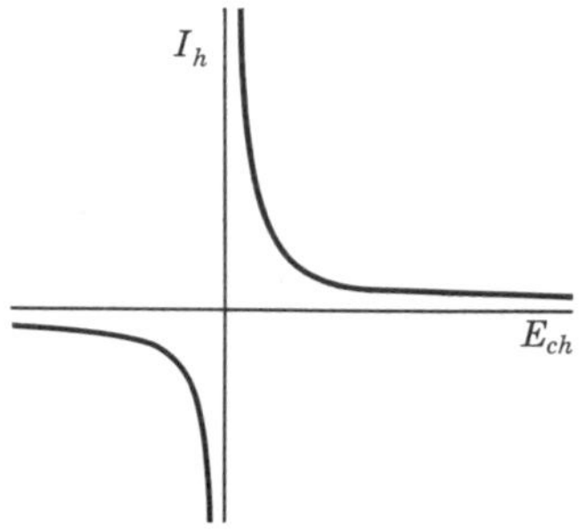

Fig. 30. An equilateral hyperbola resulting from constant-torque operation.

If, simultaneously, $a_{11} = a_{12} = a_{13} = 0$, the characteristics are linear. If the variable x_g is to be made independent of the variable x_b, the coefficients a_{11}, a_{12}, and a_{13} must be made zero, and then the variable x_g may have two different values, or only one. For stability, the last case is always obtained when $a_{22} = 0$, and $a_{23} \neq 0$, $a_{33} \neq 0$ simultaneously. Then variation of a stator-current parameter will give a family of straight lines as shown by Fig. 16.

It is important to note that the second-degree characteristics are obtainable either with a transformer metadyne, with $T_a = 0$, or with a generator or motor metadyne where $T_a \neq 0$. So far, T_a has been assumed to be constant; similar results are obtained even when T_a is an integral polynomial of the variables considered here, brush currents, brush voltages, and regulator current, provided that the degree of this polynomial is not greater than two.

In some cases the fundamental characteristics, i.e., the characteristics referred to the fundamental variables—brush currents, brush voltages, speed, regulator current, if any—may easily be derived independently of the group of fundamental Equations 42 and 56. Suppose, for instance, that the connections of the metadyne are such as to prevent any electric power from entering it except through a pair of brushes,

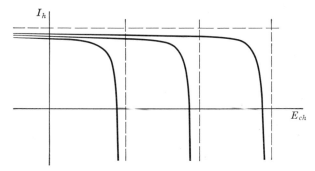

Fig. 31. Some characteristics obtained when the torque is a linear function of current and voltage.

brush c and brush h, carrying the canonical current $I_c = -I_h$; further, that the metadyne is coupled to a machine having an accelerating torque $-T_a$, and that the metadyne is provided with a speed-regulating device keeping the speed n substantially constant. Then

$$\frac{1}{2\pi n} E_{ch}I_h - T_l + T_a = 0 \qquad (69)$$

This equation gives the characteristic at once if T_l and T_a are known. Suppose, for instance, that T_a is constant and that T_l is negligible with respect to T_a; then the characteristic will be an equilateral hyperbola, as Fig. 30 shows.

Suppose, now, that T_a is made a linear function of E_{ch} and of I_h of the form

$$T_a = aE_{ch} + bI_h + c \qquad (70)$$

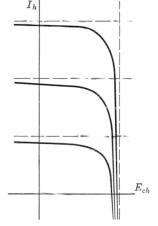

Fig. 32. Another family of characteristics obtained with a linear torque function.

Then the characteristic is a hyperbola, and a family of hyperbolas as shown by Fig. 29, or a family as shown by Fig. 31 or Fig. 32, may be easily obtained.

6 · The Metadyne with Substantially Variable Speed

Here the characteristics of a metadyne are examined briefly, first without a regulating device and second in combination with a regulator; means are described by which the speed may be controlled so that it can be made variable according to an arbitrarily defined relation.

1. BRIEF RECAPITULATION

For the reader's convenience some fundamental formulas already developed will be restated here. The group of the "fundamental equations of the metadyne" may be chosen as follows:

$$\frac{1}{n} E_{mc} = \sum_{g=a}^{m-1} K_{mc}^g I_g + \sum_{\gamma=a}^{\nu} K_{mc}^{\gamma} I_{\gamma} \qquad c = a, b, \cdots, m-1 \quad (26)$$

The electromagnetic torque developed in the metadyne may be expressed by

$$T = \frac{1}{2\pi} \sum_{c=a}^{m-1} \sum_{\gamma=a}^{\nu} K_{mc}^{\gamma} I_{\gamma} I_c \qquad (30)$$

The "regulator equation" is given by formula 56 when the speed n is constant. If instead the speed n is assumed to be substantially variable, the regulator equation becomes

$$T - T_l + T_a - 2\pi J \frac{dn}{dt}$$

$$= \frac{1}{2\pi} \sum_{c=a}^{m-1} \sum_{\gamma=a}^{\nu} K_{mc}^{\gamma} I_c I_{\gamma} - T_l + T_a - 2\pi J \frac{dn}{dt} = 0 \quad (71)$$

where J designates the moment of inertia of the rotating part of the whole set, the metadyne and the machine that is to be mechanically coupled with it.

In all the Equations 26, 30, and 71, no distinction is made between the stator currents, the number of which is assumed to be ν, as many as there are stator windings. From a consideration of the connections of the stator windings, the ν stator currents may be grouped so that the first η currents, I_α, I_β, $\cdots$, I_η, are the "independent stator currents" supplied by sources independent of the metadyne; the second group of stator currents are either brush currents or currents derived from brush voltages by a shunt connection across two metadyne brushes; and, finally, the regulator current, I_ρ, constitutes a third classification.

Upon consideration of the equations

$$I_\gamma = \frac{E_{bh}}{R_\gamma} = \frac{E_{mh} - E_{mb}}{R_\gamma} \tag{33}$$

for the shunt-connected windings, R_γ being their resistance, and of the identity of some stator currents with some brush currents,

$$I_\beta = I_c \tag{34}$$

Equations 26, 30, and 71 may be written as follows:

$$-\frac{1}{n} E_{mc} + \sum_{h=a}^{m-1} A_{mc}^h E_{mh} + \sum_{h=a}^{m-1} B_{mc}^h I_h$$

$$+ \sum_{\gamma=\alpha}^{\eta} K_{mc}^\gamma I_\gamma + K_{mc}^\rho I_\rho = 0 \qquad c = a, b, \cdots, m-1 \tag{36a}$$

$$2\pi T = \sum_{g=a}^{m-1} \sum_{\gamma=\alpha}^{\eta} K_{mg}^\gamma I_\gamma I_g + \sum_{g=a}^{m-1} \sum_{h=a}^{m-1} A_{gh} E_{mg} I_h$$

$$+ \sum_{g=a}^{m-1} \sum_{h=a}^{m-1} B_{gh} I_g I_h + \sum_{h=a}^{m-1} C_h I_\rho I_h \tag{72}$$

$$T - T_l + T_a - 2\pi J \frac{dn}{dt} = 0 \tag{71}$$

Note that generally $A_{gh}^k \neq A_{gh}$ and $B_{gh}^k \neq B_{gh}$.

Add to the preceding relations

$$I_\rho = K_\rho(n - n_0) \tag{73}$$

It should be recalled that n_0 is the critical speed of the regulator dynamo. The symbol K_ρ in the last equation is a constant indicating that the value of the regulator current is the ordinate of a point of the rectilinear part of the characteristic of the regulator current plotted against the speed n as shown in Fig. 24.

If the speed variations, because of mechanical inertia, are assumed to be so slow that the currents and voltages have their static values, then phenomena due to mutual and self-induction may be neglected. In some cases the speed varies from one value held constant for an interval of time to another value held constant for another interval of time. These particular values of n where $dn/dt = 0$ constitute a continuous succession of values which may be referred to as a domain of static values of speed. These values may be defined analytically by Equations 36a, 72, and 56.

If the metadyne is a transformer metadyne, T_a is zero. Further, if it is desired to have the voltage E_{hg} appear in the set 36a of fundamental equations instead of the variable E_{mg}, the symbol E_{mg} may be replaced by the sum $E_{mh} + E_{hg}$.

2. A METADYNE WITHOUT A REGULATING DEVICE

In this case I_ρ shall be made zero in Equations 36a and 72, and Equation 73 is neglected. There are then $2m - 1$ variables: the $m - 1$ brush currents, the $m - 1$ brush voltages, and the speed n. There are $\eta + 1$ parameters, the currents I_α, I_β, $\cdots$, I_η, and possibly the torque T_a. These satisfy the m relations 36a and 71.

If torque T_a of the machine mechanically coupled to the metadyne is completely arbitrary, this parameter above all others is of particular interest and may be considered an independent variable; on the other hand, it may be a function of other variables, particularly of the speed n, as often occurs in practice. Therefore, in this section it will be counted among the variables to be plotted in a diagram.

Thus for an exhaustive graphical representation of the characteristic, a space of $2m$ dimensions is required, $m - 1$ brush currents, $m - 1$ brush voltages, the speed n, and the torque T_a. The characteristic will be a variety $W_{(2m)}^{(m)}$ of m dimensions.

In order to investigate the shape of the global characteristic $W_{(2m)}^{(m)}$, assume that it is cut by an arbitrary variety of $m - 1$ dimensions. For such a variety, take the one defined by the group of equations

$$E_{mg} = C_g \qquad g = a, b, \cdots, m - 1$$

where C_g is a constant.

Equations 36a are then linear with respect to the brush currents and the variable $1/n$. Substitute the values of brush currents, as derived from Equations 36a, for their symbols in Equation 71, and neglect T_l corresponding to the losses. Then the following relation will be obtained:

$$\left[T_a - 2\pi J \frac{dn}{dt} \right] n^2 + N_1 n + N_2 = 0 \tag{74}$$

where the coefficients N_1 and N_2 are functions of the η parameters I_α, I_β, $\cdots$, I_η exclusively.

Now consider only the domain of static values of speed and assume that T_a is independent of n. Then Equation 74 defines two values of n for a given value of T_a, and only one value of T_a for a given value of n.

Further, assume that T_a is a function of n, an algebraic one for instance. Then Equation 74 defines a group of values for the speed n.

Finally, for the steady-state condition of a transformer metadyne, Equation 74 becomes linear, since T_a is then zero, and thus defines the following single value of n:

$$n = -\frac{N_2}{N_1} \qquad (75)$$

This result is of practical importance and deserves to be recorded:

XII. THEOREM. *Within the domain of static values of speed of a transformer metadyne without a speed-regulating device (the torque due to losses being neglected), the speed is uniquely determined when the brush voltages are given.*

Cutting the variety $W^{(m)}_{(2m)}$, the global characteristic of the metadyne, with a variety of $m - 1$ dimensions defined by a group of equations giving as constants $m - 1$ of the variables—all of them different from the speed n and from the brush voltages—leads to more laborious results.

3. MEANS FOR ARBITRARILY VARYING THE SPEED OF A METADYNE WITH A SPEED MODERATOR

When the metadyne is provided with a speed-regulating device as described in the previous chapter, it keeps its speed substantially constant independently of the value of torque T_a.

In some applications the author obtained continuous control of the speed of the metadyne set by varying the critical speed of the regulator dynamo, n_0. This was done by varying the resistance of the external circuit of the series regulator-dynamo and the resistance of the field-exciting circuit of the shunt regulator-dynamo. The resistance variations may be obtained by hand or by an auxiliary device hereafter referred to as a "speed moderator."

The speed moderator makes possible many useful metadyne applications. Only general indications are given here, but an example is described in Part II of this volume.

The speed moderator essentially consists of a resistor, inserted in the excitation circuit of the regulator dynamo, the resistance being modified according to any arbitrary relation. In a practical application, a tapped resistor is provided with a large number of contact members, a_a, a_b, $\cdots$, a_q, upon which slides another contact member, b, connected to the regulator dynamo. The relative motion of contact member b upon contact members a_a, a_b, $\cdots$, a_q, measured by the displacement x, is obtained by the action of a dynamo or a motor metadyne preferably acting through a worm gear. The speed, say s_1, of the dynamo or motor metadyne is made sensitive to certain electrical quantities, indicated here by y_1, y_2, y_3. Thus the resistance, say R_0, of the circuit of the series regulator-dynamo or of the field-excitation circuit of the shunt regulator-dynamo is made to be a function of y and therefore the critical speed n_0 another function of the same quantity y.

If x is the relative displacement of the contact member b with respect to the contact members a_a, a_b, $\cdots$, a_q, then

$$R_0 = \phi(x)$$

The function $\phi(x)$ is considered a continuous one in this section because of the large number of contact members a_a, a_b, $\cdots$, a_q. By a suitable distribution of the resistance included between two consecutive contact members a, the function $\phi(x)$ may be made the one that is wanted. Then the critical speed n_0 of the regulator dynamo of the metadyne set, if slow movements of the contact members of the speed moderator are considered, is sufficiently well determined by

$$n_0 = C_1\phi(x) \tag{76}$$

where C_1 is a constant.

The operation of the speed moderator depends on the type of its auxiliary motor and on the motor connections. Assume that this motor has an armature supplied with current of substantially constant magnitude and field windings that create a magnetic field which is a linear function, say $A + By_1 + Cy_2 + Dy_3$, of the electrical quantities y_1, y_2, and y_3 mentioned above. Then the auxiliary motor will be at standstill when this linear function is zero:

$$A + By_1 + Cy_2 + Dy_3 = 0 \tag{77}$$

In addition, assume that when the given function is different from zero the motor moves in such a direction as to tend to make this function zero.

Then a sequence of small movements will take place in one direction and in the other until the value of x causes the given linear function to be zero. Practically, it may be stated that the linear function is caused to be zero continuously by a suitable variation of the speed n_0, thus requiring the metadyne either to store kinetic energy or to transform kinetic energy into electric energy. The kinetic energy stored in the rotating masses of the metadyne is

$$\mathcal{E} = 2\pi^2 J n^2 \tag{78}$$

and therefore, when the speed n decreases, the rate of transformation of kinetic energy into electric power is

$$\frac{d\mathcal{E}}{dt} = 4\pi^2 J n \frac{dn}{dt} \tag{79}$$

if the losses are neglected.

Assume that the operation of the speed moderator involves such a small departure of speed from the critical value that we may neglect this increment with respect to the critical value itself. Therefore, the kinetic power transformed into electric power is

$$\frac{d\mathcal{E}}{dt} = 4\pi^2 J n_0 \frac{dn_0}{dt} = 4\pi^2 J C_1^2 \phi(x) \frac{d\phi(x)}{dx} \frac{dx}{dt} \tag{80}$$

Assume, now, that it is desired that this power be kept constant. Choose a dynamo as the auxiliary motor for the speed moderator, a dynamo with an applied voltage V and with a magnetic field F. Its speed, s, will be

$$s = \frac{V}{F} C_2 \tag{81}$$

where C_2 is a constant. Therefore,

$$\frac{d\mathcal{E}}{dt} = 4\pi^2 J C_3 \phi(x) \frac{d\psi(x)}{dx} \frac{V}{F} \tag{82}$$

where C_3 is another constant.

To make this power constant, the following relation may be chosen:

$$\frac{V}{F} \phi(x) \frac{d\phi(x)}{dx} = 1 \tag{83}$$

Consider, for instance, the simplest cases, in which

$$\phi(x) = A + Bx \tag{84}$$

where A and B are constants; then the ratio

$$\frac{V}{F} = \frac{1}{AB + B^2 x} \tag{85}$$

which may be very easily obtained by making voltage V constant and field F the requisite linear function of x.

More generally, if it is desired to transform this power from kinetic into an electric form, i.e., a linear function of the electric quantities y_1, y_2, y_3, as follows—

$$A + By_1 + Cy_2 + Dy_3 \tag{86}$$

this result may be obtained by making

$$\phi(x)\,\frac{d\phi(x)}{dx}\,\frac{V}{F} = A_a + B_a y_1 + C_a y_2 + D_a y_3 \tag{87}$$

where A_a, B_a, C_a, and D_a are constants. If Equation 84 is valid, this may be obtained practically by making the field F a suitable linear function of x and the voltage V an appropriate linear function of y_1, y_2, and y_3.

4. CHARACTERISTIC OF A METADYNE PROVIDED WITH A SPEED MODERATOR

Now the $m + 2$ Equations 36a, 72, and 71 must all be used. The variables are now $2m + 1$, if the regulator current I_ρ and the mechanical torque T_a are variables.

The variation of the speed is assumed to be obtained by a speed moderator, the action of which is analytically represented by one or more new equations, say **e** equations. Thus the variety $W^{(\theta)}_{(2m+1)}$ in a space of $2m + 1$ dimensions, characterizing the operation of the metadyne, will have a number of dimensions θ equal to $2m + 1 - (m + 2) -$ **e** $= m - 1 -$ **e** on the assumption that the speed moderator relates the variables taken as coordinates of the $2m + 1$ dimensional space by **e** equations:

$$\theta = m - 1 - \mathbf{e}$$

Generally the **e** equations of the speed moderator simplify the analytical problem. For instance, a function of a current or of a voltage is made constant, which means that the current itself or the voltage itself is made constant; or some currents and voltages are related by one or more linear equations. Frequently a function of the speed is made constant. For instance, its derivative dn/dt or the product, $n\,\dfrac{dn}{dt} = \dfrac{1}{2}\dfrac{d(n^2)}{dt}$, are made constant; this defines the speed n, which is the variable that enters into the equations in the most complicated manner. To simplify the problem, the deviation of the speed $n - n_0$ may be neglected with respect to the speed n itself.

7 · Metadynes Complete with Their External Connections

In this chapter a simple classification of the various types of metadynes is considered, complete with their external connections. Some general comments are made, and in particular the metadynes are divided into two categories, "reactive" and "nonreactive" types, according to the interaction of brush currents and brush voltages.

1. A CLASSIFICATION OF METADYNES THAT TAKES INTO ACCOUNT THEIR EXTERNAL CONNECTIONS

So far, the metadynes have been investigated independently of their external connections, and some general theorems and rules have been found which hold, whatever the external connections may be. So far, one metadyne was differentiated from another by the number m of its brushes per cycle, by the relative angular location of its brushes, and by its stator windings. From this chapter on, a more detailed study of the metadyne will be undertaken by considering the metadyne complete with its external connections.

There is only one way to connect the two brushes of a dynamo to an external circuit. On the other hand, there are a great number of arrangements of connections with the external circuits for a metadyne, and this number of arrangements increases very rapidly with the number m of brushes per cycle.

It is important, for a given metadyne, to find out how many different arrangements of external connections there are. Consider the following question: To what may the metadyne brushes be connected? The answer:

To one or more shunt networks, each of them having two or more wires kept at constant voltage whatever the current may be, if the output of the metadyne is assumed to be negligible with respect to the power capacity of the network.

To one or more series networks, each of them supplying a constant current through its loop whatever the voltage absorbed by the metadyne may be, the output of which is assumed negligible with respect to the power of the network.

To another electric machine, to one or more resistors, to one or more dynamos, to one or more metadynes. In order to simplify the nomenclature, a resistor or a dynamo or a metadyne in the external circuit will hereafter be called the "consumer."

Thus the term "consumer" used here is defined as any electric apparatus of which the nominal power is of the same order as or smaller than the nominal power of the metadyne.

Similarly, the term "network" will be used to designate a power distribution system or other power source capable of furnishing electric power of a magnitude compared with which the nominal power of the metadyne is negligible.

For the present, investigation will be made for combinations of metadynes chiefly with resistors and dynamos and with other metadynes. However, the external apparatus will have but two terminals.

A metadyne brush can be connected

To a wire of a network
To a terminal of a consumer   (88)
To another metadyne brush

Note that there are at least two wires per network, whether the network is a shunt or a series one; that a metadyne brush may be connected to any other of the remaining $m - 1$ metadyne brushes; and finally that the consumer may have both its terminals connected to the metadyne brushes. Thus the number of arrangements that are possible with a given metadyne is very large.

Hence, there is the problem of classification of an extensive array of metadynes. The author has adopted the following rules:

The number of brushes per cycle defines the degree.

For a given degree the external connections define the class, irrespective of the relative angular displacement of the metadyne brushes but with a definite sequence of the brushes for each class.

For a given degree and a given class the angular displacement of the brushes defines the species.

For a given degree, a given class, and a given species the metadynes differ in their stator-winding arrangements.

Some metadynes have received special names because they are used frequently, and many of these will be investigated in this volume. Here, the rules will be applied in some simple cases.

Consider, for instance, a metadyne of the third degree, and limit the possible arrangements of external connections to the case in which only a shunt network of two wires and only consumers having two terminals are considered. For subdivision into classes, only the sequence of the brushes has to be considered and not their angular displacement; therefore, the metadyne may be represented merely by ordering its brushes

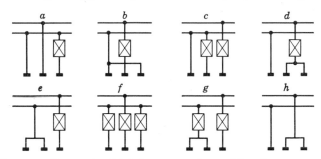

Fig. 33. Classes of a third-degree metadyne with a shunt network.

along a linear segment in a definite sequence. The classes thus obtained are eight in number as shown by Fig. 33. The consumer is represented in this figure by a small rectangle with its two diagonals.

Now consider the case of a series network instead of a shunt network; four classes are thus obtained as shown by Fig. 34. Finally, the case of

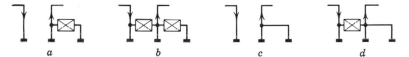

Fig. 34. Classes of a third-degree metadyne with a series network.

a shunt network with three wires gives four classes as shown by Fig. 35. For these special cases, then, the third-degree metadyne yields sixteen classes.

Consider now the metadyne of the fourth degree (very important in practical applications) and take first the case of a shunt network and

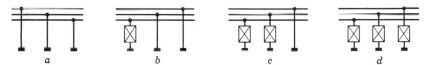

Fig. 35. Classes of a third-degree metadyne with a three-wire network.

consumers with only two terminals; fifteen classes are thus obtained, as shown in Fig. 36. Instead of a shunt network, take a series network and consumers with only two terminals; in this case there are sixteen classes, as Fig. 37 shows. Now take a shunt network of two wires and

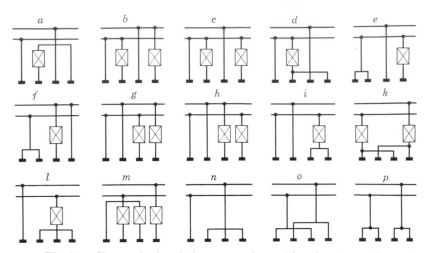

Fig. 36.   Classes of a fourth-degree metadyne with a shunt network.

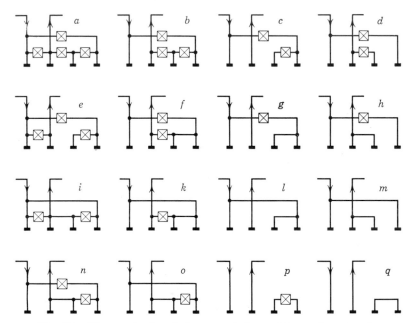

Fig. 37.   Classes of a fourth-degree metadyne with a series network.

a series network of two wires, and do not allow the two networks to have a wire in common; ten more classes are obtained as Fig. 38 shows.

The classes of the fourth-degree metadyne are not yet exhausted. For a number $m > 4$, the number of classes increases very rapidly.

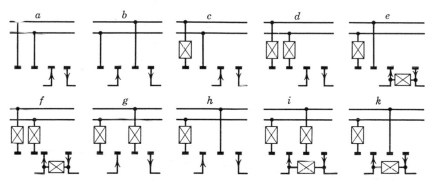

Fig. 38. Classes of a fourth-degree metadyne with both shunt and series networks.

Among such a large number of metadynes, only comparatively few have been applied in practice so far. The procedure applied in these chapters is obviously a synthesis.

2. COMMENTS ON THE VARIOUS TYPES OF METADYNES

An inspection of the diagrams of Figs. 33, 34, 35, 36, 37, and 38 will yield information on some properties of the class of metadyne involved. For instance, the scheme h of Fig. 33, scheme c of Fig. 34, schemes n and o of Fig. 36, and schemes l and m of Fig. 37 belong to a pure generator or to a pure motor metadyne, whereas the class of all other schemes yields metadynes able to be pure transformer metadynes or transformer and generator or motor metadynes simultaneously.

Metadynes of the same class but of different species, differing therefore only in the angular location of their brushes, may show a great difference in their operation. Some examples are given in Section 4 of this chapter.

Another feature not mentioned in the classification rules, although capable of greatly modifying the general characteristic of a metadyne, is the number of separate armature windings with separate commutators that a metadyne of the same degree, the same class, the same species, and the same stator windings may have. In a dynamo there is only one armature winding and only one commutator. In a metadyne, there may be as many distinct armature windings, isolated one from another and each of them connected with a separate commutator, as there are pairs of brushes. Generally, the adoption of a single armature winding with a single commutator reduces the losses, increases the efficiency, and reduces size and cost. Nevertheless, many times the adoption of more than one armature winding isolated from one another with a separate commutator for each winding improves the operation in other ways, so that it may justify the higher losses and cost, as will be apparent in some examples described in the following chapters.

Take, for instance, the case of a metadyne of the fourth degree connected to two networks only of two wires each, one being a shunt network and the other a series one. It is generally desired that the wires

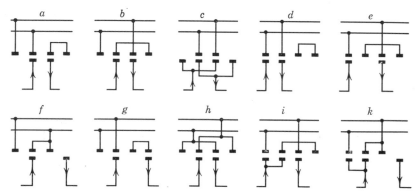

Fig. 39. Some classes of a fourth-degree metadyne having two commutators.

of the two networks shall not meet on a brush, and then only the two classes shown by Fig. 38 are possible when a single armature with a single commutator is chosen. But there may be two armature windings and two commutators, one for each of the two networks, which then never come into contact. In this case the classes of Fig. 39 may be added to the classes of Fig. 38.

The brushes in these schemes are arranged along two rows, each row for a distinct armature winding and commutator. The brushes occupying the same angular position and bearing on different commutators are considered a unit in the computation of the degree. In a later chapter, a useful example will be given of a single armature winding provided with two commutators.

The pitch of the armature winding also has a great influence on the characteristics of a given metadyne. In order to make this point more emphatic, notice that in a metadyne the pitch may vary over a large range. An example will be given later.

3. VECTOR DIAGRAMS

Generally, the voltage between two brushes varies in a metadyne, and it is desirable to have a simple graphical representation of this variation. The author uses vector diagrams in which the voltage between two brushes has a value equal to the length of the projection of the vector on a vertical line. The horizontal projection of this vector, and therefore its length, have no meaning; thus the extremities of the vectors may be moved freely along a horizontal line for the same voltage between the two contemplated brushes. This permits diagrams having two dimensions, which are therefore easier to visualize. Figure 40 gives an example; the potential of the brushes a, b, c, d, e, $\cdots$, m are represented by their ordinates on the projection axis, and the voltages between the homonymous brushes are equal to the differences of the corresponding ordinates.

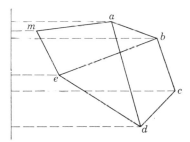

Fig. 40. A general vector diagram for the brush voltages. The vertical projections of the vectors represent the voltage magnitudes.

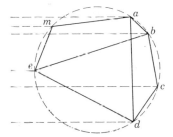

Fig 41. The voltages of Fig. 40, represented by vectors forming a polygon inscribed in a circle.

The representative points a, b, c, $\cdots$, m could easily be taken on a circle as Fig. 41 shows, but there is no advantage. In fact, the voltage distribution along the commutator of a metadyne is far from sinusoidal. A free drawing of the vector diagram allows an easier representation of the brush voltages and their relations. A similar representation applies to brush currents.

4. REACTIVE AND NONREACTIVE METADYNES

Consider an equation of the group 20,

$$\frac{1}{n} E_{bd} = \sum_{g=a}^{m-1} K_{bd}^{g} I_{g}$$

and assume that $K_{bd}^{g} = 0$, which means that current I_{g} does not induce a voltage between brushes b and d; then current I_g is said to be nonreactive with respect to brushes b and d. If $K_{bd}^g \neq 0$, current I_g is said to be reactive with respect to the same brushes.

Now consider one equation of the group 21. Similarly, if Λ_g^{bd} is zero or different from zero, brush voltage E_{bd} is said to be nonreactive or reactive with respect to current I_g, respectively.

Consider next the metadyne represented schematically by Fig. 42, where brushes a and d are diametrically opposite, chords bc and ef are

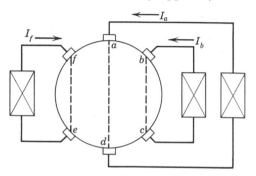

Fig. 42. Scheme of the H generator metadyne.

parallel to diameter da, and the armature-winding pitch is assumed to be substantially diametrical. The metadyne is of the sixth degree, is of a given class and species, and is called the "H generator metadyne." Because of the external connections, there results

$$I_a + I_d = 0$$

$$I_b + I_c = 0$$

$$I_f + I_e = 0$$

The fundamental group of five metadyne equations may be written as follows:

$$\frac{1}{n} E_{da} = K_{da}^{ad} I_a + K_{da}^{bc} I_b + K_{da}^{fe} I_f + \sum_{\gamma} K_{da}^{\gamma} I_{\gamma}$$

$$\frac{1}{n} E_{cb} = K_{cb}^{ad} I_a + K_{cb}^{bc} I_b + K_{cb}^{fe} I_f + \sum_{\gamma} K_{cb}^{\gamma} I_{\gamma}$$

$$\frac{1}{n} E_{ef} = K_{ef}^{ad} I_a + K_{ef}^{bc} I_b + K_{ef}^{fe} I_f + \sum_{\gamma} K_{ef}^{\gamma} I_{\gamma} \qquad (89)$$

$$\frac{1}{n} E_{ba} = K_{ba}^{ad} I_a + K_{ba}^{bc} I_b + K_{ba}^{fe} I_f + \sum_{\gamma} K_{ba}^{\gamma} I_{\gamma}$$

$$\frac{1}{n} E_{af} = K_{af}^{ad} I_a + K_{af}^{bc} I_b + K_{af}^{fe} I_f + \sum_{\gamma} K_{af}^{\gamma} I_{\gamma}$$

It is easy to see that

$$K_{da}^{ad} = K_{da}^{bc} = K_{da}^{fe} = K_{cb}^{ad} = K_{cb}^{bc} = K_{cb}^{fe} = K_{ef}^{ad} = K_{ef}^{bc} = K_{ef}^{fe} = 0$$

whereas the coefficients of the armature currents of the last two equations all are different from zero. This means that the currents I_a, I_b, I_f, the only currents supplied by the metadyne to the external circuits, do not react upon one another and that the metadyne operates as three independent electric sources.

When the external circuits supplied by the metadyne may be resolved into single circuits or groups of circuits in which the currents of one group do not interfere with the electromotive forces of the other group, the machine is called a "nonreactive" metadyne in antithesis to the more frequent "reactive" metadyne, in which the current of one external circuit reacts upon the voltage of some other external circuit. Analytically, a nonreactive metadyne is one for which the fundamental equations may be resolved into groups where the coefficient of the currents of one group are zero in the equation relative to the electromotive forces of the other group, each group comprising the electromotive forces and the currents supplied to an arrangement of external circuits.

In Fig. 43A, consider the vector diagram for the II generator metadyne when all the currents I_a, I_b, and I_f are zero, the electromotive

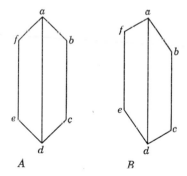

Fig. 43. Vector diagrams for the H generator metadyne.

forces da, cb, and ef being due to the magnetizing ampere-turns of stator windings. If any of the above-mentioned currents flow through the armature, the vector diagram will be distributed, for instance, as Fig. 43B shows; but the electromotive forces ef, da, and cb keep their previous values.

Suppose, now, that the chords cb and ef are equal and short-circuit the brushes e and c, f and b, as Fig. 44 shows. The class is changed, and the machine is now a "Cronos metadyne."

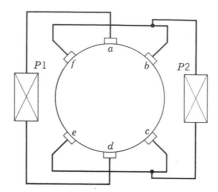

Fig. 44.   Scheme of the Cronos metadyne.

Let Fig. 45A be the vector diagram when no currents are flowing through the consumers $P1$ and $P2$. If a current flows in $P1$, the diagram will be changed from A to B or to C when consumer $P1$ supplies or absorbs current, respectively. Thus the Cronos metadyne is a reactive one.

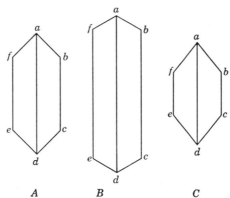

Fig. 45.   Vector diagrams for the Cronos metadyne.

In the example given above, the class has changed. In the following example the class remains the same and only the species changes; this means that only the mutual angular location of the brushes is modified. This scheme is shown in Fig. 46; it is a "K metadyne." Brushes a and b are diametrically opposite, whereas the chord cd is parallel to the diameter ba. Figure 47A gives the vector diagram when no current passes through the two consumers $P1$ and $P2$.

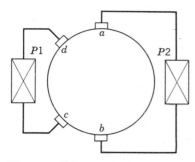

Fig. 46. Scheme of the K metadyne.

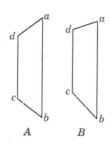

Fig. 47. Vector diagrams for the K metadyne.

When a current flows through $P1$, the vector diagram will be distorted as in Fig. 47B, but the voltages ba and cd remain constant. Thus the K metadyne is a nonreactive one.

Now modify the angular displacement of brushes c and d as shown in Fig. 48. Figure 49A shows the vector diagram when no current flows

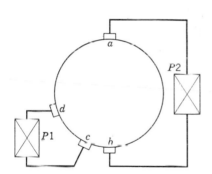

Fig. 48. Modified scheme of the K metadyne.

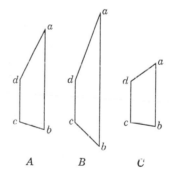

Fig. 49. Vector diagrams for the reactive metadyne of Fig. 48.

in the consumers $P1$ or $P2$; the vector diagram will be modified as Fig. 49B or Fig. 49C shows, according as the direction of the current and the value of the brush voltages are modified. Thus the metadyne of Fig. 48 is a reactive metadyne.

8 · Quasi-Static Characteristics and Static Stability

In this chapter, the metadyne is considered complete with its external connections, and its operation is investigated as a function of time t; the variation of the currents and of the voltages is assumed to be so slow that the effects due to self- and mutual magnetic and electric induction may be neglected.

The currents and electromotive forces plotted against time t give the quasi-static characteristics.

Particular attention is given to the singular points of the static and the quasi-static characteristics in order to obtain some information on the stability of operation of the metadyne.

1. QUASI-STATIC CHARACTERISTICS

So far the metadyne has been considered independently of the external connections of its brushes to the loads and to the networks. Now these connections will be studied.

These external connections establish some relations between brush currents and brush voltages, and these relations may be expressed analytically by equations that allow for an immediate reduction of the $2(m - 1)$ brush currents and brush voltages, say to only q independent ones, which may be designated by the letters x_a, x_b, $\cdots$, x_q; to these brush currents and brush voltages are added the regulator current, which will be represented by x_r, and the speed n. These $q + 2$ variables satisfy the $m - 1$ fundamental equations of the metadyne, which may be written in the form

$$0 = n \sum_{h=a}^{r} G_{gh}x_h + \sum_{h=a}^{r} H_{gh}x_h + nG_g + H_g \qquad g = a, b, \cdots, m - 1 \quad (90)$$

where G_{gh}, H_{gh}, G_g, H_g are constants and where r equals $q + 1$.

Further, the $q + 2$ variables satisfy other relations due to the particular operation of the consumers. If the consumers are resistors, dynamos, and metadynes, these relations are generally expressed analytically by $q - m + 1$ other linear equations of the form

$$\sum_{h=a}^{q} F_{gh}x_h + F_g = 0 \qquad g = a, b, \cdots, q - m + 1 \quad (91)$$

where F_{gh} and F_g are constants.

In general, Equations 90 and 91 uniquely define the q variables x_a, x_b, $\cdots$, x_q, if the regulator current x_r and the speed n are given. The values of the $q + 2$ variables x_a, x_b, $\cdots$, x_q, x_r, n constitute the co-ordinates of a point P in a space of $q + 2$ dimensions. If the regulator Equation 56 for constant speed is satisfied by these values, P is a point on the static characteristic.

If the speed n is very close to the critical speed n_0, then it may be assumed that the regulating device is operating correctly, and Equation 73 may be dropped. Then the regulator Equation 56 for constant speed added to Equations 90 and 91 defines all the $q + 1$ variables: x_a, x_b, $\cdots$, x_q, x_r, for a given value of the speed n; and thus a point P belonging to one static characteristic is determined. A similar procedure applies when there is no regulating device, except that x_r vanishes.

Generally, however, the regulator Equation 56 is not satisfied and then Equation 71 must be considered instead. The electromagnetic torque T of the metadyne expressed in terms of the symbols x_a, x_b, $\cdots$, x_q, x_r takes the following form:

$$T = \sum_{g=a}^{r} \sum_{h=a}^{r} Q_{gh} x_g x_h + \sum_{h=a}^{r} Q_h x_h + Q_0$$

where Q_{gh}, Q_h, and Q_0 are constants. Equations 71 and 73, in turn, take the form

$$\sum_{g=a}^{r} \sum_{h=a}^{r} Q_{gh} x_g x_h + \sum_{h=a}^{r} Q_h x_h + Q_0 - T_l + T_a - 2\pi J \frac{dn}{dt} = 0 \quad (71A)$$

$$x_r = K_\rho (n - n_0) \tag{73}$$

First, suppose that there is no speed-regulating device. Then x_r vanishes and Equations 90 and 91 define the q variables x_a, x_b, $\cdots$, x_q for a given value of n.

Suppose that these values do not satisfy the regulator Equation 56. If the variables x_a, x_b, $\cdots$, x_q are replaced in Equation 71A by their expressions as functions of the variable n given by Equations 90 and 91, the resulting differential equation determines the value of the speed n.

The values of x_a, x_b, $\cdots$, x_q and n are then given as functions of time t, and these $q + 2$ variables may be considered as coordinates of a point P in a space of $q + 2$ dimensions. For varying time t, point P moves in this space and describes a "quasi-static characteristic." This characteristic is obtained from equations where the variation of the variables x_a, x_b, $\cdots$, x_q with respect to time is assumed to be so slow that the effect of the magnetic and of the electric induction may be neglected.

The constants that appear in Equations 90 and 91 and 71A are functions of the parameters I_α, I_β, $\cdots$, I_η and of those voltages and currents defined independently by the external connections of the metadyne. But these parameters and the voltages and currents may vary with time sufficiently slowly that the effect of magnetic and electric induction may be neglected; the corresponding point P will then describe another quasi-static characteristic.

The form of Equations 90 shows what the analytical expression of the variables x_a, x_b, $\cdots$, x_q may be as a function of the variable n. This makes it apparent that the solution of the differential Equation 71A in a "closed form" is generally difficult or impossible.

The following case has a simple solution. Consider the fundamental Equations 36; they are linear with respect to the brush currents and the variable $1/n$. Assume that all the brush voltages are kept constant because of the external connections of the metadyne. Then substitute the values of the brush currents as derived from Equations 36 for their symbols in Equation 71A, neglect T_l, and the following relation is obtained:

$$\left(T_a - 2\pi J \frac{dn}{dt}\right) n^2 + N_1 n + N_2 = 0 \tag{74}$$

where N_1 and N_2 are constants. From Equation 74 is obtained

$$2\pi J \frac{dn}{dt} = T_a - \frac{N_1}{n} - \frac{N_2}{n^2}$$

This equation obviously leads to a simple integral when T_a, N_1, and N_2 are independent of time, and it can lead to only two integrations when T_a, N_1, and N_2 are certain functions of time, for instance when each is the sum of a constant and of the same function of time. The former case often occurs in practical applications, since the voltages of the networks and the voltages induced by the consumers are often kept constant.

For the general case, the following procedure gives approximate but satisfactory practical results: The speed n is given a probable value; then Equations 90 and 91 determine the variables x_a, x_b, $\cdots$, x_q directly. Upon substitution into Equation 71A, the value of the derivative dn/dt is obtained, and from this value a further value of n results, with which the procedure is repeated. Thus one may obtain a sufficiently accurate segment of the quasi-static characteristic.

Assume now that there is a speed-regulating device and a moderator device, and that the latter causes such slow speed variations that the effect of magnetic and electric induction may be neglected. Then the variables x_a, x_b, $\cdots$, x_q, x_r, and n satisfy not only Equations 90, 91, 71A, and 73 but also another equation, say

$$Y\left(x_a,\ x_b,\ \cdots,\ x_q,\ n_0,\ \frac{dn}{dt}\right) = 0 \qquad (92)$$

assumed to be the analytical expression of the operation of the moderator.

To obtain a solution, in practice it is assumed that the regulator device is powerful enough to force the speed n to follow the value n_0 of the critical speed so closely that one may take $n = n_0$ and $dn/dt = dn_0/dt$. Then Equation 73 may be dropped; x_a, x_b, $\cdots$, x_q may be determined from Equations 90 and 91 for a given value of n and as a function of x_r; x_a, x_b, $\cdots$, x_q may be replaced in Equations 92 and 71A by their values determined above; and from the last two equations the values of x_r and of dn/dt may be obtained by simple algebraic operations. Point P_1, determined by the coordinates x_a, x_b, $\cdots$, x_q, x_r, n, and t_1 in a space of $q + 3$ dimensions, is thus defined.

A second application of this procedure makes it possible to pass from point P_1 to a second point, P_2, relative to the instant t_2 and to the second value of the speed defined with the aid of the first value and its derivative with respect to time. The sequence of points P_1, P_2, P_3, $\cdots$ thus obtained determines, practically speaking, a quasi-static characteristic. A similar procedure is possible when the parameters with which the constants are constructed are themselves functions of the time t.

2. STATIC STABILITY REGARDING CURRENTS AND VOLTAGES

Consider a system of electric circuits, fixed or moving with respect to one another with a uniform motion at constant speed, and construct the equations satisfied by the currents and the voltages of these circuits and the equations expressing the two Kirchhoff's laws. If the equations uniquely determine all the given currents and voltages with definite values, the state of operation so determined is uniquely definite and it may, in general, continue without modification for an indefinite time; i.e., this state is then stable.

Now if the parameters appearing in the given equations are modified, the values of the voltages and of the currents are generally modified. It may happen that for some special values of the parameters not all the values of the currents and of the voltages are uniquely determined and finite, but for at least one of them there is more than one finite value, or there is an infinite value, or, finally, there is more than one finite value and simultaneously an infinite one.

These special values of the parameters, currents, and voltages constitute the singularities of the contemplated assembly. The resulting singular state is indefinite or involves infinite currents or voltages, or it may have both characteristics. Thus for a uniform motion there are generally an infinity of stable states and some singular ones.

But the motion may be a function of the voltages and of the currents considered here. It is not generally uniform; on the contrary, it is generally variable. Then it may happen that, upon departing from a definite motion corresponding, if it were maintained uniform, to a stable state, the system is gradually shifted to a singular state. The investigation of this dynamic change of state is beyond the scope of this study of quasi-static operation.

Having investigated the static characteristics and the quasi-static ones, one may try to determine the singular state in order to remain as far as possible from it in practical applications or in order to use them appropriately, as the author many times does.

The points of the static or quasi-static characteristics corresponding to the singular state are called singular points. For the operation of the metadyne, four kinds of singular points may be distinguished:

For a finite value of the speed n, and of one or more of the variables x_a, x_b, $\cdots$, x_q, x_r, one or more of the latter become infinite; such a point is called a common polar point of the characteristic.

For a finite value of the speed, and of one or more of the variables x_a, x_b, $\cdots$, x_q, x_r, one or more of the latter are indefinite; the corresponding point is called a common surge point.

For a finite value of the speed, all the variables x_a, x_b, $\cdots$, x_q, x_r are indefinite; this type of point is called a general surge point.

For finite values of the parameters the speed becomes infinite; this condition is called a flight point.

A singular point may have more than one characteristic singularity. A nonsingular point of the characteristic is called a regular point.

The finite speed corresponding to a singular point is called a critical speed; it is a critical polar speed in the case of a polar point, and a critical surge or critical building-up speed in the case of a surge point. The points corresponding to the asymptotes of the hyperbola in Figs. 29, 31, and 32 are polar points.

The point for which $nA = 1$ (see Section 2 of Chapter 4) for a shunt dynamo is a common surge point, and the corresponding value of the speed is a surge (or building-up) critical speed. This value has been found from the static characteristic, and it has since been confirmed from considerations of the dynamic characteristic of the same machine used as a regulator dynamo.

The singular points are best determined during investigation of each particular case of metadyne. However, a procedure is given here which applies to the general case.

Consider Equations 90, 91, 71A, 73, and 92. For a given value of the time, t, they correlate the q variables x_a, x_b, $\cdots$, x_q, brush currents or brush voltages; the regulator current, x_r; the speed, n; and the critical speed of the regulator dynamo, n_0—in all, $q + 3$ variables. Simplify the data by admitting, as experience frequently demonstrates, that the regulator device is efficient enough to oblige speed n to remain so very close to the critical speed as to permit taking $n = n_0$ and dropping Equation 73; then $q + 2$ variables remain with $q + 2$ equations. Neglect T_l also.

Choose from among the $r = q + 1$ variables x_a, x_b, $\cdots$, x_q, x_r one variable, say x_α, a current or a voltage, and call the others "temporary variables." Solve systems 90 and 91 of q linear equations with respect to the temporary variables. The solution may be written

$$x_h = \frac{D_h(n, x_u)}{D_0(n, x_\alpha)} \tag{93}$$

where the index, h, may have any value a, b, $\cdots$, q, r except the value α, where $D_0(n, x_\alpha)$ is the determinant of the coefficients of the temporary variables in the linear Equations 90 and 91, and where $D_h(n, x_\alpha)$ is the determinant corresponding to the variable x_h. All these determinants are evidently functions of speed n and variable x_α.

If the equation

$$D_0(n, x_\alpha) = 0 \tag{94}$$

is satisfied, there is a singular point. Further, if one or more than one or all the determinants $D_h(n, x_\alpha)$ appearing in Equations 93 are different from zero,

$$D_h(n, x_\alpha) \neq 0$$

there is a polar point. If Equation 94 is satisfied and, further, one or more or all determinants $D_h(n, x_\alpha)$ are equal to zero,

$$D_h(n, x_\alpha) = 0$$

there is a surge point.

If the choice of the variable x_α allows it to be expressed linearly as a function of the temporary variables by means of any of the Equations 71A and 92, then the variable x_α is replaced in Equations 90 and 91 by its expression, these equations are solved with respect to the temporary variables, and the solution may be written

$$x_h = \frac{D_h(n)}{D_0(n)} \tag{95}$$

where index h may have any value a, b, $\cdots$, q, r, except the value α, and where the determinant of the coefficients $D_0(n)$ and the determinants $D_h(n)$ are functions of speed only. The roots of the algebraic equation

$$D_0(n) = 0 \tag{96}$$

are then the values of the critical speeds.

If for these values of the critical speeds one or more than one or all the determinants $D_h(n)$ are different from zero, there is a polar point. If for the values of the critical speeds one or more than one or all the determinants $D_h(n)$ are zero, there is a surge point. We are naturally led to Equations 95 and 96 when there is no regulator device and consequently no speed moderator.

3. STATIC STABILITY REGARDING SPEED

The static characteristic of the metadyne gives the corresponding value of speed n and of the currents and voltages x_a, x_b, $\cdots$, x_q, x_r. Although it almost grants the stability of the currents and voltages, in the event that these are uniquely definite and the speed is maintained constant, it does not give any information regarding the stability of speed n. Speed n may remain constant or have a tendency to increase or to decrease.

On the other hand, this information is very important for the practical operation of the metadyne; it is fundamental for the choice of the location and size of the regulator winding, if there is one. This information may be clearly enough indicated from only the static behavior of the metadyne without use of the variable time or the derivatives with respect to time. Hence the designation of this section.

The total torque acting upon the shaft of the metadyne has a moment equal to $T - T_l + T_a$. Neglect T_l in order to simplify the calculation. Assume that the speed variations are so slow as to permit neglecting the effect of the magnetic and the electric induction. The necessary and sufficient condition of having the speed unchanged is expressed by the relation

$$\frac{dT}{dn} + \frac{dT_a}{dn} < 0 \tag{97}$$

From the expression of T appearing in Equation 71A, there results by differentiation with respect to speed n

$$\frac{dT}{dn} = \sum_{g=a}^{r} \sum_{h=a}^{r} Q_{gh} \left(x_h \frac{dx_g}{dt} + x_g \frac{dx_h}{dt} \right) + \sum_{h=a}^{r} Q_h \frac{dx_h}{dt} \qquad (98)$$

Differentiate Equations 90, 91, and 73 with respect to n:

$$0 = \sum_{h=a}^{r} G_{gh} x_h + n \sum_{h=a}^{r} G_{gh} \frac{dx_h}{dn}$$

$$+ \sum_{h=a}^{r} H_{gh} \frac{dx_h}{dn} + G_g \qquad g = a, b, \cdots, m - 1 \quad (99)$$

$$0 = \sum_{h=a}^{q} F_{gh} \frac{dx_h}{dn} \qquad g = a, b, \cdots, q - m + 1 \qquad (100)$$

$$\frac{dx_r}{dn} = K_\rho \qquad (101)$$

There are $q + 1 = r$ derivatives of the form dx_h/dn, and Equations 99, 100, and 101 yield r independent linear equations with respect to the r derivatives, from which the derivatives can generally be determined. Substitution of the values thus obtained in place of the corresponding derivatives in Equation 98 yields the value of the first member of the relation 97, on the assumption that dT_a/dn is given. Then:

If $dT/dn + dT_a/dn < 0$ the speed is stable.
If $dT/dn + dT_a/dn = 0$ the speed is indifferent.
If $dT/dn + dT_a/dn > 0$ the speed is unstable.

The condition 97 for stable operation must be fulfilled for the whole length of the segment of the static or quasi-static characteristic corresponding to the contemplated application. The absolute value of the first member of relation 97, this relation supposedly being satisfied, gives a measure of the stability. This value may also be considered as a criterion for a good choice of the location and size of the eventual regulator winding.

Relation 97 may be satisfied even when the derivative dT/dn is positive, provided that the negative value of dT_a/dn is large enough. This property has sometimes been used to investigate the operation of the metadyne outside of its proper stability limits. As a rule, the derivative dT/dn is made negative and its absolute value as large as possible.

Sometimes an indication for the right choice of the regulator winding may be obtained by an investigation of the elementary torques developed in the metadyne. In fact, the value of the total torque is the algebraic sum of as many elementary torques as there are summations in the double sum appearing in Equation 30.

One or more of these elementary torques are due to the action of the regulator current I_ρ, and the sign of the derivative of these elementary torques with respect to the speed is promptly recognized; some other elementary torques are due to currents affected by the regulator current or by the speed, and the value of their derivative with respect to the speed is easily recognized; finally, some other elementary torques are independent of the speed. Thus the sign of the algebraic sum of these derivatives may be determined.

4. A REMARK ON DYNAMIC STABILITY

Dynamic stability takes into account all the derivatives with respect to time, particularly the derivatives of the currents and of the voltages. Only a brief remark will be made here in order to permit a complete description of the metadyne stator windings which will become necessary in the successive development of this volume.

A simple means for obtaining dynamic stability consists in the insertion of resistors in many of the electric circuits of the metadyne, but this involves large losses. Since the first appearance of the metadyne, the author has instead utilized the stabilizing-series stator windings as defined in Section 1 of Chapter 4. In fact, the voltage created by a resistor of resistance R carrying a current I, a voltage favorable to dynamically stable operation, is expressed by $-RI$; the voltage induced by a stabilizing-series stator winding excited by the current I in an armature rotating at n revolutions per second is expressed by nKI, where the constant K may be given a negative sign by proper choice of the connections of the stabilizing-series stator winding. The stabilizing effect is therefore the same as the one due to a resistor of resistance $R = -nK$, and the losses become negligible.

Although stabilizing-series stator windings may have an undesirable effect on the static or quasi-static characteristics of the metadyne, this undesirable effect may be partially or almost completely compensated by the use of other stator windings. In addition, the series stabilizing windings may be replaced by other kinds of windings, the action of which cannot be explained completely from the static viewpoint alone.

In order to recall the presence of stabilizing-series stator windings and of the eventual windings used for compensating the effect of the stabilizing windings on the static characteristics, the schemes of the metadynes will hereafter frequently show two blocks for a brush. One block, bearing on the circumference representing the armature, indicates the brush proper, and a second block, just above the first one, represents the terminal corresponding to that brush. Then between the brush proper and its terminal the series stator windings are assumed to be inserted, such as stabilizing windings or commutating pole windings not otherwise represented in the figure.

9 · Consideration of the Anisotropic Metadyne and of the Saturated Iron

The effect of iron saturation upon the theory previously developed is considered, and a procedure is given for taking this effect into account approximately; further, some anisotropic metadynes are considered, and a general remark is made showing that the theory based on isotropic and nonsaturated metadynes retains its value.

1. ISOTROPIC METADYNES WITH SATURATED IRON

The theory so far developed is simple and may be convenient although the problems considered have sometimes not been very simple, and a number of useful theorems and rules have been stated, but all this strictly applies only to an isotropic metadyne with unsaturated iron.

The ampere-turns required by the iron part of the whole magnetic circuit are frequently only a small fraction of the ampere-turns required by the air gap; therefore their nonlinear relation with respect to the magnetic induction may frequently be replaced by a properly chosen linear relation so that the linear relations so frequently used in the theory developed in the previous chapters may be retained. But cases exist in which iron saturation is too large to be neglected, and these require close attention.

In the equations established in the previous chapters, the coefficients K_{ab}^{cd}, K_{ad}^{g}, and their linear combinations are continuously used; and they are constant as long as iron saturation is not present. These coefficients have the same dimensions and are of the same nature as the coefficients of self-inductance and mutual inductance, and they are numerically equal to the brush voltages of a metadyne revolving at one revolution per second and excited by unit current. When iron saturation occurs, these coefficients are rather complicated functions of the currents of the circuits interlinked with the flux concerned. The author has devoted a chapter in *Elettromeccanica* to the calculation of the coefficients of self-inductance and mutual inductance,* in which many relations are established that facilitate the calculation of their value with an exactitude dependent only on the amount of work devoted to it. Here, only a brief consideration will be given.

* *loc. cit.*, Volume I, Chapter V.

Let the voltage E_{cd} be due to the action of two currents, x_a and x_b:

$$\frac{1}{n} E_{cd} = K_{cd}^a I_a + K_{cd}^b I_b$$

where the coefficients K_{cd}^a and K_{cd}^b are functions of the values I_a and I_b of the currents.

The voltage per revolution, $(1/n)E_{cd} \equiv Z$, may be graphically represented in three-dimensional space by the value of the ordinates of a

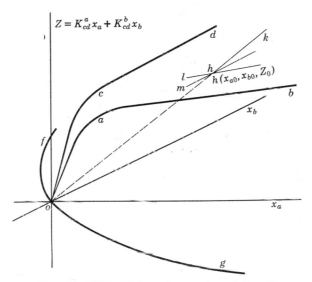

Fig. 50.   Graph of the voltage per revolution, Z.

surface S having as plane abscissas the value of currents x_a and x_b as Fig. 50 shows. Then oab is the upper section of surface S, cut by the plane x_aoZ; its upper section cut by the plane x_boZ is ocd; the section cut by the plane x_aox_b is fog. Only the upper part is represented, for simplicity.

Consider the particular value $Z_0 = K_{cd}^a x_{a0} + K_{cd}^b x_{b0}$, having x_{a0} and x_{b0} as coordinates and corresponding to point h of the surface. Expand the function according to the Taylor series

$$Z = Z_0 + (x_a - x_{a0}) \frac{dZ_0}{dx_a} + (x_b - x_{b0}) \frac{dZ_0}{dx_b} + \cdots \qquad (102)$$

where the derivatives dZ_0/dx_a and dZ_0/dx_b are the slopes of the two tangents, lh and mh, parallel to the planes x_aoZ and x_boZ, respectively.

Take only the first three terms of the development, the terms that are written in Equation 102, and replace the voltage per revolution $(1/n)E_{cd}$ in the group of fundamental Equations 90 of the metadyne, for instance, by the three specified terms. Then those equations, linear with respect to x_a, x_b, $\cdots$, x_r, will still remain linear with respect to the same variables and will permit a further easy adjustment of the problem, provided that the actual operating point, say P, of the electromotive force per revolution $(1/n)E_{cd}$ is a point on surface S near to the selected point, h. If the choice of point h has been so fortunate as to coincide with the point P finally resulting from the calculation, then the form of the equations is exact. Thus, in general, iron saturation will affect the numerical results of the operating characteristic, but it will only slightly modify the nature of the characteristic.

2. ANISOTROPIC METADYNES WITH NONSATURATED IRON

In most cases, a metadyne actually constructed cannot be said to have true isotropy. Therefore, for an exact design, all the results obtained in the previous chapter have to be reviewed.

Consider, for instance, the first theorem, which has served as a basis for many further developments. It does not apply in the simple case of a dynamo with two diametrically opposite brushes and diametrical pitch of its armature windings, the stator of the dynamo being constructed as usual with polar segments, when the commutation axis is not symmetrically located with respect to the geometrical axis of the polar segments as Fig. 51 shows.

In fact, a current flowing through brushes a and b will create armature ampere-turns that may be subdivided into two parts: one part, lying entirely under the polar segments and not represented in the figure, will not give any flux capable of inducing an electromotive force between brushes a and b; and another part, lying in the interpolar free space and limited exactly between diameters ab and $a'b'$, symmetrical with respect to the axis of symmetry XX' of the whole magnetic circuit, shown by dots and crosses. The latter part creates a flux that passes through the magnetic circuit as shown by the arrowed loops in the figure. This flux induces an electromotive force between brushes a and b, contrary to the statement of Theorem I. The machine will then operate as a series-excited machine; and if there is some permanent magnetism and the sense of rotation is correct, the machine will build up at its critical speed. If the commutating axis is along the axis XX' of symmetry, the electromotive force is zero, whatever the current in the armature may be.

As a second example, consider a four-brush metadyne with no stator windings and with an elliptical stator bore, the armature being perfectly circular, as shown in Fig. 52. Let the brushes be equidistant and the armature winding have a substantially diametrical pitch; let brushes a and c be connected to a constant voltage, V, as the source, and brushes b and d to a consumer. Assume first that the air gap has a constant depth, the stator bore being presumably circular. Then the torque will be zero according to Theorem IX and the metadyne will operate

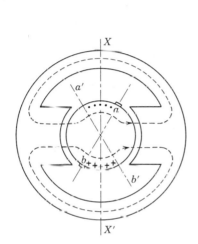

Fig. 51. The ordinary two-pole   Fig. 52. A fourth-degree metadyne
dynamo is anisotropic.   with an anisotropic magnetic circuit.

as a pure transformer metadyne, the energy supplied by the secondary brushes, b and d, to the consumer being drawn entirely from the source at constant voltage V connected to the primary brushes. The expression of the torque T is

$$T = \frac{1}{2\pi} [K_{ca}^{bd} I_a I_b - K_{bd}^{ac} I_b I_a] = 0$$

because $K_{ca}^{bd} = K_{bd}^{ac}$.

Now consider the elliptical stator bore, which gives an air gap of variable depth, and assume that the minor depth is along the commutating axis ca; then $K_{bd}^{ac} > K_{ca}^{bd}$, and, therefore, a torque will appear on the shaft. The metadyne will then operate partly as a generator (or as a motor) and partly as a transformer, and the output supplied to the consumer will be taken only partly from the source of constant voltage V. This type of operation is desirable for some applications. It should be noted that a geometrically isotropic metadyne may also be rendered anisotropic by asymmetrical iron saturation.

3. GENERAL REMARKS

It is obvious that only rarely will a metadyne comply exactly with the theory developed in the previous chapters. Further, a metadyne will frequently be the object of a particular investigation, and its design will require some special procedure. Some of those used by the author will be briefly indicated in the second part of this volume.

But, for a general investigation and a first, approximate design, the theory of an isotropic, saturated-iron metadyne may prove a useful and, sometimes, a powerful tool. This method is particularly valuable in the hands of a designer able to look at the symbols with intuitive good judgment.

10 · On Commutation

A fundamental theory of commutation is given as applied to a very simple armature; the investigation is limited for the sole purpose of justifying the devices that, when applied to a metadyne, allow it to commutate under practically the same conditions as a dynamo.

1. GENERALITIES ON COMMUTATION

What has been said so far would have slight practical interest if commutation in the metadyne were not made possible to an extent sufficient to insure good operation for machines of large output. From the description already given, it appears that commutation in a metadyne takes place not only along the so-called "neutral zone" separating two magnetic poles of opposite signs in the machine but also, and more frequently, in the middle of the magnetic flux and not rarely under the very axis of that flux.

Before the advent of the metadyne, the author developed a theory of commutation in dynamos, and this theory facilitated his task with the metadyne. Further developments have produced such good results that there is now justification for stating that the field of good commutation is wider for metadynes than for dynamos. Since commutation alone might be discussed in an entire volume, in this chapter there are briefly developed only those principles that insure that good commutation in a metadyne may be obtained under practically the same conditions as in conventional dynamos.

Consider a rectangular circuit interlinked with a laminated magnetic circuit and carrying a current i, as Fig. 53 shows, and assume that the current must be modified from an initial value I to a final value $-I$ in a time T_c. At the terminals of the electric circuit an electromotive force $-e$ must be applied to overcome the induced electromotive force e due to the change of the flux ϕ created by current i in the interlinked magnetic circuit:

$$e = -\frac{d\phi}{dt} = -L\frac{di}{dt} \tag{103}$$

the electric circuit having a single turn, the saturation of the iron and the relatively small ohmic drop being neglected.

89

122934

LIBRARY
MISSISSIPPI STATE COLLEGE

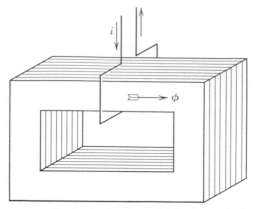

Fig. 53.   A simple magnetic circuit that is useful in the analysis of commutation.

Whatever the law of variation of current i may be, the total electric impulse supplied to the circuit is

$$\int_0^{T_c} e \, dt = +2\phi_0 = 2LI \tag{104}$$

where ϕ_0 is the original value of the flux at the instant $t = 0$ when the current has the value $+I$.   The mean value of the induced electromotive force is

$$e_m = \frac{2}{T_c} LI \tag{105}$$

Let the magnetic circuit be modified as Fig. 54 shows, the electric circuit being wound around a rotating cylindrical armature; and assume that, during time T_c of the commutation of current i, the armature ro-

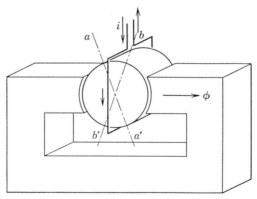

Fig. 54.   A modification of Fig. 53, showing the location of the armature in the magnetic circuit.

tates between the two extreme positions aa' and bb' so that the cylindrical wire segments of the electric circuit are moving through the interpolar space all the time of commutation. The relations 103, 104, and 105 are still valid.

Now assume that instead of one electric circuit there are two identical ones, as Fig. 55 shows, having their terminals diametrically opposite and each of them carrying the current $+I$ for $t = 0$ so that both of

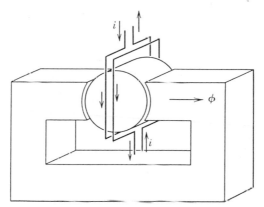

Fig. 55. Another modification of Fig. 53, emphasizing the two armature-winding layers.

them will create a flux equal to $2\phi_0$ for $t = 0$. Assume further that this current is inverted in the same time, T_c, under the same conditions.

For the sake of symmetry, it should be conceded that the currents in the two circuits will have the same value as current i in Figs. 53 and 54, at any instant of time t between zero and T_c. During this time of commutation, the conductors along the generatrices of the cylinder do not enter the air gap under the polar segments but always remain in the interpolar region. Then, instead of Equations 103, the equation

$$e = -2\frac{d\phi}{dt} = -L\frac{di_1}{dt} - M\frac{di_2}{dt} = -2L\frac{di}{dt} \tag{106}$$

will be valid, because the two circuits are supposed to be so close together that

$$L = M$$

and because the currents of the two circuits will be equal at any instant. The total impulse for each circuit will be

$$\int_0^{T_c} e\, dt = 4\phi_0 = 4LI \tag{107}$$

and the mean value of the voltage induced in each circuit will be

$$e = +\frac{4}{T_c}LI \qquad (108)$$

For a dynamo having a winding of diametrical pitch, two diametrically opposite brushes, and no excitation current, these arguments may be applied to the two armature sections commutating simultaneously, if the commutation of the two armature sections is considered independently of any interference of the other commutating and noncommutating sections of the armature.

It is easy to obtain some indication of the value of the voltage given by Equation 108 for ordinary dynamos. The commutation time, T_c, is about 1/1000 of a second; LI is the flux created by the ampere-turns of a section carrying its normal current; the total armature ampere-turns, assuming that all interlink the whole area of the magnetic circuit of the machine, create in an average dynamo a flux practically equal to the normal flux of the dynamo. In a metadyne these armature ampere-turns are about four times the magnetizing ampere-turns for creating the normal flux. On the other hand, the average number of segments of a one-cycle armature may be taken equal to 50; therefore the value LI may be calculated as follows:

$$LI = K\frac{1}{50}\phi_N \qquad (109)$$

where ϕ_N is the normal flux of the machine, and K is equal to 1 for a dynamo and to 4 for a metadyne.

The normal voltage induced in the section of the machine is due to the variation of the flux ϕ_N during the time, T_d, necessary for a peripheral point of the armature to cover one pole pitch, and the average frequency of the armature magnetizing cycle is about 25; thus T_d may be taken equal to $\frac{1}{50}$, and finally e_m is, on the average, equal to

$$e_m = 4K\frac{1}{50}E_N\frac{T_d}{T_c} = E_N 4K\frac{1}{50}\cdot\frac{1000}{50} = 1.6KE_N$$

where E_N is the normal voltage induced in a section of the armature. In a dynamo the value of e_m is thus equal to 1.6 times the maximum voltage induced per section; therefore, e_m is about 40 volts. In a metadyne it is four times as much.

This result is in striking contrast with the fact that in dynamos the commutating poles induce only a very small voltage, about 2 volts, in the commutating sections for obtaining a smooth reversal of the currents. The theorems stated below will give a satisfactory explanation.

2. THE THEOREM ON COMMUTATION FOR ISOTROPIC MACHINES

A revolving armature will now be considered with two commutating sections and many other noncommutating ones carrying current. First some simplifications will be made:

An even number of bars on the commutator.
Two diametrically opposite brushes.
An exact diametrical pitch for the armature winding.
A single turn per winding section.
One single section per slot; i.e., two peripheral conductors per slot.
The width of the brushes is exactly equal to the width of the bars of the commutator, and the width of the mica sheets between the commutator bars is negligible.

All these restrictions will be implied by the phrase "elementary armature."

In this section, the armature is assumed to rotate in an isotropic magnetic medium, for instance, in a concentric nonsaturated circular iron ring, or even in the air far from any magnetic mass, as Fig. 56 shows. The brushes short-circuit the two armature sections embedded in the two diametrically opposite slots 1 and 13; during the time T_c, axis nn' of these two slots moves from position aa' to position bb'. During this time, no other sections commutate; when the commutation of the sections embedded in slots 1 and 13 finishes, the commutation of the two sections embedded in slots 24 and 12 begins, and so on. Only two diametrically opposite sections are commutating at a given instant.

The magnetic field created by the ampere-turns of the armature, say ϕ, is the resultant of two component fields: the first is one created by the ampere-turns of the two commutating sections, say ϕ_c, and the second one is created by the ampere-turns of all the noncommutating sections, say ϕ_n. The latter field, seen by an observer moving with the armature, is invariable, it is independent of time, and it rotates with the armature; the former, as seen by the same observer, keeps the same direction at all points of the surrounding space but varies in magnitude and in sense with time, always being proportional to the commutating current i, variable with time, and changing from the value $+I$ to the value $-I$.

Obviously, the electromotive force induced in any of the two commutating sections is due exclusively to the variation of the flux ϕ_c, the noncommutating sections having no action whatever on the commutating ones. Let $(\phi_c)_t$ be the value of the flux ϕ_c at the time t inter-linked by each of the two commutating sections. Then

$$(\phi_c)_0 = -(\phi_c)_{T_c} \equiv 2LI$$

The mean value of the electromotive force which must be imposed on a commutating section for compensating this action is, then,

$$-2\frac{2LI}{T_c} = -\frac{4LI}{T_c} \tag{110}$$

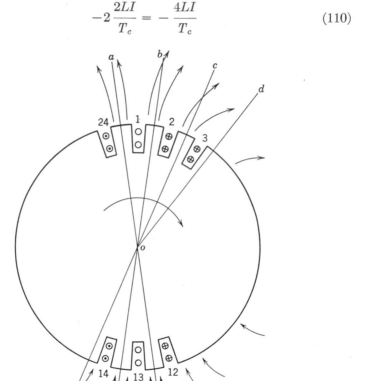

Fig. 56.   An armature located in an isotropic magnetic medium.

Now assume that the flux ϕ_n does not rotate with the armature but remains fixed in space and that it is cut by a rotating commutating section in the time T_c; then calculate the mean value of the electromotive force. Under the given postulate, the flux cut by one side along a generatrix of the armature of the commutating section, say the side embedded in slot 1, is the sum of the fluxes created by each noncommutating section coming out of the armature along the dihedral angle *aob*. Consider the two sections embedded in slots 3 and $12 + 3 = 15$; they create a flux along angle *aob* which is exactly the same as the one created by the two commutating sections along the dihedral angle *cod*, if these commutating sections are carrying current I.

If all the commutating sections are considered in the same way, the flux cut by one wire of the commutating section will be found to be exactly equal to $2LI$. Consideration of the other side of the section, the one embedded in slot 13, shows that the total electromotive force induced in the commutating section is equal to that induced by cutting a total flux $4LI$ during the time T_c, and therefore its mean value is given by Equation 110. Hence the following theorem:

XIII. Theorem of Commutation for Isotropic Machines. *The mean value of the electromotive force induced in the commutating section of an elementary armature equals the mean value of the electromotive force which would be induced in the commutating section by cutting the flux created by the noncommutating sections if the flux were fixed in space during the commutation period T_c.*

The theorem obviously holds when a magnetic ring surrounds the armature, leaving an air gap of constant depth.

If the depth of the air gap is the normal one of a dynamo or of a metadyne, the theorem easily yields a mean value of the electromotive force necessary for commutation: about 40 volts for a dynamo and 160 for a metadyne, as found in Section 1 by another method.

3. THE FIRST THEOREM ON COMMUTATION FOR ANISOTROPIC MACHINES *

To simplify the argument, it will be assumed here that the armature is not slotted but smooth and that the conductors of the armature winding are distributed along the smooth cylindrical surface of the armature in two regular layers, an internal and an external. In Fig. 57, the conductors of the external layer are indicated by a small letter, and the internal ones belonging to the same section of the armature are indicated by the same letter primed.

Suppose, now, that a smooth elementary armature is rotating, no longer in an isotropic stator, but in an anisotropic one as represented by the figure, as is customary for dynamo machines; the commutating zone

* See a communication by this author to the Academy of Sciences of Turin (*Atti accad. sci. Torino*, Volume 75, 1937).

is left free, not covered by iron, and the inductor is assumed to be without field windings. The flux created by the armature ampere-turns may
be resolved into two components: the flux that, upon coming out of the
armature, penetrates into the polar segments, and the one that does not.
The former is called the "anisotropic flux." *

In this and the following section, only the anisotropic flux is considered. Thus the reader must now take into account only the flux lines
passing through the iron, such as the ones indicated in Fig. 57.

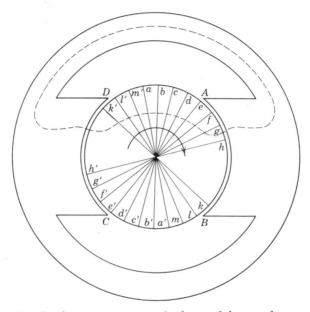

Fig. 57.   An elementary armature in the usual dynamo frame.

Let aa' and bb' be the initial and final positions of the commutating
section, respectively; in the figure, only one section is represented, for
the sake of simplicity, and the other one is assumed to overlap practically the entire section shown in the diagram. Let $L_{aa}I$ be the anisotropic flux created by the commutating section aa' at the time $t = 0$ at
its initial position aa'. Then the positive sense in the armature of the
anisotropic flux created by the commutating section aa' will be the one
indicated by the arrow, from left to right in the armature.

Let i be the instantaneous value of the current in the commutating

---

* A broader definition of the anisotropic flux can be stated, a definition based on
the behavior of the flux with respect to the moving commutating section; the anisotropic flux is not modified by this motion. The simple definition given above will be
used here.

section aa' at the time t. The total electromotive force, say e, induced in the commutating section is

$$e = -2L_{aa}\frac{di}{dt} - 2\frac{d}{dt}\sum_{h=b}^{m} - IL_{ha} = -2L_{aa}\frac{di}{dt} + 2I\frac{d}{dt}\sum_{h=b}^{m} L_{ha} \quad (111)$$

where the coefficient 2 takes into account the second layer of the winding and where $2m$ is the total number of sections of the armature winding. The sum that appears in Equation 111 may be resolved into two parts: a first part containing all the sections that during the whole time of commutation are interlinked with the total anisotropic flux created by the two (overlapping) commutating sections, say sections b, c, d and l, m; let the other ones be e, f, g, h, $\cdots$, j, k, which during a part of or during the whole time T_c of commutation move under the polar segments. The former have a coefficient of mutual induction, say L_{ca}, which is equal to L_{aa} because of the assumption made to consider the anisotropic flux alone:

$$L_{aa} = L_{ab} = L_{ac} = -L_{ma} \quad (112)$$

These evidently yield a partial sum equal to zero because neither the current nor the coefficient of mutual induction varies during the commutation time. Therefore,

$$e = -2L_{aa}\frac{di}{dt} + 2I\frac{d}{dt}\sum_{g=e}^{k} L_{ga} \quad (113)$$

In order to calculate the second member of Equation 113, consider the flux ϕ that is created by a commutating section at the instant $t = 0$. Then

$$L_{aa}I = \phi \quad (114)$$

and

$$L_{ga}I = \phi_{gB} - \phi_{Ag} \quad (115)$$

where the flux ϕ_{gB} is the part of the flux ϕ extending from point g to point B of the air gap under the polar segment, and ϕ_{Ag} the part extending from point A to point g. There is, therefore,

$$\phi = \phi_{Ag} + \phi_{gB}$$

From Equation 115 the following relation is obtained by differentiation:

$$\frac{d}{dt}(L_{ga}I) = I\frac{dL_{ga}}{dt} = (-B_g + B_{g'})A\Omega R \quad (116)$$

where B_g is the induction at point g due to the flux ϕ; where $B_{g'}$ is the induction due to the same flux at point g', the positive sense of the induction being the centripetal one; and where Λ, Ω, and R are the length, the angular speed, and the radius of the armature, respectively. Thus Equation 113 may be transformed as follows:

$$e = -2L_{aa}\frac{di}{dt} - 2\Lambda\Omega R \sum_{g=e}^{k} (+B_g - B_{g'})$$ (117)

Integrate both members of this equation from the time $t = 0$ to $t = T_c$:

$$\int_{t=0}^{t=T_c} e\, dt = 4L_{aa}I - 2\Lambda\Omega R \sum_{g=e}^{k} \left[\int_{t=0}^{t=T_c} B_g\, dt - \int_{t=0}^{t=T_c} B_{g'}\, dt \right]$$ (118)

If x is the peripheral length of the armature, the relation

$$\Omega R\, dt = dx$$

results, and the last member appearing in Equation 118 may be written

$$2\Lambda\Omega R \sum_{g=e}^{k} \left[\int_{t=0}^{t=T_c} B_g\, dt - \int_{t=0}^{t=T_c} B_{g'}\, dt \right]$$

$$= 2\Lambda \sum_{g=e}^{k} \left[\int_{x_g}^{x_h} B_g\, dx - \int_{x_{g'}}^{x_{h'}} B_{g'}\, dx \right] = 4\phi$$ (119)

and Equation 118 may be written

$$\int_{t=0}^{t=T_c} e\, dt = 4L_{aa}I - 4\phi = 0$$ (120)

Hence the following theorem:

XIV. First Theorem regarding Commutation in Anisotropic Machines. *The integral of the total electromotive force induced in the commutating section, extended over the total duration of commutation, or the total electric impulse induced in this same commutating section, or the mean value of the total induced electromotive force of an elementary smooth armature is zero when only the anisotropic flux is taken into account.*

In the first section of this chapter it has been shown that the counter-electromotive force, for the reversal of the normal current in a section of the winding when two diametrically opposite sections are commutating simultaneously and when the other sections carry no current, is about $25 \times 1.6 = 40$ volts in a dynamo, and about $4 \times 25 \times 1.6 = 160$ volts in a metadyne, whereas the usual commutating poles induce only about 2 volts in the commutating section. The theorem stated above shows that the 38 volts left over in a dynamo or the 158 volts left in a metadyne are compensated by the action on the commutating section of the noncommutating sections by means of their mutual induction, owing to the variation of the coefficient of this mutual induction because of the angular rotation of the armature.

4. THE SECOND THEOREM ON COMMUTATION IN ANISOTROPIC MACHINES

In this section the action of only the anisotropic flux acting upon a smooth elementary armature will again be discussed. Consider the instantaneous value of the electromotive force induced in the commutating section as given in the preceding section and add to it the ohmic drop ri. The following equation is obtained:

$$-2L_{aa}\frac{di}{dt} + 2I\frac{d}{dt}\sum_{g=e}^{k} L_{ga} - ri = 0 \tag{121}$$

determining the instantaneous current i in the commutating sections for a smooth elementary armature. The resistance r comprising the resistance of the commutating section and the apparent resistance of the brush contact is a complicated function of the current i, but the total amount of the voltage drop ri is small with respect to the absolute value of each of the other two members of Equation 121.

If the angular speed Ω is a constant, the second term of Equation 121 may often be made a constant in practice. By means of Equation 116 it is then easy to see that the condition necessary and sufficient for obtaining the second member of Equation 121 constant is to satisfy the relation

$$\sum_{g=e}^{k} (B_g - B_{g'}) = \text{constant} \tag{122}$$

during the entire time of commutation. It is recalled that the positive sense of the induction is centripetal.

B_g and $B_{g'}$ are the values of the induction in the air gap under the polar segments for flux ϕ created by the commutating section itself when it is carrying current I. Equation 122 is obviously satisfied when the air gap has a constant depth, and this occurs very often in practice. Nearly all practical machines can be shown to satisfy Equation 122. Here, for the sake of brevity, the reader should limit attention to an air gap of constant depth.

Assume, then, that Equation 122 is satisfied, and let $2KI$ be the value of the second term of Equation 121. After Equation 115 is applied, the relation

$$K = \frac{1}{I}\sum_{g=e}^{k} \left[\frac{d\phi_{gB}}{dt} - \frac{d\phi_{Ag}}{dt}\right] \tag{123}$$

is obtained for any instant of commutation. Multiply each member by dt, and integrate for the whole duration of commutation:

$$KT_c = \frac{1}{I} \sum_{g=e}^{k} \left[\int_0^{T_c} d\phi_{gB} - \int_0^{T_c} d\phi_{Ag} \right] = -\frac{1}{I} 2\phi \qquad (124)$$

whence

$$K = -\frac{2L_{aa}}{T_c}$$

Equation 121 may then be written

$$\frac{di}{dt} + \frac{2I}{T_c} + \frac{r}{2L_{aa}} i = 0 \qquad (125)$$

which is a very simple equation if r is a constant. Suppose that $r = 0$; remember that, for $t = 0$, $i = I$. Then Equation 125 gives this important result:

$$i = I \left(1 - 2\frac{t}{T_c} \right) \qquad (126)$$

Figure 58 gives a graphical representation of current i.

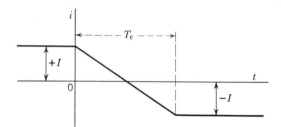

Fig. 58.   Current i during linear commutation.

When the linear law 126 occurs, the current density under the brush remains constant at any point of the contact surface, the losses have a minimum value, and the temperature of the commutator itself is the lowest. The commutation is then sometimes called "ideal," but here it will be referred to as "linear commutation."

The following theorem may now be stated:

XV. SECOND THEOREM ON COMMUTATION IN ANISOTROPIC MACHINES. *In a smooth elementary armature the commutation that occurs under the action of only the anisotropic flux is linear when Equation 122 is satisfied, as happens in nearly all practical cases, and when the total resistance of the circuit, short-circuited by the brushes, is zero.*

Further study shows that the last two theorems may be extended not only to various types of air gaps of variable depth but also to slotted armatures.

Consider Equation 125; even for a constant value of r, the solution—an exponential law—gives a commutating current less favorable than the linear current of Equation 126. If condition 122 is satisfied, the linear law, Equation 126, is obtained only when $r = 0$, as is easily proved. Thus commutation would be at its best when metallic brushes with very low contact resistance are used, when only the anisotropic flux is considered. However, experience with normal machines has shown that far better commutation is obtained with high-contact-voltage graphitic brushes; this is so because in an actual machine one must consider both electromotive forces, the one induced by the anisotropic flux and the other induced by the isotropic flux.

Taking into account the average numerical results of the first section of this chapter, one may say that in ordinary machines, dynamos or metadynes, 95% to 99% of the total electromotive force e, induced in the commutating section when the two commutating sections reverse their current while all other armature sections carry no current, is balanced by the action of the noncommutating sections when they carry their normal current. Only the remaining 5% to 1% of e must be considered for further compensation.

A departure from Equation 122 means a departure from linear commutation, as far as the anisotropic flux is concerned. Now the first member of Equation 122 may also be written

$$\frac{1}{2(k - e + 1)} \left(\sum_{g=e}^{k} B_g - \sum_{g'=e'}^{k'} B_{g'} \right) = (B_g)_m \qquad (127)$$

where $2(k - e + 1)$ is the number of armature sections moving through the polar space during the time T_c, and where $(B_g)_m$ indicates the mean value of the induction along the armature conductors corresponding to the flux created by the commutating section assumed to be carrying current $+I$. Either this mean value remains constant for any position of the commutating section during commutation and then the law 122 is valid, or it does not remain constant and then commutation is perturbed.

The oscillation during the time T_c of the value of the first member of Equation 122 around its mean value may give a measure of the disturbance of the commutation from the ideal linear law, when only the anisotropic flux is considered. This oscillation may be investigated, and any step reducing it may generally be regarded as an improvement of commutation. The curve of $\Psi(t)$, a function of the time t extended over T_c, and defined as

$$\Psi(t) = \sum_{g=e}^{k} (B_g - B_{g'}) - \frac{1}{T_c} \int_0^{T_c} \sum_{g=e}^{k} (B_g - B_{g'}) \, dt \qquad (128)$$

may be considered a criterion for the quality of commutation, as far as the shape of the magnetic circuit of the iron is concerned.

5. SOME APPLICATIONS OF THE THREE THEOREMS ON COMMUTATION

Many times the author has had to consider proposed machines having a commutator, but of such construction that the two theorems on commutation for anisotropic machines could not apply. His judgment is that such suggestions are practically impossible of execution except for very small outputs.

Figure 59 shows schematically one of these machines: it is a static converter from three-phase alternating current to direct current; in the

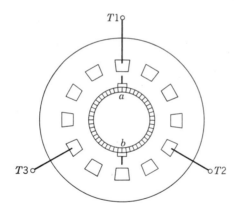

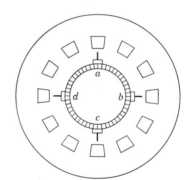

Fig. 59. A static three-phase synchronous converter.

Fig. 60. A constant-current generator. Commutation is tolerable only for small outputs.

slots is embedded a closed winding connected on one side to a three-phase network by the three taps $T1$, $T2$, and $T3$ and on the other side to a commutator upon which bear two brushes, a and b, which are assumed to rotate at an angular speed equal to the pulsation of the alternating current in the three-phase network. This machine satisfies only the theorem for isotropic machines, and it does not comply with the theorems on commutation of anisotropic machines. The full value of the electromotive force e must be compensated by some device; further, e is much higher here than in the ordinary dynamo or metadyne because there is no air gap at all. This machine will not commutate and cannot be made useful unless new commutating devices, unknown so far, are applied.

As a second example, certain machines that have been proposed and even constructed may be considered; these consist essentially of stationary windings arranged as on a static transformer, divided into sections and connected, one section after another, to a commutator, with a relative motion between commutator and brushes, either of these two elements to remain stationary. The "Transverter" and the "Panchahuteur" belong to this class of machines. The two theorems of commutation in anisotropic machines do not apply; the electromotive force e is not compensated at all; and the value of e is again very high.

Figure 60 shows schematically a third example: a closed winding is embedded in the slots and is divided in sections connected to a commutator upon which bear four equidistant brushes; a relative rotation is created between brushes and commutator. This is a semistatic pseudo-metadyne; if a constant-voltage direct-current source is applied between brushes a and c, a constant current may be derived from brushes b and d approximately inversely proportional to the speed of the mutual rotation between brushes and commutator, and approximately proportional to the impressed voltage on brushes a and c. However, commutation is impossible for an output exceeding a few kilowatts at 110 volts.

6. ACTION OF THE STATOR WINDING ON COMMUTATION OF A DYNAMO

The first theorem for anisotropic machines may be stated as follows: the total variation of the anisotropic flux interlinked with the commutating section is zero. The second theorem for anisotropic machines may be stated as follows: the instantaneous variation of the anisotropic flux interlinked with the commutating section is zero within the conditions for which the second theorem applies.

Therefore, the flux having its closed flux lines similar to the one drawn in Fig. 57 is practically invariable during commutation, and, therefore, a field winding on the stator will have practically no damping or any other action on commutation.

It is well known that large dynamos generally commutate in the same way when they are short-circuited (while there are practically no field ampere-turns) and when they are fully loaded (while the field ampere-turns have their normal value). Commutation may be somewhat better in one or in the other case, but not radically different. For the same reason, a laminated stator has no noticeable action on commutation, although many writers think it has an unfavorable action. The author had the opportunity to make accurate tests with laminated and non-laminated stators and could not detect any difference; this result may be considered a confirmation of the statement made above.

7. ON THE FLUXES ACTING ON THE COMMUTATION OF AN ACTUAL DYNAMO

Consider again Fig. 57 and restrict attention to an elementary armature. The flux interlinked with the commutating section aa' may be subdivided into three components:

A first component is the anisotropic flux created by the commutating section. Owing to the rotation of the noncommutating sections with respect to this flux, its total action is zero according to the first theorem for anisotropic machines.

A second component is the flux created by the commutating sections other than the anisotropic. One part of it spreads around the conductors of the section in the air comprised in the space between two consecutive polar segments, and a second part of it spreads along the front connection on both sides of the armature. The theorem for isotropic machines may be applied to this second part of the second component.

A third component is the flux created by a stator field winding and cut by the conductors of the commutating section during commutation.

In order to compensate the electromotive force induced by the last two components, commutating poles may be used, and their action upon the commutating section may be calculated either as a modification of mutual inductance or as an electromotive force induced by cutting the flux emerging from the commutating poles. The analysis of the phenomenon of commutation in a dynamo is now followed by a similar consideration of commutation in a metadyne. For this purpose the generalization developed in the following paragraph is necessary.

8. GENERALIZATION OF THE THEOREMS FOR ANISOTROPIC MACHINES

The machine schematically shown by Fig. 61 is an anisotropic one but of a more complicated shape than the one of Fig. 57. Let aa' and bb' be the two extreme positions within which lie the zone of commu-

tation and an axis of symmetry for the magnetic circuit. The anisotropic flux created by the current, I, flowing through the commutating
zone may be resolved into two others, ϕ_{DA} passing through the polar
segments D and A, and ϕ_{CB} passing through the polar segments C and
B. Each of the two theorems may be applied upon each of the fluxes
ϕ_{DA} and ϕ_{CB} separately, and the combined result may be stated by the
same theorems applied to the more complex shape of the magnetic cir-
cuit. The fluxes ϕ_{CA} and ϕ_{BD} could be taken instead of the fluxes ϕ_{BA}
and ϕ_{CB}.

Instead of four polar segments, any even number may be considered
with the same result. The generalization is easily extended to magnetic

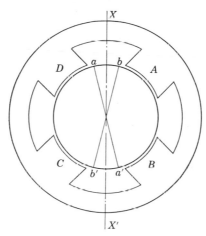

Fig. 61. An anisotropic machine of more complex form than that in Fig. 57.

circuits where the commutation axis, XX', is no longer an axis of symmetry for the magnetic circuit by subdividing the total flux into elements which must only satisfy the condition that, during the whole
time of commutation T_c, each element is constantly and completely
interlinked with the commutating section.

9. DEVICE FOR GOOD COMMUTATION IN A METADYNE

Consider in Fig. 62 a metadyne with four brushes and a diametrical
winding pitch, and assume that the four brushes, a, b, c, and d, lie on
two diameters, ac and bd. Then these diameters coincide with the four
commutating axes.

Now consider a stator provided with a winding; in order to insure
good commutation at the two brushes a and c, an anisotropic stator is

created by opening the interpole slots A and C wide enough to allow the commutating zones to be free as Fig. 63 shows. These same slots may be used for embedding the straight sides of the stator windings; their circular sides are shown in the figure by dotted lines. Application of the same procedure to the commutation of brushes b and d and to the location of the straight sides of the corresponding stator windings yields a stator as shown in Fig. 64, with four slots and four polar segments, each slot containing the straight side of two stator coils and surrounded by a third coil.

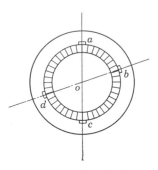

Fig. 62. A fourth-degree metadyne in which the brush axes and commutation axes coincide.

The stator coils create a flux along the commutating zone, which induces an electromotive force in the commutating section generally adverse to commutation. In order to eliminate this flux, the stator coils are divided into two other smaller

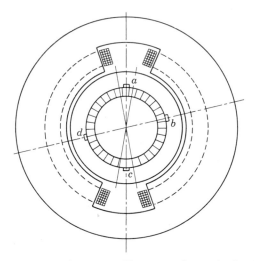

Fig. 63. Stator construction to provide a neutral zone for brushes a and c.

coils, each coil interlinked with only one polar segment as Fig. 65 shows. Hence the following rule:

XVI. RULE. *Above each commutating zone of a metadyne, a space must be provided larger than the commutating zone; and any coil of a stator winding which is thus found to be interlinked simultaneously with more than one polar segment must, generally, be subdivided into as many separate coils as there are polar segments, so that each coil will be interlinked with only one polar segment.*

The word "generally" mentioned in the rule is due to the fact that in some cases the proposed stator winding may also be used for the compensation of the ampere-turns of the armature reaction. In Part II some examples of these cases are pointed out.

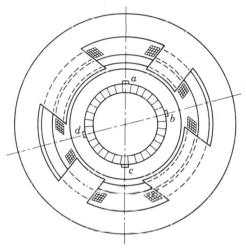

Fig. 64.   Additional stator slots required by brushes b and d.

Finally, in order to minimize the effect of the stator coils on commutation for the arrangement of Fig. 65, the slots opened in the stator must be made liberally wider than the commutation zone, as Fig. 63 shows. Thus the commutation of the four brushes, a, b, c, and d, of the metadyne, with the stator arranged as in Fig. 65, will take place under the favorable conditions pointed out by the first theorem for anisotropic machines, according to its generalization as developed in Section 8, and with the considerations made in Section 7.

The conditions under which commutation takes place in a dynamo and in a metadyne differ in another respect. In a dynamo there is only one diametrical commutating axis; in the metadyne of Fig. 65 there are two of them, and their mutual influence must be investigated.

If bd is perpendicular to ca, the mutual induction is zero. If these two diameters are not perpendicular, there is mutual induction and therefore a mutual interaction, particularly when the brush currents vary quickly. This interaction may be favorable or unfavorable to commutation; the result obviously depends on the sense and the value of the commutated currents, and the interaction must be investigated case by case. Nevertheless, it may generally be observed that the whole flux interlinked with commutating sections belonging to different diameters of the armature, far apart the one from another, is also interlinked with armature and stator windings that are practically short-circuited; therefore the variation of this flux is severely damped, and the mutual interaction of the commutating sections is considerably reduced. However, it is also possible to construct devices that minimize the interaction of the comutating sections even if the interlinking flux is not damped out.

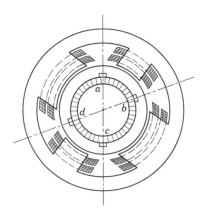

Fig. 65. Rearrangement of stator windings for good commutation in the metadyne of Fig. 64.

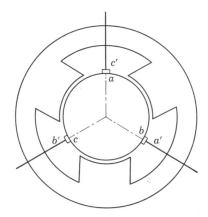

Fig. 66. A third-degree metadyne with coincident commutating axes.

So far, a diametrical winding pitch and diametrically opposite brushes have been considered. Now remove these limitations: the two radial commutating axes corresponding to each brush generally lie in different directions (in the case of nondiametrical pitch), and therefore two stator slots must be provided for each brush. In order to obtain reasonable utilization of the material, arrangements must be made to reduce the number of stator slots by causing the radial commutating axes to coincide whenever this is possible.

Figure 66 shows a metadyne with three equidistant brushes and a winding pitch of 120°. Here the internal radial commutating axis of a brush coincides with the external radial commutating axis of the preceding brush, and only three stator slots are necessary.

The same procedure may be applied to a metadyne with four equidistant brushes and a winding pitch of 90°, and so on, to m brushes and a winding pitch equal to $k(360°/m)$, where k is an integer. This device, sometimes useful for small machines where commutating poles are not needed, is not always adopted when commutating poles on large machines are necessary because the commutating flux may not meet the conditions required for good simultaneous commutation of two different armature currents.

10. COMMUTATING POLES ON METADYNES

The ampere-turns interlinked with a commutating pole in a dynamo first must compensate the ampere-turns of the armature and secondly must develop a supplementary number of ampere-turns sufficient to create the flux for inducing the right electromotive force in the commutating section.

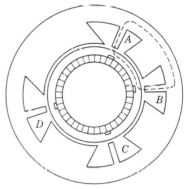

The compensation of the ampere-turns of the armature is more difficult in a metadyne than in a dynamo. Consider Fig. 67, showing schematically a metadyne with m brushes and with, say, Q stator slots, which means Q commutating zones. Commutating poles are provided in each stator slot, and now the problem is to determine the ampere-turns of their coils.

Fig. 67. Scheme of a general metadyne, illustrating the procedure for designing commutating poles.

Several cases will be considered by assuming that in the commutating zone commutation involves:

(a) A single brush current.

(b) Two brush currents having a constant ratio of intensity.

(c) Two brush currents having a variable ratio of intensity.

(d) More than two brush currents having a constant ratio of intensity.

(e) More than two brush currents having a variable ratio of intensity.

In case a there is only one radial commutating axis; case b concerns the usual dynamos and many metadynes with two overlapping radial commutating axes; all other cases correspond to metadynes with two or more coincident radial commutating axes. Cases d and e occur more frequently with armatures provided with a wave winding. It is to be noted that a commutating brush does not necessarily correspond to every commutating pole.

Let B_H be the induction along the axis of the air gap under the commutating pole of slot H. Then for proper commutation it follows that

$$B_H = \sum_g K_{Hg} I_g \qquad H = A, B, \cdots, Q \qquad (129)$$

Let X_H be the ampere-turns that must be interlinked with the commutating pole of slot H, their positive sense being along the centrifugal direction with respect to the armature. Trace a closed line through the geometrical axis of the commutating pole of slot H, then through the geometrical axis of any other commutating axis, say the one in slot q, then through the corresponding air gaps of depth a_H along a radius of the armature, and finally along a line, say l_H, completely immersed in the iron magnetic circuit of the machine. Let the positive sense of this line be centrifugal through the commutating pole of slot H. Upon application of Maxwell's law of circuitation, the following equation is obtained:

$$\frac{1}{\mu_0}[a_H B_H - a_q B_q] + \int_{l_H} \frac{B_s}{\mu_s} \cos \theta_s \, ds = X_H - X_q$$

$$+ \sum_h N_{Hh} I_h \qquad H = A, B, \cdots, P \quad (130)$$

where the induction in the air gap of a commutating pole has its positive sense in the centrifugal direction, where s is the length in the positive sense along the line l_H, where B_s is the magnetic induction in this part of the path, where θ_s is the angle between the positive direction of the magnetic induction and the positive direction of the tangent to the line l_H at the point of abscissa s, and finally where $N_{Hh} I_h$ are the armature ampere-turns created by the current I_h and interlinked with line l_H.

There are as many Equations 130 as there are different integral lines traced according to the rule given above; that means $\frac{1}{2}Q(Q - 1)$ equations. It is easy to see that all these equations are not independent of one another and that only $Q - 1 = P$ of them are independent. In order to trace the integral lines corresponding to the independent equations, one may follow the same procedures given for obtaining the $m - 1$ independent canonical currents in the armature; for instance, one may trace $Q - 1 = P$ loops comprising two consecutive commutating poles, or one may trace $P = Q - 1$ loops comprising a fixed commutating pole and any one of the other P commutating poles. Thus P Equations 130 independent of one another may be obtained; hence any reference to group 130 will imply that the group comprises P independent equations.

The addition to the group 130 of P equations of an arbitrary complementary relation between the values X_H, for instance a linear relation between them—in particular if one of them is set equal to an arbitrary value, for example zero—a group of Q equations is obtained that defines the ampere-turns X_A, X_B, $\cdots$, X_Q.

The value of the integral appearing in Equations 130 depends to some extent on the stator windings, but its net value is generally small enough compared with the value of the other terms that the following rule may be considered correct without great error:

XVII. RULE. *The magnetic field under the commutating poles, necessary for good commutation in a metadyne, is generally obtained by ampere-turns created by as many coils as there are independent armature currents, i.e., m − 1 coils.*

In a dynamo there is only one brush current, $m = 2$, and therefore there is a single coil around the commutating poles. However, skillful design of a metadyne may reduce the number of the coils of the commutating poles so far that there may finally be only a single coil. But it is important to notice that, even when there are many coils, the total value of their ampere-turns is practically the same as the value of the ampere-turns of a dynamo of comparable size.

Although the study of commutation has been restricted here, enough has been said to justify the following statement:

In a metadyne in which Rules XVI and XVII are satisfied, the commutation is as good, other things being equal, as in a dynamo having a similar armature rotating at the same speed.

Closer investigation of commutation has shown that commutation in a metadyne may be made better than in a comparable dynamo; in other words, for the same armature and the same speed, the current satisfactorily commutated in a metadyne is higher than in the corresponding dynamo. If Rules XVI and XVII do not apply, the machine is said to be a "pseudometadyne." Commutation is then possible or tolerable only for small outputs and relatively low speeds.

11. NOTES CONCERNING ANISOTROPIC METADYNES

The free spaces above the commutating zones give an anisotropic magnetic circuit, but a magnetic circuit may be anisotropic because of its geometrically unsymmetrical shape or because of local iron saturation. Only the first cause will be considered here. The question then arises how the theorems so far developed will be affected.

The first theorem will hold if the radial magnetic axis of the flux created by the armature, when it is carrying a canonical current corresponding to a particular pair of brushes, say the brushes g, h, is an axis of symmetry of the magnetic circuit in spite of the free spaces provided on the stator above the commutating zones. Then $K_{gh}^{gh} = 0$.

If this condition of geometrical symmetry of the magnetic circuit occurs for all the $m - 1$ independent canonical currents, then all the elements of the main diagonal of the matrix of the coefficients K_{gh}^{bd} will be zero. Further, if this condition of geometrical symmetry holds for any of the $m(m - 1)/2$ canonical currents, Theorem VII, expressed by the relation $K_{gh}^{bd} = -K_{bd}^{gh}$, also holds and then the matrix of the $(m - 1)^2$ coefficients K corresponding to the $m - 1$ independent canonical currents is still a skew-symmetric one.

SPECIAL CASES OF METADYNES

11 · Introduction

1. GENERAL REMARKS ON DISTRIBUTION SYSTEMS

In this second part, special cases of metadynes are investigated. For this purpose the means made available by the general theory developed in Part I will be used, and the particular properties of each special case will be pointed out. Further, a brief description will be given of some applications actually in operation.

Every machine receives electric energy supplied by a network, or it operates to supply energy to the network, or it is supplied by an electric network and it supplies electric energy to another network. Thus we must first consider the mode of distribution of electric power.

Conventionally, electric power is split into two elements, voltage and current; and, if there is a network for supplying energy to a number of consumers that are variable in operation and in output with time, it is desirable, on the one hand, to keep as many characteristics of the energy constant as possible to provide satisfactory continuous operation of the consumer and, on the other hand, to keep the regulation of the machines generating the energy as invariable as possible. Thus electric power is generally supplied at constant voltage because the main generators, dynamos and alternators, inherently supply power at substantially constant voltage, and because consumers supplied at constant voltage operate satisfactorily in general. Such a constant-voltage system is then a shunt network.

The operation of many consumers is better with constant current than with constant voltage, but the well-known main generators are not suitable for supplying electric power at constant current. Consumers that operate better from constant-current than from constant-voltage sources are very numerous, and only the general habit of using a constant-voltage supply prevents many electrical engineers from acknowledging this fact. However, some highly skilled engineers have tried to produce generators capable of supplying power at constant current; prominent among them is Thury of Switzerland, who succeeded in developing constant direct-current networks large enough to supply many important towns. He used as main generators dynamos with shiftable brushes so that the impressed voltage at any instant is set to the value necessary to keep the current constant at a predetermined value. By means of very ingenious devices, Thury overcame the difficulty of commutation with shiftable brushes.

Many types of metadyne can supply constant direct current quite naturally without the aid of any additional device, because their inherent characteristic requires no setting whatever; thus they are generators suitable for a series network and may bring again into a more favorable light the system of supplying electric power at constant current. The particular metadynes considered in Part II are often connected to a constant-voltage shunt network or to a constant-current series network, or to both kinds.

It is appropriate now to give equal attention to shunt networks supplied with constant voltage and series networks carrying constant current. The question then arises whether there are some other useful distribution systems outside of these two.

For a large distribution network comprising all kinds of consumers, a constant-voltage or a constant-current regulation seems the most suitable or at least the most equitable with respect to the operation of the various consumers. But the consumers may be subdivided into large classes, each class having some special operation, with special requirements and special dangers to avoid. For each class a particular function correlating the current and the voltage, different from the ones given above, appears to be more desirable.

Usually a substation is installed to reduce the voltage when the energy is supplied from a long transmission line to an aggregate load. If this local area comprises consumers of a special class, the substation might not only modify the voltage value, as is done now, but might also change the current-voltage relationship characterizing the distribution system from the constant-voltage or the constant-current rule to another current-voltage function more suitable to the class of consumer supplied by the substation.

Further, even with shunt networks at constant voltage or series networks at constant current, safety reasons may require certain limitations. Hence, for such conditions there must be some particular relation between voltage and current different from the function observed during normal operation.

A given desirable function correlating voltage and current in steady state is not generally valid when quick changes occur—for instance, when a fault occurs. Then it is desirable that, even for very rapid variations with respect to time, the desired regulation be maintained or at least be closely followed. Thus the dynamic behavior of a plant must be as carefully investigated as its static operation. Therefore, the choice of an appropriate distribution for a metadyne plant is a question that must be considered with the aid of dynamic analysis.

The facility with which constant current may be supplied by a metadyne creates the impression that a metadyne is a constant-current machine; this notion is incorrect. Most of the metadyne generators may supply electric power with an inherent characteristic that may be expressed analytically by an equation,

$$f(v, i) = 0 \tag{1}$$

which may, by suitable modification of easily adjusted parameters, cover a very large field of graphic characteristics, algebraic or other curves, as has been pointed out already in Part I.

Equation 1 may sometimes be reduced to a linear function:

$$Av + Bi + C = 0 \tag{2}$$

where A, B, and C are constants; in particular, the usual cases are

$$v = -\frac{C}{A}$$
$$i = -\frac{B}{A} \tag{3}$$

An extensive new field is opened by metadynes; it has a nonlinear characteristic expressed by Equation 1. Detailed investigation of this field, with special emphasis on dynamic operation of these machines, goes beyond the concepts of static behavior presented here.

2. CONVENTIONS

For the sake of simplicity, the ohmic drops are rarely considered in Part II. In fact, they do not change the linear form of the expression of the electromotive force as a function of the brush currents, and thus practically they interfere very little with the main operation.

It has been shown in Part I that with a given number of brushes per cycle, and with a given angular location of these brushes (i.e., from a metadyne of a given degree, a given class, and a given species), many different types of metadynes are derived by modifying the number and the connections of the stator windings. In order to simplify the investigation, attention will often be directed to the general case; then the equations will be specified by the particular sign and value of the coefficients that correspond to the particular type of metadyne. Accordingly, the scheme will be represented, as Fig. 68 shows, by a circle with the brushes placed at their relative angular locations, and with a square block above the brushes, the block representing the terminal of the machine leading to the corresponding brush; both the brush and ter-

minal are indicated by the same small Roman letter. Between brush
and terminal there may be one or many stator coils carrying the homonymous brush current. As the ohmic drop along these coils is generally
neglected, the potential of the brush and corresponding terminal are
assumed to be the same.

Generally, a shunt stator winding is connected between two brushes;
therefore, the current entering the brush is the sum of the currents
entering the homonymous terminal and the currents in the shunt stator

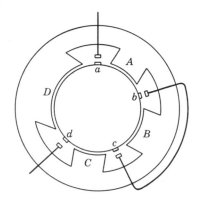

Fig. 68.   A generalized fourth-degree metadyne.

windings connected to that brush. Since the shunt currents are generally neglected with respect to the brush currents, it follows that the
brush current is identical with the homonymous terminal current and
that it passes unchanged through any stator windings connecting the
brush and the terminal.

It is recalled that the brush is represented in the diagram at just that
radial position which corresponds to its commutating axis relative to the
external layer of the winding. The latter is assumed to be a right-handed
one, and the armature is assumed to rotate in the clockwise sense when
the speed n is positive. The polar segment immediately following a
brush in the clockwise sense is indicated by the homonymous capital
Roman letter for that brush, as Fig. 68 shows.

12 · The Cross Transformer Metadyne at Substantially Constant Speed

1. THE METADYNE OF DEGREE $m = 4$ WITH TWO NONCONSECUTIVE BRUSHES CARRYING THE SAME CURRENT

The metadyne of degree $m = 4$ is investigated in many chapters of Part II. Frequently in metadynes of this degree the two nonconsecutive brushes carry the same current. For this reason the main properties of the general case are considered in this first section.

If two nonconsecutive brushes are carrying the same current, the general scheme must be the one of Fig. 69, in which the consumers 1 and

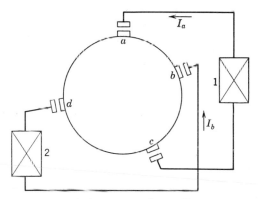

Fig. 69. The general fourth-degree metadyne with cross-connected brushes.

2 may supply or absorb electric power, or even may be reduced to a simple short circuit. In the figure the four brushes, a, b, c, and d, have a definite angular location, but this location does not enter into the equations developed here; therefore it does not limit the results, which thus apply to any type of metadyne, the scheme of which is derived from Fig. 6 by modification of the relative angular location of the brushes while their sequence is left unchanged. Since

$$I_a + I_c = 0$$
$$I_b + I_d = 0$$

(4)

there are thus only two different currents left, say I_a and I_b.

119

There are three independent brush voltages because $m = 4$, and these are chosen as follows: E_{ca}, E_{bd}, E_{ba}. The first two are obviously of practical interest, and the third one defines the relative potential of consumers 1 and 2.

For the sake of generality, assume that there are the following stator windings:

Two series stator windings, the one carrying the current I_a, $(I_\alpha = I_a)$, and the other the current I_b, $(I_\beta = I_b)$.

Three shunt windings connected across brushes a and c, brushes b and d, and brushes b and a, respectively; through these windings pass the currents I_γ, I_δ, I_ς, respectively.

An independent stator winding carrying the independent current I_ε.

A speed-regulator stator winding through which the regulator current, I_ρ, is flowing.

Further, assume that a mechanical torque, T_a, is applied to the shaft of the metadyne; that the speed is n while n_0 is the critical speed of the regulator, the value of n_0 being left constant; that the metadyne is isotropic and its iron nonsaturated. The metadyne losses are neglected.

The fundamental equations are

$$\frac{1}{n} E_{ca} = K_{ca}^b I_b + \sum_{\gamma=\alpha}^{\rho} K_{ca}^\gamma I_\gamma$$

$$\frac{1}{n} E_{bd} = K_{bd}^a I_a + \sum_{\gamma=\alpha}^{\rho} K_{bd}^\gamma I_\gamma \tag{5}$$

$$\frac{1}{n} E_{ba} = K_{ba}^a I_a + K_{ba}^b I_b + \sum_{\gamma=\alpha}^{\rho} K_{ba}^\gamma I_\gamma$$

And the regulator equations are

$$\sum_{\gamma=\alpha}^{\rho} [K_{ca}^\gamma I_a - K_{bd}^\gamma I_b] I_\gamma + 2\pi T_a = 0 \qquad I_\rho = K_\rho (n - n_0) \tag{6}$$

Thus there are five equations between seven variables: I_a, I_b, E_{ca}, E_{bd}, E_{ba}, I_ρ, and n.

Therefore, add to Equations 5 and 6 the two equations determining the relation between I_a and E_{ca} pertaining to consumer 1, and the relation between I_b and E_{bd} pertaining to consumer 2; then all the variables will be defined. If Equations 5 and 6 are added to just one more, and if five variables are eliminated from these six equations, the resulting relation between the two remaining variables will be a plane characteristic of the metadyne.

After substitution of the brush currents for the stator currents passing through a series winding, and of the brush voltage for the product of the stator current flowing in a shunt winding with the resistance of that winding, and after similar terms have been collected, Equations 5 and 6 are transformed into the following:

$$
\left.
\begin{aligned}
-\frac{1}{n} E_{ca} + A_{ca}^{bd}E_{bd} + A_{ca}^{ba}E_{ba} + A_{cu}^{ca}F_{ca} + B_{ca}^{a}I_a + B_{ca}^{b}I_b \\
+ K_{ca}^{\varepsilon}I_{\varepsilon} + K_{ca}^{\rho}I_{\rho} = 0 \\
-\frac{1}{n} E_{bd} + A_{bd}^{bd}E_{bd} + A_{bd}^{ba}E_{ba} + A_{bd}^{ca}E_{ca} + B_{bd}^{a}I_a + B_{bd}^{b}I_b \\
+ K_{bd}^{\varepsilon}I_{\varepsilon} + K_{bd}^{\rho}I_{\rho} = 0 \\
-\frac{1}{n} E_{ba} + A_{ba}^{bd}E_{bd} + A_{ba}^{ba}E_{ba} + A_{ba}^{ca}E_{ca} + B_{ba}^{a}I_a + B_{ba}^{b}I_b \\
+ K_{ba}^{\varepsilon}I_{\varepsilon} + K_{ba}^{\rho}I_{\rho} = 0 \\
2\pi nT_a + A_{ca}^{bd}E_{bd}I_a + A_{ca}^{ba}E_{ba}I_a + A_{ca}^{ca}E_{ca}I_a + B_{ca}^{a}I_a^2 + B_{ca}^{b}I_aI_b \\
+ K_{ca}^{\varepsilon}I_{\varepsilon}I_a + K_{ca}^{\rho}I_{\rho}I_a - A_{bd}^{bd}E_{bd}I_b - A_{bd}^{ba}E_{ba}I_b - A_{bd}^{ca}E_{ca}I_b \\
- B_{bd}^{a}I_aI_b - B_{bd}^{b}I_b^2 - K_{bd}^{\varepsilon}I_{\varepsilon}I_b - K_{bd}^{\rho}I_{\rho}I_b = 0
\end{aligned}
\right\} \quad (7)
$$

$$
I_{\rho} = K_{\rho}(n - n_0) \tag{8}
$$

where A and B are constants that depend on the construction of the machine.

Since the value of n is very near to n_0, the system of equations may be simplified with the assumption that $n = n_0$. Substitute n_0 for n in Equations 7 and drop Equation 8.

One of the supplementary equations defining the operation of the consumers, an equation that corresponds most frequently to practical cases, is one of the two following:

$$
E_{ca} = \text{constant} \tag{9}
$$

$$
I_a = \text{constant} \tag{10}
$$

Select the supplementary Equation 9, for instance. From the three first equations of system 7 are obtained I_{ρ}, I_a, and E_{ba}. If these are substituted in the last equation of system 7, a relation between I_b and E_{bd} results which is represented by a conic, in which E_{ca} and I_{ε} may be considered parameters to allow for a doubly infinite set of conics.

In practice, it is important to know what kind of conics may be obtained under these conditions. To know this, it is sufficient to solve Equations 7. The solution is straightforward but laborious because of the large number of terms appearing in these equations. Instead of undertaking it, adequate information may be obtained by means of the following procedure:

For the sake of simplicity put $E_{bd} = x$, $E_{ca} = C$ (constant) and $I_b = y$, $I_a = z$.

1. Recall that the characteristics

$$f_1(x, y) = 0$$

$$f_2(x, z) = 0$$

are conics, as has been demonstrated in Part I.

2. Observe that the fourth equation of group 7, the equation of the regulator dynamo, may also be written

$$xy = zC + 2\pi n T_a \equiv zC + P \tag{11}$$

where $2\pi n T_a = P$ represents the power supplied to the metadyne through the mechanical shaft.

3. Observe that the voltage $E_{bd} = x$ may have any value positive or negative, and that to any of these values corresponds at least one value of the current $I_b = y$.

At this point, assume first that the mechanical power, P, supplied by the shaft is constant. Now consider the case in which the characteristic is a straight line; the conic degenerates and the equation $f_1(x, y) = 0$ may be split into two linear ones. Then

$$ax + y + c = 0$$

Substitute in Equation 11 the value of y obtained from the last equation; the corresponding characteristic $f_2(x, z) = 0$ thus obtained is

$$x(ax + c) + zC + P = 0 \tag{12}$$

Since

$$\begin{vmatrix} a & 0 & \dfrac{c}{2} \\ 0 & 0 & \dfrac{C}{2} \\ \dfrac{c}{2} & \dfrac{C}{2} & P \end{vmatrix} = -\dfrac{aC^2}{4}$$

and

$$\begin{vmatrix} a & 0 \\ 0 & 0 \end{vmatrix} = 0$$

Equation 12 will be represented by a straight line if $C = 0$ or if $a = 0$, and otherwise by a parabola having its axis parallel to the z axis. See Figs. 70 and 71.

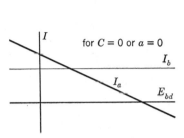

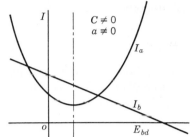

Fig. 70. Straight-line character-istic for constant shaft power.

Fig. 71. Parabolic characteristic for constant shaft power.

Conversely, if the characteristic $f_2(x, z) = 0$ is a straight line,

$$ax + z + c = 0$$

substituting the value of z obtained from this equation in Equation 11 yields the corresponding characteristic $f_1(x, y) = 0$ as follows:

$$xy + C(ax + c) - P = 0 \tag{13}$$

Since

$$\begin{vmatrix} 0 & \dfrac{1}{2} & \dfrac{Ca}{2} \\ \dfrac{1}{2} & 0 & 0 \\ \dfrac{Ca}{2} & 0 & Cc - P \end{vmatrix} = \dfrac{P - Cc}{4}$$

and

$$\begin{vmatrix} 0 & \dfrac{1}{2} \\ \dfrac{1}{2} & 0 \end{vmatrix} = -\dfrac{1}{4}$$

Equation 13 will give a straight line if $P - Cc = 0$ (for instance, if $P = 0$ and $c = 0$, or if $P = 0$ and $C = 0$); it will give a hyperbola if $P - Cc \neq 0$. See Figs. 72 and 73.

Since this study has examined the possible cases for which at least one of the two characteristics is a straight line, the only case left is that for which both characteristics are nondegenerate conics. From observation 3 mentioned above, it may be deduced that the characteristics $f_1(x, y) = 0$ cannot be:

A circle.
An ellipse.

A parabola lying completely on one side of the y axis.

A parabola lying on both sides of the y axis but not having its axis parallel to the y axis.

A hyperbola with neither asymptote parallel to the y axis.

In other words, the characteristic $f_1(x, y)$ can be only either of the following:

A parabola having its axis parallel to the y axis.

A hyperbola having one of its asymptotes parallel to the y axis.

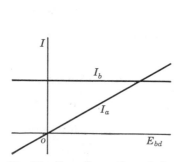

Fig. 72. Some linear characteristics possible with the shaft power equal to zero.

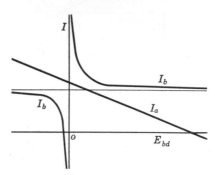

Fig. 73. Hyperbolic characteristics possible with the cross-connected metadyne.

Now a parabola having its axis parallel to the y axis is, in the general case, represented analytically by the equation

$$y = ax^2 + bx + c$$

After substitution for y in Equation 11 of the value given above, the following equation is obtained:

$$x(ax^2 + bx + c) = zC + P$$

which is a cubic and not a conic. Therefore, the characteristic of $f_1(x, y) = 0$ cannot be a parabola at all.

On the other hand, the general equation of a hyperbola having one of its asymptotes parallel to the y axis is

$$ax^2 + xy + bx + cy + d = 0$$

This equation may be solved for y immediately; substituting this value in Equation 11 again yields an equation of the third degree if $a \neq 0$. Therefore, the only possible hyperbola is the one having the equation

$$xy + bx + cy + d = 0$$

This is a hyperbola having asymptotes such that one is parallel to the x axis and the other is parallel to the y axis. Then the equation $f_2(x, z) = 0$ becomes

$$bx^2 + Cxz + x(P + d) + zcC + Pc = 0 \qquad (14)$$

which is a hyperbola having an asymptote parallel to the z axis, as Fig. 74 shows.

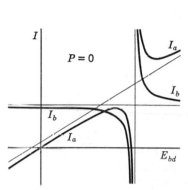

Fig. 74. Hyperbolic transformer characteristics may result when the two partial characteristics are non-degenerate conics.

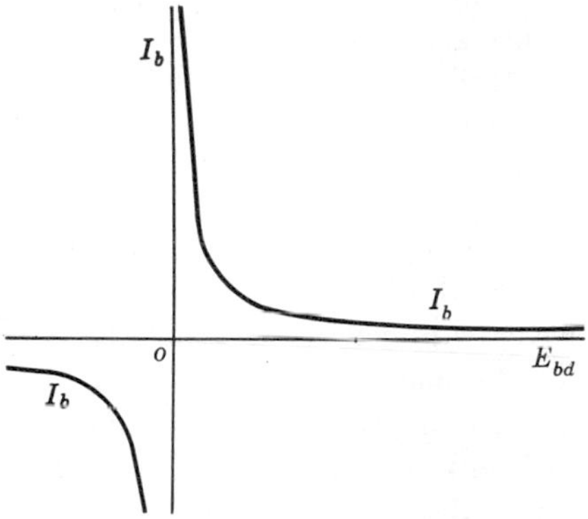

Fig. 75. An equilateral hyperbola is a possible partial characteristic.

In particular, consider the special operating condition in which the voltage $E_{bd} = x = 0$, obtained, for instance, when the brushes b and d are short-circuited. Then Equation 11 yields only one value for z:

$$z = \frac{-P}{C} \qquad (15)$$

Equation 15 yields a finite value for z if the following conditions are not satisfied simultaneously:

$$P \neq 0$$
$$C \neq 0 \qquad (16)$$

If both relations 16 are satisfied, the equation $f_1(x, y)$ becomes

$$xy = P \qquad (17)$$

corresponding to an equilateral hyperbola, as Fig. 75 shows.

To summarize, the characteristic $f_1(x, y) = f_1(E_{bd}, I_b) = 0$ may be a straight line or a hyperbola having its asymptotes parallel to the x and

y axes, respectively, the center being at any position. The characteristic $f_2(x, y) = f_2(E_{bd}, I_a) = 0$ may be a straight line, a hyperbola, or a parabola. An ellipse or circle is impossible under the conditions postulated: $E_{ca} = C$ and $2\pi n T_a = P$, where C and P are two constants.

If $P = 0$, the metadyne is a pure transformer.

If $P > 0$, the metadyne is a generator and may simultaneously be a transformer; if $P > 0$ and $C = 0$ simultaneously, the metadyne is a pure generator.

If $P < 0$, the metadyne is a motor and may simultaneously be a transformer; if $P < 0$ and $C = 0$ simultaneously, the metadyne is a pure motor.

These results have been obtained from the assumption that not only the speed n but also the torque on the shaft, and hence the mechanical power supplied to the metadyne, are constant. But this power, P, may be made a function of the electric variables of the metadyne, for instance, of E_{bd}, or of I_b, or of I_a. If this function is a linear one, then the shape of the characteristic will remain substantially the same as shown above; if P is a more elaborate function of the electric variables, then the shape of the characteristic changes.

Instead of the complementary Equation 9, take Equation 10, and put $I_a = C$, $x = E_{bd}$, $y = I_b$, and $E_{ca} = v$. Then the regulator-dynamo equation may be written

$$P + Cv = xy$$

which is substantially the same as Equation 11; therefore, the resulting characteristic will remain substantially the same.

So far the regulator dynamo has been considered operating. If the regulator dynamo is omitted, the last equation of group 7 is dropped, and the group will consist of the remaining first four equations, all linear in the five variables E_{bd}, E_{ca}, E_{ba}, I_a, and I_b. If a complementary arbitrary equation between these variables is given, and if it is a linear one such as either of the two Equations 9 and 10, the characteristics will be linear and will be represented by straight lines.

If the complementary arbitrary equation is nonlinear, for instance, algebraic of the second degree as is possible with a metadyne, then generally the characteristic considered here will also be algebraic and nonlinear. Current I_ε may be considered a parameter of great practical value because it allows modification by easy means of the position of the characteristics with respect to the coordinates.

2. THE "CROSS" TRANSFORMER METADYNE

This name denotes a metadyne having four equidistant brushes per cycle, say a, b, c, d, and having its brushes a and c connected to a power system and its brushes b and d connected to a consumer, as Fig. 76 shows. Further, it will be assumed that the armature winding pitch is substantially diametrical. In this case

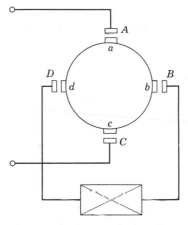

$$E_{ba} = E_{cd}$$
$$E_{cb} = E_{da} \tag{18}$$

and the vector diagram will then have the shape of a parallelogram as Fig. 77 shows.

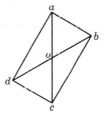

Fig. 76.   Scheme of the Cross transformer metadyne.

FIG. 77.   Vector diagram for the Cross transformer metadyne.

Let o be the intersection of the two diagonals; then

$$E_{ba} = E_{bo} + E_{oa} = \tfrac{1}{2}(E_{ca} + E_{bd})$$
$$E_{cb} = E_{co} + E_{ob} = \tfrac{1}{2}(E_{ca} - E_{bd}) \tag{19}$$

That means that only two electromotive forces are independent; choose these as the electromotive forces E_{ca} and E_{bd}, and for the sake of simplicity put

$$E_{bd} = x$$
$$I_b = y$$
$$E_{ca} = v \tag{20}$$
$$I_a = z$$

The fundamental Equations 5 of the metadyne are then reduced to the two first ones, where evidently

$$K_{ca}^b = K_{bd}^a \tag{21}$$

The corresponding first two equations of group 7 and the equation of the regulator dynamo may be written

$$-\frac{1}{n}v + A_v v + A_x x + A_z z + A_y y + K_{ca}^{\varepsilon} I_{\varepsilon} + K_{ca}^{\rho} I_{\rho} = 0$$

$$-\frac{1}{n}x + B_v v + B_x x + B_z z + B_y y + K_{bd}^{\varepsilon} I_{\varepsilon} + K_{bd}^{\rho} I_{\rho} = 0 \qquad (22)$$

$$2\pi n T_a = P = xy - vz$$

Now assume that the terminals A and C are connected to a constant-voltage network. Let

$$v = C$$

The variables reduce to four in number, and the global characteristic $W_{(4)}^{(1)}$ becomes a line in a four-dimensional space. Therefore, a complete representation of this line may be obtained by its projections on the coordinate hyperplanes.

Consider that the stator has no series windings; then from relation 21 results

$$A_z = B_y = 0$$

$$A_y = B_z = K$$

and Equations 22 may be simplified as follows:

$$C\left(A_v - \frac{1}{n}\right) + A_x x + Ky + K_{ca}^{\varepsilon} I_{\varepsilon} + K_{ca}^{\rho} I_{\rho} = 0$$

$$B_v C + x\left(B_x - \frac{1}{n}\right) + K_z + K_{bd}^{\varepsilon} I_{\varepsilon} + K_{bd}^{\rho} I_{\rho} = 0 \qquad (23)$$

$$P + Cz = xy$$

Elimination of the two variables I_{ρ} and z from this system of equations yields the following equation of the characteristic $f_1(x, y) = 0$:

$$(x - a)(y - b) = c$$

where

$$a = -C\frac{K_{bd}^{\rho}}{K_{ca}^{\rho}}$$

$$b = \frac{C}{K}\left[B_x - \frac{1}{n} - A_x\frac{K_{bd}^{\rho}}{K_{ca}^{\rho}}\right] \qquad (24)$$

$$c = P + ab + C\left[\left(A_v - \frac{1}{n}\right)\frac{K_{bd}^{\rho}}{K_{ca}^{\rho}} - B_v\right] + I_{\varepsilon}\left(K_{ca}^{\varepsilon}\frac{K_{bd}^{\rho}}{K_{ca}^{\rho}} - K_{bd}^{\varepsilon}\right)$$

This characteristic is represented by a hyperbola having as its center the point with coordinates $x = a$ and $y = b$, having c as its power, and having its asymptotes parallel to the coordinate axes. As Fig. 78 shows, such a characteristic is invaluable in many applications because the operation of the consumer is then similar to operation at substantially constant current at low voltages, which generally means operation at low speed, and similar to operation at substantially constant voltage at high voltages, which generally means operation at high speed. Suppose, for instance, that the consumer is an independently excited motor,

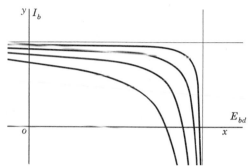

Fig. 78. The hyperbola provides regions of constant-current and constant-voltage operation.

or a series motor; it will start under constant current and it will reach high speeds with constant voltage, conditions very desirable for each sort of operation.

From Equations 24 it follows that varying the value of the independent current, I_e, keeps the center and therefore the asymptotes fixed, and varies only the power of the hyperbola, thus generating a family of characteristics as Fig. 78 shows. The abscissa of the asymptote parallel to the y axis is the highest voltage that may be applied to the consumer.

The abscissa of the center may be modified, for a given network supplying brushes a and c, only by modification of the ratio

$$\rho = \frac{K_{bd}^\rho}{K_{ca}^\rho} \tag{25}$$

that is, by modification of the angular position of the magnetic axis of the regulator winding.

The ordinate of the center may be modified not only through this ratio, ρ, but also through the resistances of the shunt stator windings across brushes b and d, i.e., by modification of the constants A_x and B_x, a very easy procedure.

If the power of the hyperbola, c, is made equal to zero, the hyperbola degenerates into two straight lines, its asymptotes. If the center of the hyperbola is removed to infinity and simultaneously the power of the hyperbola is made infinite, a segment of the degenerate hyperbola is obtained at a finite distance; this means that the characteristic becomes a straight line. This result is achieved simply with infinite increase of the ratio ρ; in other words, when simultaneously

$$K^{\rho}_{bd} \neq 0$$

and   (26)

$$K^{\rho}_{ca} = 0$$

This means that the magnetic axis of the regulator winding coincides with the commutation axis of brushes a and c.

The direction of the straight line representing the characteristic depends on the direction in which the center of the hyperbola is removed to infinity. If this is the direction of the x axis, the characteristic will be a straight line parallel to the x axis; i.e.,

$$I_b = \text{constant} \tag{27}$$

To satisfy Equation 27, it is sufficient to make $a = \infty$ and b finite, and therefore to satisfy conditions 26 and simultaneously to put

$$A_x = 0$$

Hence, there can be no shunt stator winding across brushes b and d having its axis along the commutating axis of the same brushes. The value of the constant indicated in relation 27 may then be changed by modification of the power of the hyperbola, through change of the independent current, I_ε, or of the shunt stator winding across the brushes a and c, as Fig. 79 shows.

Removing the center of the hyperbola to infinity in a direction not parallel to either of the two axes makes the characteristic a straight line inclined with respect to both axes. Its equation will be

$$\alpha x + \beta y + \gamma = 0 \tag{28}$$

To do this it is sufficient that conditions 26 are satisfied. The direction of the straight-line characteristic depends on the ratio b/a, which, under these conditions, becomes

$$\frac{\alpha}{\beta} = \lim \frac{b}{a} = \frac{A_x}{K} \tag{29}$$

Therefore the direction may be modified easily with a variation of the resistance of the shunt stator winding connected across brushes b and d

and having its magnetic axis directed along the commutating axis of the same brushes.

Equation 28 is readily obtained from the first equation of group 23 when $K_{ca}^{\rho} = 0$,

$$C\left(A_v - \frac{1}{n}\right) + A_x x + Ky + K_{ca}^{\varepsilon} I_\varepsilon = 0 \tag{30}$$

from which we obtain

$$\gamma = K_{ca}^{\varepsilon} I_\varepsilon + CA_v - \frac{C}{n} \tag{31}$$

This value is easily controlled by A_v and still more easily by I_ε.

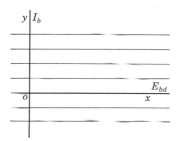

Fig. 79. A family of constant currents.   Fig. 80. A family of linear currents.

Suppose that a family of parallel, inclined straight-line characteristics is desired, as Fig. 80 shows. Then A_x must be kept constant, and I_ε, or A_v, or both I_ε and A_v, may be varied.

Suppose that a family of straight, linear characteristics is desired, forming a bundle around a point lying on the y axis, as Fig. 81 shows. Then γ/K, that is, γ, must be kept constant while the ratio 29 must vary. In other words, the sum $K_{ca}^{\varepsilon} I_\varepsilon + CA_v$ must be kept constant. Either I_ε and A_v must both be held constant, or both must simultaneously be modified inversely to one another, while A_x is varied.

In a similar way a bundle is obtained having any desired point of the plane as center and having as coordinates the arbitrary values m and n. It is sufficient to let

$$\alpha m + \beta n + \gamma = 0$$

and to vary β. And so on for other kinds of families.

Finally, suppose that the desired characteristic is a single straight line parallel to the y axis; i.e.,

$$E_{bd} = \text{constant} \tag{32}$$

Then the center of the hyperbola must be removed to infinity in the direction of the y axis; b of Equations 24 must be made infinite while a must remain finite. These conditions are impossible with the stator windings chosen for this example; however, there can be a straight-line characteristic of the kind in Fig. 80 as near to the vertical as desired but not exactly vertical.

On the contrary, a possible characteristic is composed of two straight lines, one of which corresponds to relation 32 and the other corresponds to relation 27. To obtain this characteristic it is necessary to make the

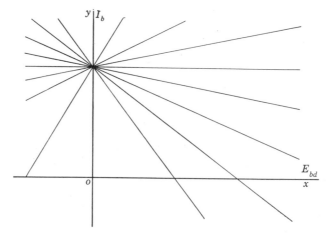

Fig. 81.   A family of linear currents all having the same initial value.

power $c = 0$ (see formula 24) and thus to degenerate the hyperbola into its two asymptotes passing through the center having coordinates a and b; and, further, to choose for a the value of the constant appearing in Equation 32 and to choose for b a value far above the maximum value that current I_b reaches during practical operation.

Thus, to summarize, any straight-line characteristic may be obtained. The expression of the characteristic $f_2(x, z) = 0$ may easily be found as follows:

If the corresponding characteristic $f_1(x, y) = 0$ is linear, as Equation 28 shows, then the characteristic $f_2(x, z) = 0$ is given by

$$P + Cz + x\left(\frac{\alpha}{\beta}x + \frac{\gamma}{\beta}\right) = 0 \qquad (33)$$

which is a straight line only if $\alpha/\beta = 0$, and which is a parabola in all other cases.

If $f_1(x, y)$ is a hyperbola, eliminate I_ρ between the first two Equations 23. A linear expression is obtained in x, y, and z, say,

$$dx + y + ez + f = 0$$

Substitution of the expression thus derived for y in the third Equation 23 yields the equation

$$P + Cz + x(dx + ez + f) = 0$$

This is a hyperbola having one of its asymptotes parallel to the z axis; evidently this asymptote, and the asymptote parallel to the y axis of the hyperbola of the corresponding characteristic $f_1(x, y) = 0$, have the same abscissa.

For the characteristic $f_3(x, I_\rho) = 0$, the procedure is as follows: If Equation 28 is valid, substitute in Equation 33 the value of z derived from the second Equation 23. The corresponding characteristic is a straight line only if Equation 27 is satisfied; otherwise it is a parabola.

If $f_1(x, y) = 0$ is a hyperbola, then derive y and z from the corresponding first and second Equations 23 and substitute in the third one. The corresponding characteristic $f_3(x, I_\rho) = 0$ is then a hyperbola having an asymptote parallel to the I_ρ axis. The asymptotes parallel to the y axis, to the z axis, and to the I_ρ axis all have the same abscissa.

If the metadyne is inserted into a loop of a series distribution system through its terminals A and C (see Fig. 76), and if the relation

$$z = I_a = C \qquad \text{(a constant)} \tag{34}$$

holds in this loop, then instead of Equations 23 there are the following ones:

$$v\left(A_v - \frac{1}{n}\right) + A_x x + Ky + K_{ac}^\varepsilon I_\varepsilon + K_{ac}^\rho I_\rho = 0$$

$$B_v v + x\left(B_x - \frac{1}{n}\right) + KC + K_{bd}^\varepsilon I_\varepsilon + K_{bd}^\rho I_\rho = 0 \tag{35}$$

$$P + Cv = xy$$

Comparing systems 23 and 35 leads to the deduction that the resulting characteristics will be similar.

So far it has been tacitly assumed that $2\pi n T_a = P$ is constant. If P is a linear function of x, y, z, I_ρ, then the characteristics do not change substantially; a substantial change does occur if P is a more elaborate function.

The primary brushes, a and c, of the Cross metadyne may be connected to an electric source, the voltage and current characteristics of which are different from the constant-voltage and constant-current types examined above. Then, more complicated characteristics may be obtained. It should be recalled that what is developed in this section applies not only to a pure transformer metadyne, to a pure generator metadyne, and to a pure motor metadyne, but also to a complex metadyne; i.e., a metadyne operating simultaneously as a transformer and as a generator or motor.

3. A SWITCHING LOCOMOTIVE WITH A CROSS TRANSFORMER METADYNE

There is now sufficient background to develop, at least statically, an important application of the metadyne to switching locomotives. Consider the case of the Italian State Railways, for which the normal line voltage is 3000 volts.

The particular requirements that a shunting locomotive must meet are the following:

(*a*) Frequent stops, startings, and braking.

(*b*) Very large starting and braking effort.

(*c*) Frequent operation at very low speed, say one kilometer or two per hour, with a very gradual speed control.

(*d*) The best utilization of the adhesion on rails.

(*e*) Frequent operation at relatively high speed, say 40 kilometers per hour, with a relatively low tractive effort.

(*f*) Easy, handy, quick, and intuitive control.

Figure 82 shows the proposed arrangement. The transformer metadyne has four equidistant brushes: *a*, *b*, *c* and *d*. Brushes *a* and *c* are connected to the overhead line, brushes *b* and *d* supply current to the four motors $M1$, $M2$, $M3$, and $M4$. The locomotive is assumed to be of the well-known *B-B* type involving full adhesion. On the same shaft with the metadyne are mounted a regulator dynamo, RD, and a base dynamo, BD, both dynamos being shunt-excited.

Before the locomotive is started, it is necessary to start the metadyne itself. For this purpose a series stator winding, SW, is provided on the stator of the metadyne. Thus when the contactor, $C1$, is closed, the current supplied by the overhead line and limited by the resistor, R_1, passes through the metadyne, creating the strong torque of a series motor upon starting and of a metadyne motor just as soon as the speed becomes appreciable. In a very short time, say 20 to 30 seconds, the speed reaches its normal value, the regulator dynamo and base dynamo set is operating, and the regulator current is flowing in the regulator

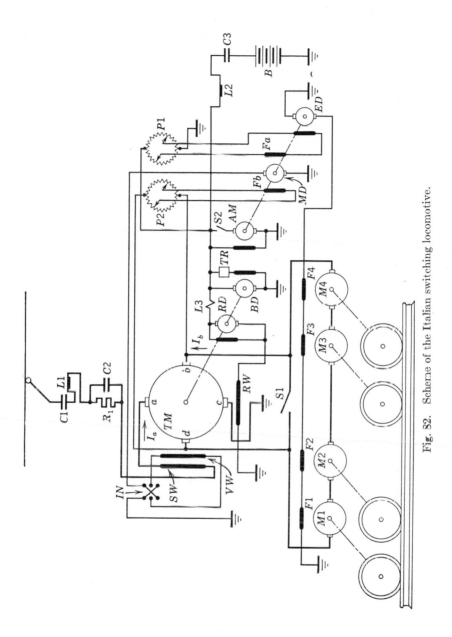

Fig. 82.   Scheme of the Italian switching locomotive.

winding, RW. The speed is then automatically maintained at its normal value. The secondary current, I_b, then excites the metadyne, the primary current, I_a, drops very nearly to zero, the ohmic drop along resistor R_1 becomes practically zero, and the breaker, $C2$, closes automatically, short-circuiting resistor R_1 and thus completing the start. This maneuver takes, say, 30 to 40 seconds and is initiated with a push button.

The best utilization of the adhesion of the locomotive on the rails is a requirement common to all locomotives, but it is particularly important for a shunting locomotive. The coefficient of adhesion on the rails is a complex function of the speed, the temperature, the state of the rail, and the previous speed, but it may be roughly approximated by the curve abc of Fig. 83, which gives the corresponding tractive effort T as a

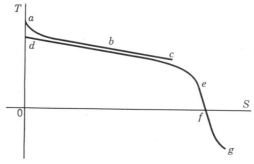

Fig. 83.   Maximum possible tractive effort, abc, is limited by coefficient of adhesion. Ideal tractive effort is given by $defg$.

function of the speed S. Thus the ideal arrangement would be to cause the metadyne to supply the motors with a current automatically varying with speed and following such a law as to give a tractive effort varying proportionally to the ordinates of the curve abc of Fig. 83.

On the other hand, it is important for any locomotive that once the train is started the acceleration rate be kept the highest possible until a predetermined speed is reached, and then the torque must quickly drop in order to secure speed stability. Further, it is desirable that the predetermined speed is not exceeded, and, if this happens for some reason (for instance, if the inclination of the profile of the line becomes negative), it is highly desirable that the locomotive automatically develops a braking effort.

Thus the ideal characteristic for the tractive effort may be represented by $defg$ of Fig. 83, very closely following the line abc, corresponding to the maximum tractive effort allowed by the adhesion on the rails, until the predetermined high speed is reached. In the neighborhood of this speed, the tractive effort drops quickly, along the segment *ef*, to insure good stability of the speed of the train; and when the maximum speed is surpassed, the tractive effort becomes negative and increases rapidly along the segment *fg* to provide for an energetic braking action.

The scheme of Fig. 82 gives such a characteristic. The variator winding, *VW*, with its magnetic axis along the direction of the commutating axis of the secondary brushes, *b* and *d*, is energized by a special auxiliary dynamo, *MD*, called the modulator dynamo. This dynamo shows intense iron saturation and is excited by two field windings, the first field winding, *Fa*, being fed by a constant-voltage source, the small battery *B*, and having its ampere-turns controlled by potentiometer *P1*, and the second field winding, *Fb*, being fed by the brush voltage E_{bd} and having its ampere-turns controlled by potentiometer *P2*.

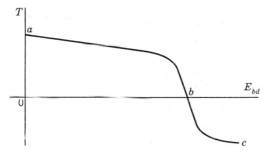

Fig. 84. Tractive effort (and modulator-dynamo output) versus secondary voltage of the metadyne.

The modulator dynamo is driven at constant speed by the shunt-excited auxiliary motor, *AM*. Because of its field windings, the modulator dynamo, *MD*, produces a voltage that is a function of brush voltage E_{bd}, as represented in Fig. 84, showing a sharp bend due to severe iron saturation.

The corresponding characteristic of brush current I_b as a function of brush voltage E_{bd} is very similar to the characteristic of Fig. 84, because there is no action of the ampere-turns of regulator winding *RW* on brush current I_b and the action of series winding *SW* is rather favorable, as one may easily check. This is the reason why the ordinates of the diagram of Fig. 84 have been shown as the tractive effort, *T*, directly.

Field windings *F1*, *F2*, *F3*, and *F4* of the motors, fed by the exciter dynamo, *ED*, create a constant field independently of brush voltage E_{bd}; therefore, the abscissas of diagram 84 are proportional to the speed *S* of the locomotive. Thus, the desired ideal characteristic of the tractive effort is obtained as a function of the speed of the locomotive.

By modification of the position of potentiometer *P*2, only the abscissa
of the intersection of the characteristic with the axis of speed is modified;
this intersection corresponds to the no-load speed. Thus a family of
characteristics is obtained, as Fig. 85 shows, for which the maximum

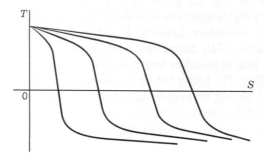

Fig. 85. A family of characteristics having the same starting effort for various
no-load speeds.

tractive effort is kept constant and the value of the no-load speed is
modified. This family of characteristics is particularly interesting for
shunting maneuvers.

Modifying the position of potentiometer *P*1, only, provides another
family of characteristics as shown by Fig. 86, for which both the maximum tractive effort and the no-load speed are modified. Potentiometer
*P*1 simultaneously regulates the maximum value of brush current I_b
and the constant value of the ampere-windings *F*1, *F*2, turns of field

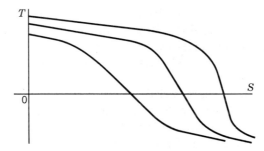

Fig. 86. The maximum tractive effort may be changed as easily as the no-load speed.

*F*3, and *F*4; this means that the current in the armature of the motors
and in the field windings are modified in the same sense and a reasonably
good distribution of copper losses is thus obtained. This is the main
reason why the author adopted the exciter dynamo *ED* indicated in
Fig. 82. The exciter dynamo and the modulator dynamo are driven by

the auxiliary motor, AM; this three-machine set is of small capacity and produces a low voltage, say 100 volts.

The voltage provided for each of the traction motors is one-fourth of brush voltage E_{bd}, thus simplifying their construction. The value of the no-load brush voltage, i.e., the value of the abscissa of point b in Fig. 84, may be considered the maximum value of the voltage impressed on the traction motors for normal operation. Take into consideration the whole family of characteristics put at the disposal of the engineer, and choose the characteristic showing the highest no-load brush voltage E_{bd}. The highest voltage impressed on the traction motors for normal

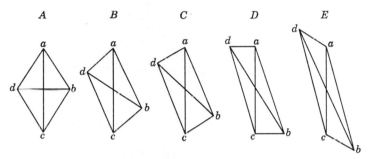

Fig. 87. Some vector diagrams for the metadyne of the Italian switching locomotive.

operation will thus be determined. Indicate this voltage by $(E_{bd})_{0 \text{ max}}$, the symbol $(E_{bd})_0$ indicating the no-load brush voltage E_{bd} for a given characteristic.

The maximum no-load brush voltage $(E_{bd})_{0 \text{ max}}$ is fixed for a given equipment; it depends on the battery voltage and is independent of the overhead-line voltage. In order to fix the value of this maximum closely, a voltage regulator, TR (see Fig. 82), may be applied to the base dynamo, BD. The voltage induced by the base dynamo is chosen equal to the full charging voltage of the battery, which is thus kept "floating" during the whole operation.

One important result is that the maximum voltage impressed on the traction motors is arbitrarily predetermined for a given equipment and is independent of the variations of the overhead-line voltage. The maximum no-load voltage $(E_{bd})_{0 \text{ max}}$ may be chosen equal to the normal overhead-line voltage, V_L, or it may be lower or even higher.

In the event that $(E_{bd})_{0 \text{ max}} < V_L$, the vector diagrams will be the ones indicated by A, B, and C of Fig. 87, if the projection axis is assumed vertical; diagram A corresponds to standstill, diagram B to a low-speed acceleration, and diagram C to running at high speed with the maximum voltage on the motors. In the event that $(E_{bd})_{0 \text{ max}} = V_L$, diagram D, corresponding to this equality, must be added to the previous diagrams. Finally, diagram E belongs to the case $(E_{bd})_{0\,max} > V_L$.

Now suppose that the locomotive is running at a speed corresponding to the abscissa of point p of the characteristic $apbc$ of Fig. 88 and that

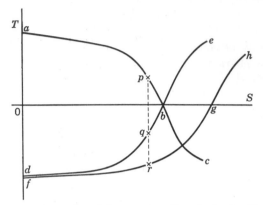

Fig. 88.   Behavior of the tractive effort during braking.

the engineer wants to brake. He will simply reverse the current in field windings $F1$, $F2$, $F3$, and $F4$ of the traction motors; the characteristic will be indicated by the line $dqbe$, and the representative point of operation will be displaced from p to q; and afterwards it will slowly slide along the segment qd. The corresponding vector diagrams are given by Fig. 89 for the assumption that $(E_{bd})_{0\,max} > V_L$.

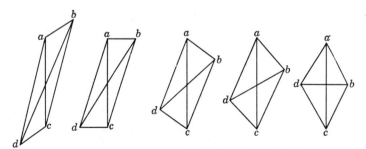

Fig. 89.   Vector diagrams of the voltages during braking.

If the braking effort corresponding to point q is not sufficient, the engineer may choose the characteristic $frgh$. Further, if it is recalled that the accelerating effort is diminished by the drag corresponding to the mechanical losses of the train, while the braking effort is increased by the same amount, it becomes obvious that the same I_b versus E_{bd}

characteristic of the metadyne provides, for a given value of speed S of the locomotive, a braking deceleration that is about 20% to 30% higher than the corresponding motoring acceleration.

A few remarks will complete the description of the scheme of Fig. 82. Switch $S1$ is used for short-circuiting the armatures of the motors at standstill.

To change from motoring to braking operation, the current in field windings $F1$, $F2$, $F3$, and $F4$ is reversed by moving the handles of the potentiometers, $P1$ and $P2$, the external circuit of the exciter dynamo, ED, being left permanently closed as it possesses a large inductance and it stores a relatively large amount of electromagnetic energy. The ampere-turns of the variator winding, VW, must instead remain in the same direction; it is for this reason that the inverter, IN, has been used, the electromagnetic energy stored by the variator winding, VW, being much smaller than that stored by the field windings of the traction motors.

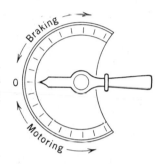

Fig. 90. Control lever for the Italian switching locomotive.

Normally, contactor $C1$ opens only when line current I_a is very nearly zero; nevertheless, a safety overload relay, $L1$, is provided for tripping it in case of emergency. A similar relay, $L2$, protects the battery, B. The two potentiometers, $P1$ and $P2$, which directly control a very small power, are combined with inverter IN and are operated by means of a single handle as shown by Fig. 90.

Figure 91 shows an internal view of a French shunting locomotive equipped with a metadyne, although wired according to a different scheme described in a following chapter; the handle of the master controller may be seen without any dial, since a very large number of positions are possible. For "forward movement" the handle is turned to the right, and for "backward movement" the handle is turned to the left. If the locomotive is moving "forward," braking is obtained when the handle is moved to the left; if the locomotive is moving "backward," braking is obtained when the handle is moved to the right. Thus, control of the locomotive is easy and instinctive, and the engineer may concentrate his attention on the work outside the cab.

In contrast with what happens with ordinary locomotives, the engineer of the metadyne locomotive may handle its controller very roughly, pushing it abruptly from one extreme position to another, without danger and without causing peaks of current or mechanical damage.

Fig. 91.   Interior of a French switching locomotive, showing the control for the metadyne equipment.   (*Courtesy of Als-Thom, Paris.*)

Therefore, with some skill, he may perform many useful maneuvers: pushing a train, or stopping it, or giving it the right impact.

     It is important to note that all the machines in the locomotive, except the metadyne, are removed from direct action with the overhead line, thus being independent of the variations of the overhead-line voltage (3600 volts to 2400 volts) which sometimes occur very suddenly. It should also be noted that all the auxiliary machines are at low voltage.

Suppose that a motor is damaged and must be put out of service; it is disconnected from the secondary circuit, which is reestablished by connecting together the two terminals corresponding to the damaged motor. If a fault prevents variator winding VW from creating the proper ampere-turns, in the worst cases current I_b drops to the value of the magnetizing current. Suppose that an accidental overspeed puts the metadyne in danger; the regulator current will then increase very quickly and overcurrent relay $L3$ will trip the main contactor, $C1$.

4. REMARKS ON THE TRACTIVE EFFORT AND THE SIZE OF THE MOTORS OF THE SWITCHING LOCOMOTIVE

During the tests of the first switching locomotive equipped with a metadyne, a train was formed comprising a locomotive having a weight on drivers of 72 tons and provided with a standard rheostatic equipment and series motors, the metadyne-equipped locomotive having a weight on drivers of 58 tons. The number of cars hauled was progressively varied to obtain a practical comparison between the standard and the metadyne locomotive. Although the two locomotives have a different mechanical resistance to movement, this difference did not matter because they were always hauled together. A practical comparison of the useful tractive effort could be obtained by counting the largest number of cars driven by each locomotive, without skidding, along the same track sections, either straight or curved.

It had been expected that the metadyne locomotive would haul about 80% (58/72 = 0.80) of the number of cars hauled by the standard locomotive. It was repeatedly found, however, that the metadyne locomotive started a train slightly longer, apparently having an adhesion coefficient about 25% higher than that of the standard locomotive.

After accurate dynamometric research, this unexpected favorable result was explained as follows: During starting of the rheostatic locomotive, the tractive effort versus speed characteristic has a toothed shape, shown by Fig. 92, because of the rheostat. To the toothed segment of the characteristic there corresponds a practical mean tractive effort, T_0, shown in the figure; skidding will occur if the peak value, T_p, reaches the value corresponding to the coefficient of adhesion.

For the metadyne locomotive, the characteristic is a smooth one without teeth or peaks, and therefore the practical mean tractive effort may be made equal to that value corresponding to the adhesion coefficient. This reasoning explained a value about 18% higher for the practical maximum tractive effort for the metadyne locomotive. The remaining 25% − 18% = 7% was due to the actual reduction of the coefficient of adhesion when the wheels were driven by the quickly varying torque of the standard locomotive while the metadyne locomotive showed a torque of steady value. Practically, this result means that a metadyne equipment causes the weight on drivers of the locomotive to be about 20% to 25% more effective.

The metadyne equipment has lighter control elements than the rheostatic equipment and has negligibly small resistors; on the other hand, it

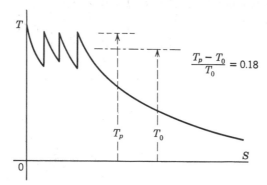

Fig. 92.   Starting characteristic of a standard locomotive.

must comprise the metadyne itself. Thus the question arises whether the traction motors may be made lighter when supplied by a metadyne. Such a reduction has been found possible to the extent of about 10% to 15%, and it is due to the following reasons:

> If the motors must withstand the overhead-line voltage, they must be constructed to withstand the maximum line voltage, which is 20% higher than the normal voltage, V_L; and, on the other hand, they must be able to develop the maximum tractive effort required for the locomotive even when the line voltage reaches its minimum, which is about 20% lower than normal voltage V_L. On the contrary, the motors supplied by the metadyne always operate under the same maximum voltage, say $\frac{1}{4}$ $(E_{bd})_{0\,max}$, whatever the value of the overhead-line voltage, V_L, may be, and in addition they are fed by the same maximum current, I_b, independently of V_L.
>
> To develop the maximum tractive effort, required when the train is starting, the current is increased in the armature and in the field winding; and, although the torque is proportional to the armature current, it is far from being proportional to the field-winding current because of the severe iron saturation. Thus in a series motor, the copper losses in the field are very large while the maximum tractive effort is being developed, and their contribution to the torque is

practically negligible. With the metadyne equipment the armature current of the traction motors may be increased at will, while the current of the field winding is kept at a value corresponding to reasonable iron saturation.

Dynamic stability requires that motors built for direct connection to the line have a relatively large number of ampere-turns for the field, whereas the motors inserted in the metadyne circuits do not require special precautions for insuring dynamic stability. Therefore, the total stator ampere-turns for the traction motors of the metadyne locomotive are smaller, other things being equal.

Thus when considering the additional weight of the metadyne, one must take into account the reduction of the weight of the motors; further, one must consider that the weight of the metadyne is fully sprung on the truck, whereas the weight of the motors is partially hung directly on the wheel axles.

After the weight, the space occupied by the equipment must next be considered. This is also smaller for the metadyne locomotive, because of the elimination of the main resistors and the great reduction of switchgear, in spite of the presence of the metadyne itself. Such a favorable difference is even more apparent when the rheostatic locomotive is provided with dynamic braking, and still more when such a locomotive is equipped with the necessary switchgear for braking with partial regeneration of the power to the overhead line.

5. THE BEHAVIOR OF THE METADYNE SWITCHING LOCOMOTIVE AGAINST FLASHOVER

Traction motors are exposed to severe operation by quick load variations, sudden current changes, and abrupt voltage jumps; and these disturbances sometimes cause a flashover, i.e., an arc extending over the commutator and sometimes joining brushes of opposite sign and damaging the motor. Great care is given to the design of traction motors to prevent flashover or at least to divert it.

The traction motors inserted in the metadyne circuit are very safely protected against the possible causes of flashover; but the metadyne itself, being directly connected to the overhead line, is openly exposed to these causes. Since flashover of the metadyne is closely connected with its dynamic behavior and its commutation, both of these aspects of the metadyne theory must be investigated thoroughly for complete understanding of flashover. Nevertheless, one may consider here the static aspect of this trouble and compare, at least from this point of view, the metadyne with the dynamo.

The electric arc along the commutator starts while a segment of the commutator leaves a brush that is sparking because of poor commutation, and the arc is further fed by the voltage induced between two consecutive commutator segments. Hence it is necessary to reduce this voltage to a value lower than the one necessary for maintaining an electric arc. Now this value is not well defined when the air surrounding the commutator is strongly ionized.

If the small successive arcs between two consecutive segments are fed by a sufficient voltage over the whole region between two brushes of opposite sign, the full electric arc bursts. It is thus important to investigate the value of the voltage induced between two consecutive

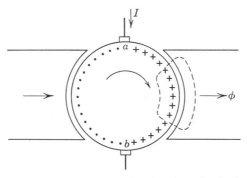

Fig. 93.   Current and flux distributions in a simple dynamo.

commutator segments as they pass from one brush to another brush of opposite sign. This voltage is proportional to the local value of the magnetic induction; therefore, an investigation of the distribution of the magnetic induction along the air gap from one brush to another brush of opposite sign is in order.

First consider a dynamo, reference being made to Fig. 93, the depth of the air gap being assumed constant. The magnetic induction at a given point of the air gap depends on the ampere-turns of the field winding and on the armature ampere-turns. The field-winding ampere-turns create a magnetomotive force of constant value under the polar segments as is indicated by the ordinates of the broken line *ahfmnqkb* in diagram *A* of Fig. 94, in which the distance along the periphery of the commutator has been taken as the abscissa.

The armature ampere-turns create a magnetomotive force varying along the periphery of the armature as the ordinates of the straight line *gfrs*, as is immediately proved by the application of the circuitation law along a closed line that is symmetrical to the magnetic axis of the polar segment, similar to the one indicated by a dotted line in Fig. 93. Thus the resultant magnetomotive force will be represented by the ordinates of the line *gfmpqkrs.*

If the iron saturation is taken into account, as well as the fringing of the magnetic field near the end of the polar segments, the magnetic induction will be found to be distributed along the periphery of the armature as the ordinates of the curve indicated by C of Fig. 94. The

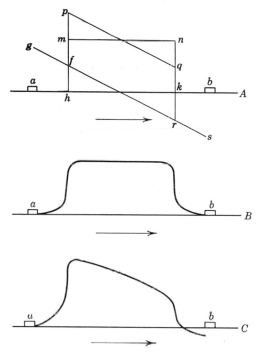

Fig. 94. Ampere-turns and flux density along the air gap of the dynamo of Fig. 93.

curve indicated by B of the same figure gives the distribution of the magnetic induction when the field is excited but when there is no current in the armature; thus the difference between B and C gives the distortion caused by the armature ampere-turns.

Now consider the case corresponding to C, the dynamo being loaded, and assume that the arrows in Figs. 93 and 94 give the direction of the movement of the commutator. Since the arc, which is started when the segment leaves brush a, enters the zone where the induction is the highest, it is well fed and thus increases; it ionizes the air so strongly that it may continue to burn, even through the zone where the induction decreases, until it reaches brush b. If the direction of motion were the opposite, the probability of a flashover would have been much less: as soon as the arc had started under brush b, it would enter the zone where the induction is low and it would be extinguished.

Now consider the Cross transformer metadyne and take the particular case of the switching locomotive as described in the previous paragraph. Reference is made to diagrams A, B, C, and D of Fig. 95.

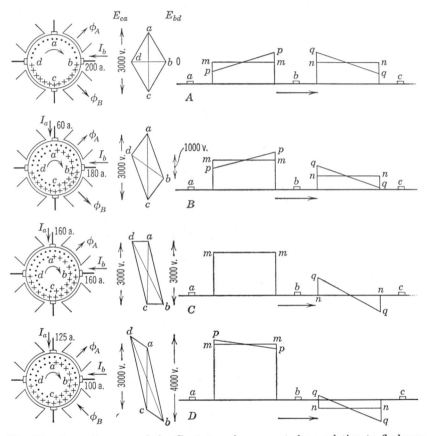

Fig. 95. Some diagrams of the Cross transformer metadyne relative to flashover during motoring operation of the locomotive.

At the extreme left of each diagram is a single schematic of the metadyne with the value of the brush currents I_a and I_b and the distribution of the ampere-turns along the periphery of the armature, the external rows of crosses and dots corresponding to current I_b, and the internal rows corresponding to current I_a. A vector diagram is given next, showing the brush voltages, brushes a and c assumedly being connected to the overhead line that supplies its normal voltage: 3000 volts.

At the extreme right, the distribution of the magnetomotive force is given. Assume, for the sake of simplicity, that the iron of the metadyne is not saturated and neglect the effect of fringing of the magnetic field. Thus the same broken lines will, by their ordinates, represent the magnetic induction and the voltage induced between two consecutive commutator segments.

Diagram A corresponds to the beginning of the starting period, the voltage supplied to the motors being zero, $E_{bd} = 0$, and the load current, I_b, being at its maximum value, 200 amperes. Current I_a is then zero since the losses are being neglected.

Because of the combined action of the stator and rotor currents, the value of the resulting ampere-turns along the axis of polar segment A (the polar segment located immediately after brush a in the clockwise direction) is represented by the ordinate of segment mm; hence, the value of the magnetic induction along this is sufficient to induce $\frac{1}{2}(3000)$ = 1500 volts between brushes b and a. Starting from this mean value and considering the rotor ampere-turns extending from one side of this axis to the other, as was done for Fig. 93, one obtains the inclined line pp, which, with its ordinates, gives the magnetic induction at every point of the air gap. Similarly, the inclined line qq is obtained for segment B (the polar segment coming immediately after brush b in the clockwise direction).

When the locomotive is accelerating while running at low speed (about a third of its normal speed), diagrams B are obtained. Current I_b supplied to the traction motors has decreased to 180 amperes, and the voltage E_{bd} has increased to 1000 volts; the overhead-line current, I_a, is 60 amperes; and the magnetic induction under the polar segments is given by the ordinates of the inclined, straight segments pp and qq for polar segments A and B, respectively. Notice that under polar segment A the ampere-turns due to current I_a and those due to current I_b are opposing, whereas under polar segment B their effect is cumulative.

Diagrams C correspond to full-speed operation. The voltage E_{bd} on the traction motors equals the overhead-line voltage, and current I_b supplied to the motors equals the overhead-line current. The armature ampere-turns under polar segment A due to currents I_a and I_b completely compensate one another, and therefore the magnetic induction remains constant all along polar segment A. Under polar segment B, the mean value of the induction is zero while the local action of the rotor ampere-turns then reaches its maximum.

Finally, diagrams D correspond to running overspeed; the voltage E_{bd} reaches 4000 volts, 1000 volts more than the overhead-line voltage. The inclined segment pp reappears, but in the opposite direction, and shows a very small local action of the rotor ampere-turns under polar segment A.

Inspection of Fig. 95 shows that the deviation of the magnetic induction under a given polar segment from a constant value is much less pronounced than with a dynamo; in fact, in the metadyne examined here, the polar segment covers only a part, say two-thirds, of a half rotor-winding pitch, whereas in a dynamo it generally covers about two-thirds of the whole pitch. It should be noted that the electromotive force induced between two consecutive brushes by a given polar segment varies continuously, and that the higher the voltage, the smaller the deviation of the distribution of the magnetic induction from a constant value; when the polar segment must induce a voltage equal to the overhead-line voltage, the local action of the armature ampere-turns is zero. This fact allows a higher value of the safe mean voltage induced between two consecutive commutator segments and therefore a higher utilization of the material.

Now trace the path of a small arc between two consecutive commutator segments started under brush a and moving towards brush c of opposite sign. Entering the region covered by polar segment A, it encounters: a value of magnetic induction lower than the mean value under that polar segment (as diagrams A and B show), or the mean value (as diagram C shows), or a slightly higher one (as in diagram D). The case of diagram D is an exceptional one not generally met in practice.

After having left the region under polar segment A, the arc must traverse the free zone of brush b, where there is no electromotive force to feed it. Finally, the arc, on its way to reach brush c, must traverse the region under polar segment B, which obviously is a region discouraging and even opposing the permanence of the arc. For instance, in diagrams C and D there is an induced electromotive force in a direction opposite to the arc current, and this action opposing the arc becomes stronger as the voltage favorable to the arc under segment A becomes higher.

Figure 96 gives the diagrams corresponding to operation during regenerative braking: diagram E corresponds to the beginning of braking while the locomotive is running at very high speed; diagram F corresponds to normal high speed; diagram G corresponds to low speed; and, finally, diagram H corresponds to the end of the braking stage, the locomotive having been brought to a complete standstill. Reasoning as with Fig. 95 leads to the same conclusions.

Thus we may say that the metadyne is less subject to flashover than the dynamo. As a matter of fact, the French switching locomotives that will be described in a further chapter have proved this statement very clearly; these locomotives must frequently cross the main traffic lines, thus abruptly cutting off the overhead-line voltage before crossing and receiving the impact of the total line voltage abruptly after having crossed the main lines. The question of the arc joining brushes *a* and *b* with a flashover will be considered again in a further chapter, of this

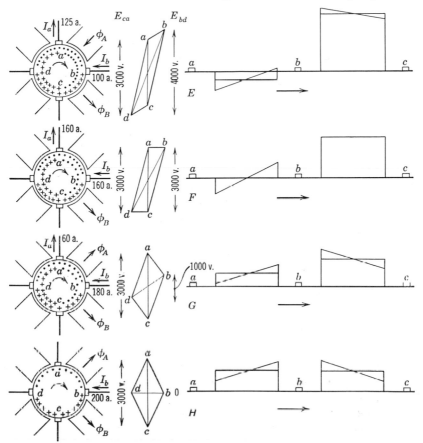

Fig. 96. Behavior of the locomotive metadyne during regenerative braking.

volume, where the high-speed motor coaches proposed for the Italian State Railways are described.

6. THE COMMUTATION AND ARMATURE HEATING EFFECT IN THE ITALIAN SWITCHING LOCOMOTIVE

Apply the rules developed in Chapter 10. Figure 97 indicates two ways of drawing the integral lines for application of the circuitation theorem; the brushes are indicated only by the letters *a*, *b*, *c*, and *d*, and the dotted lines show the integral paths.

The scheme of Fig. 97B is simpler, and it gives the following two equations:

$$\frac{1}{4} NI_a + A_a + A_c = H_a a + H_c a + \int_S \frac{\overline{B}}{\mu} \cdot \overline{ds}$$

$$\frac{1}{4} NI_b + A_b + A_d = H_b a + H_d a + \int_S \frac{\overline{B}}{\mu} \cdot \overline{ds}$$

(36)

where the positive direction has been taken as the one indicated by the arrows on Fig. 97B, where N indicates the number of peripheral conductors of the armature winding, A indicates the ampere-turns on the

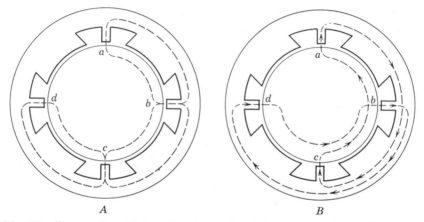

Fig. 97. Some paths of integration for study of the commutation of the Italian switching locomotive.

commutating pole, H the magnetic field in the air gap of depth a under the commutating poles, and $\overline{B}$ the vector representing the magnetic induction at a point of the integral path having $\overline{ds}$ as the vectorial differential length and S as the total length immersed in the iron. H is measured in amperes per meter, a and S in meters, and $\overline{B}$ in webers per square meter. The dot indicates the scalar product.

Since there are only the two Equations 36 for determining the four unknown quantities A_a, A_b, A_c, and A_d, two other conditions may be arbitrarily chosen, say the following:

$$A_a = A_c$$

$$A_b = A_d$$

(37)

Equations 36 and 37 determine the ampere-turns A_a and A_c and the ampere-turns A_b and A_d just as for two independent dynamos having the same armature as the metadyne: the one provided with brushes a and

c, and the other with brushes b and d, respectively. From the diagram of Fig. 97A, one will come to the same result by a proper choice of the supplementary arbitrary conditions.

To investigate the heating effect in the armature, indicate by R_a the resistance of the armature winding between two diametrically opposite points, and consider the distribution of the currents I_a and I_b in the armature winding as indicated schematically by the diagrams at the extreme left of Fig. 95. The total heating effect is obviously

$$R_a \left(\frac{I_a}{2} - \frac{I_b}{2} \right)^2$$

for segment ab (taken in the clockwise direction) and segment cd, respectively, and

$$R_a \left(\frac{I_a}{2} + \frac{I_b}{2} \right)^2$$

for segments bc and da, respectively. Therefore for the whole winding it will be

$$\tfrac{1}{4} R_a [2(I_a - I_b)^2 + 2(I_a + I_b)^2] = R_a I_a^2 + R_b I_b^2 \tag{38}$$

This result may be stated as follows: The heating effect given by either one of the brush currents I_a or I_b is unaffected by the presence of the other current. This important result is a chief reason for the high efficiency of the metadyne considered here.

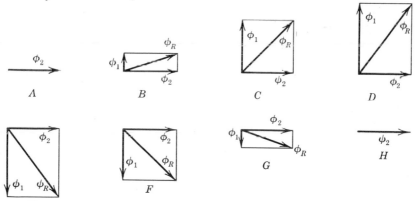

Fig. 98. Flux diagrams for the locomotive metadyne.

Figure 98 shows the diagrams of the flux in the metadyne corresponding to the four cases A, B, C, and D of Fig. 95. The total flux ϕ_R is indicated by its two components ϕ_1 and ϕ_2 along the two commutating axes of brushes ca and brushes bd, respectively.

For case A, the total flux coincides with its component ϕ_2; for all other cases, the component ϕ_1 appears. The diagrams E, F, G, and H correspond to the diagrams of Fig. 96 and illustrate the operation during regenerative braking. The total flux oscillates between two extreme positions located more than 90 electrical degrees apart. The horizontal component ϕ_2 is constant.

7. ON THE SPEED STABILITY OF THE TRANSFORMER METADYNE OF THE ITALIAN SWITCHING LOCOMOTIVE

Apply the method indicated in Section 3 of Chapter 8 of Part I. The fundamental equations of the metadyne are

$$\frac{1}{n} E_{ca} = KI_b + K_\alpha I_a + K_\beta I_\beta$$

$$\frac{1}{n} E_{bd} = KI_a + K_\gamma I_\rho \tag{39}$$

where I_β is the variator current, I_ρ is the regulator current, and K, K_α, K_β, and K_γ are constants. For the regulator current,

$$I_\rho = K_\rho(n - n_0) \tag{40}$$

where K_ρ is a constant, and n_0 the critical speed of the regulator dynamo. The expression for the torque is

$$T = \frac{1}{2\pi} (K_\alpha I_a^2 + K_\beta I_\beta I_a - K_\gamma I_\rho I_b) \tag{41}$$

If these equations are differentiated, with E_{ca}, E_{bd}, and I_β held constant, the following expressions are obtained:

$$2\pi \frac{dT}{dn} = 2K_\alpha I_a \frac{dI_a}{dn} + K_\beta I_\beta \frac{dI_a}{dn} - K_\gamma I_b \frac{dI_\rho}{dn} - K_\gamma I_\rho \frac{dI_b}{dn} \tag{42}$$

$$\frac{1}{n^2} E_{ca} + K \frac{dI_b}{dn} + K_\alpha \frac{dI_a}{dn} = 0 \tag{43}$$

$$\frac{1}{n^2} E_{bd} + K \frac{dI_a}{dn} + K_\gamma \frac{dI_\rho}{dn} = 0 \tag{44}$$

$$\frac{dI_\rho}{dn} = K_\rho \tag{45}$$

Determine the values of the derivatives of I_a, I_b, and I_ρ with respect to the speed n, and substitute them in Equation 42. The following relation is obtained:

$$2\pi \frac{dT}{dn} = -\left[\frac{1}{K^2 n^2} E_{bd} + \frac{K_\gamma K_\rho}{K}\right][2K_\alpha I_a + K_\beta I_\beta]$$

$$- K_\gamma K_\rho I_b - K_\gamma I_\rho \left[\frac{K_\alpha E_{bd}}{K^2 n^2} + \frac{K_\alpha K_\gamma K_\rho}{K^2} - \frac{E_{ca}}{K n^2}\right] \quad (46)$$

The value of this function investigated over the whole range of operation of the locomotive will demonstrate the way to insure speed stability for any point of practical operation, by means of an appropriate choice of the values of K_γ and K_ρ.

8. OHMIC DROP, LEAKAGE FLUX, AND IRON SATURATION IN THE METADYNE OF THE ITALIAN SWITCHING LOCOMOTIVE

Consider the ohmic drop in the armature winding between brushes c and a; it is equal to

$$\tfrac{1}{2}R_a(I_a - I_b) + \tfrac{1}{2}R_a(I_a + I_b) = R_a I_a$$

The ohmic drop between brushes b and d is found in a similar way to be equal to $R_a I_b$, where R_a is the armature resistance between two diametrically opposite points. Thus, the armature ohmic drop between primary brushes is independent of the secondary current, and the armature ohmic drop between secondary brushes is independent of the primary current.

To represent the ohmic drop, the vector diagrams of Fig. 95 may be used; in this way Figs. 99I and 99II are obtained, where the ohmic drop has been exaggerated in order to make it conspicuous. Figure 99I corresponds to diagram A of Fig. 95; diagram $abcd$ has been repeated, and to it have been added the armature ohmic drop, bB, and the ohmic drop, dD, in the stator windings due to current I_b; there is no ohmic drop due to current I_a, as the latter is zero; diagram $ABCD$ corresponding to the voltages between the terminals A, B, C, and D has been thus obtained. In a similar way diagram II of Fig. 99 has been derived from the vector diagram of A of Fig. 95; now the ohmic drops of both currents I_a and I_b are evident.

It is well known that in the field of a dynamo a flux ϕ_S must be created which is about 12% stronger than the flux ϕ_R passing through the armature; in other words, the leakage is about 12%. An exact definition of

the leakage flux is given in the first volume of *Elettromeccanica,* already
mentioned by the author.   Here a rough, intuitive definition, such as
the one given above, will be satisfactory.   Hence, in the stator of the
metadyne only 90% of the flux will be passing through the armature
and contributing to useful operation of the metadyne.

In fact, the variator winding tends to demagnetize the magnetic
circuit, and the magnetization is insured by the armature ampere-turns.
Thus only a part of the flux in the iron laminations of the armature

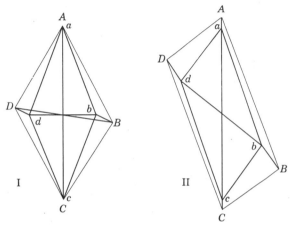

Fig. 99.   Distortion of vector diagrams resulting from consideration of ohmic drops.

passes through the laminations of the stator, as well.   Further, the flux
interlinked with the armature end windings and created by the armature
ampere-turns is inoperative in a dynamo, whereas it contributes to the
normal operation of the metadyne.

For these reasons the stator iron core of the metadyne needs about
20% less magnetic cross section than the iron of the inductor of a corresponding dynamo, for the same flux to induce the same useful electromotive force between the brushes.   This allows a noticeable reduction
of the total size of the metadyne as compared with an equivalent dynamo.

The trial and error method may be employed to take into account
the iron saturation, guided by the magnetic characteristic of the iron
laminations and of the cast steel used for the machine.   In order to
obtain exact information, the circuitation theorem may be applied
repeatedly to many paths of integration drawn along the magnetic
circuit.

Apply the circuitation theorem along the two closed lines *oahco* and
obgdo drawn along the magnetic axis of the polar segments as shown in

Fig. 100. Point q thus obtained, with the magnetic induction as ordinate and with the distance along the air gap measured from the magnetic axis of the polar segment as abscissa, is plotted in Fig. 100II. Further, many integral paths, symmetrical with respect to the magnetic axis of

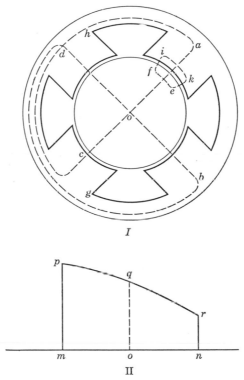

I

II

Fig. 100. The effect of saturation can be computed by repeated application of the circuitation theorem to many integral paths.

the polar segment (such as the loop $efik$, as indicated on Fig. 100I) are considered, and the circuitation theorem is applied reiteratively for each such integral path; thus, each time, a pair of points of the curve pqr is obtained. By integration of the curve pqr, the flux under the polar segment is obtained. Hence, the values of the various "constants" in the fundamental equation are derived, and a general checking-up is then possible. This procedure must be followed for many operating points. It is laborious, but it yields reliable results.

13 · Some Transformer Metadynes of Degree $m = 4$

The transformer metadyne may operate as a typical direct-current transformer, and one may use it even in those applications for which the voltage of the direct-current source is very different from the voltage required by the load. In this chapter, certain solutions to this problem are considered, each solution having been sanctioned by a practical application. Such an application appeared naturally when existing electrified railway lines changed the value of the overhead-line voltage, since it was desirable to continue to use the traction motors built for the old voltage value.

1. THE CROSS TRANSFORMER METADYNE WITH TWO COMMUTATORS

The stator is the same as for the ordinary metadyne with a single commutator, but the rotor has two separate windings, each winding being associated with a separate commutator. The scheme of Fig. 101 represents this machine clearly.

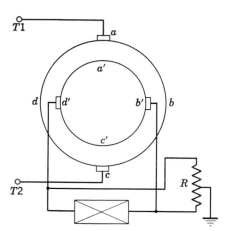

Fig. 101. The Cross transformer metadyne with two commutators.

Assume that the commutator bearing the brushes a and c is connected with the constant-voltage line, having its terminals at $T1$ and $T2$, and that the commutator bearing the brushes b' and d' supplies a consumer with current. The consumer, removed from direct contact with the main line, will be supplied with a current I_b related to the voltage $E_{b'd'}$ by any predetermined law, the maximum value of this voltage being governed by the ratio of the conductors per slot corresponding to the two separate windings. Suppose this ratio is 3; then the maximum value of $E_{b'd'}$ will be one-third of the maximum value of E_{bd}, say about one-third of the line voltage E_{ca}.

158

Suppose, further, that some arrangement has been made for bringing to zero the mean value of the potentials of brush b' and brush d'. One way to obtain this result, for instance, is to ground the middle point of the resistor R connected across brushes b' and d', as Fig. 101 indicates; another way is to ground the middle connection point between consumers when these consumers are even in number and operate in a similar way at any moment, as is true for the traction motors of a locomotive. When the ground point is at the middle of an even number of consumers, the vector diagram may be represented by two separate rectangles, $abcd$ and $a'b'c'd'$, the center of the latter being brought to zero potential. The maximum stress that the insulation of the consumers must withstand will then correspond to $\frac{1}{2}(E_{b'd'})$ max. Suppose that the overhead line is a 3000-volt electric-railway line; then the motors will never be brought to a voltage higher than 500 volts with respect to the ground potential. See Fig. 102.

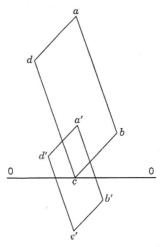

Fig. 102. Vector diagram of the two-commutator metadyne.

Since the armature now has two separate windings, the heating effect in it will not show the desirable reduction found in Section 6 of the previous chapter. Therefore, the size of a two-commutator Cross transformer metadyne will be larger than the size of the corresponding single-commutator Cross metadyne.

2. THE TRIDENT TRANSFORMER METADYNE

The problem of using a 1500-volt overhead line with a locomotive equipped with old traction motors, built for a 600-volt overhead line, has confronted many railway companies. The first company to adopt the metadyne equipment was the Paris-Orleans Company, under the technical direction of Hippolyte Parodi, a man of great initiative.

The distrust held by technical men against a two-winding armature of a direct-current machine is widespread for the dynamo, but its generalization to the metadyne is unjustified. In fact, in a dynamo having an armature with two windings, two pairs of brushes must commutate under the same pair of commutating poles; and if the flux emitted by these commutating poles is adequate for the current of one pair of brushes, it is generally inadequate for the current of the other pair of brushes. Thus a dynamo with two armature windings generally gives trouble with commutation, and one is never constructed except for small power.

In a metadyne with two armature windings, one set of commutating poles corresponds to the brushes bearing on one commutator, and another

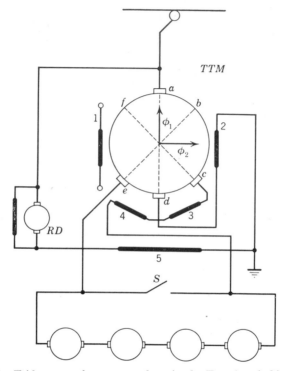

Fig. 103. The Trident transformer metadyne in the French switching locomotive.

set of commutating poles corresponds to the brushes bearing on the other commutator. Thus, the different brush currents are separately given an adequate commutating flux.

The solution adopted by the author for the first traction metadyne in the French switching locomotive was welcome because of its single-winding armature in spite of the great difference of voltage between overhead line and traction motors. The type of metadyne adopted was the Trident transformer metadyne, clearly indicated by the scheme of Fig. 103.

The degree of the metadyne is $m = 4$. Two brushes, a and d, are diametrically opposite and are connected to the overhead line; the other two brushes, c and e, connected to the four traction motors of the B-B

locomotive, are located symmetrically near brush d, at about 45 electrical degrees from it. On the same shaft a shunt-excited regulator dynamo, RD, is mounted, which is connected to the overhead line through the regulator winding, 5.

In addition to regulator winding 5, the metadyne is provided with a variator winding, 1, having its magnetic axis electrically normal to the commutating axis of the primary brushes, a and d; with a series winding, 2, having the same magnetic axis as variator winding 1 and carrying the primary current, $I_a = -I_d$; and, finally, with another series winding carrying the secondary current, $I_c = -I_e$, having two members, 3 and 4. Member 3 has its magnetic axis along the axis of polar segments C (immediately following brush c in the clockwise direction) and F (immediately following point f diametrically opposite to brush c), and member 4 has its magnetic axis along the axis of polar segments D and A (immediately following brushes d and a, respectively, in the clockwise direction). The latter two windings were chosen to stabilize the operation during regenerative braking even if the traction motors should be left series-excited.

Because the scheme of Fig. 103 is simplified, no contactors or starting rheostat have been shown, and the nature of the excitation of the traction motors has not been indicated. For all these and other minor details one may refer to the scheme of Fig. 82 of the Italian shunting locomotive.

Primary current I_a creates, by means of its rotor ampere-turns, the primary flux ϕ_1 along the commutating axis of primary brushes a and d; secondary current I_c creates, by means of its armature ampere-turns, the secondary flux ϕ_2 along the bisector of the two commutating axes, cf and eb, corresponding to brushes c and e, respectively.

The fundamental equations are three:

$$\frac{1}{n} E_{da} = K_b I_c + K_\alpha I_a + K_\gamma I_\gamma + (K_\varepsilon - K_\delta)I_c$$

$$\frac{1}{n} E_{ce} = K_a I_a + K_\beta I_c + K_\rho I_\rho \tag{47}$$

$$\frac{1}{n} E_{cd} = K_c I_a + K_d I_c + K_\delta I_c + K_\sigma I_\rho$$

where the constants K with a Roman index (for the sake of simplicity, a single index has been adopted instead of the usual three) refer to the rotor-current action, where the constants K with a Greek index refer to a stator-current action, where I_ρ is the regulator current, and where I_γ is the variator current.

It is obvious that

$$K_c = \tfrac{1}{2}K_a$$

$$K_\sigma = \tfrac{1}{2}K_\rho \tag{48}$$

$$K_b + K_a = 0$$

The ratio K_β/K_α depends on the proportion between polar segment B and polar segment A.

In addition, write the equation relative to the brush voltage E_{de}:

$$\frac{1}{n}E_{de} = \frac{1}{2}K_aI_a - K_dI_c + K_\varepsilon I_c + \frac{1}{2}K_\rho I_\rho \tag{49}$$

In designing the stator windings 3 and 4, the author has chosen the predetermined relations

$$K_d + K_\delta = \tfrac{1}{2}K_\beta$$

$$-K_d + K_\varepsilon = \tfrac{1}{2}K_\beta \tag{50}$$

which enable a simplification of the fundamental equations as follows:

$$\frac{1}{n}E_{da} = K_bI_c + K_aI_a + K_\gamma I_\gamma + 2K_\beta I_c$$

$$\frac{1}{n}E_{ce} = K_aI_a + K_\beta I_c + K_\rho I_\rho \tag{51}$$

$$E_{cd} = E_{de} = \tfrac{1}{2}E_{ce}$$

The corresponding vector diagrams are given by Fig. 104. This is a case of complete compensation of the armature reaction with respect to E_{cd} and E_{de}.

Diagram A corresponds to standstill, diagram B to motoring at low speed, and diagram C to motoring at high speed. At this speed, the voltage impressed on the traction motors reaches its maximum 1000 volts, while the highest difference of potential of any point of the traction motors with respect to ground is only 500 volts, 100 volts less than the old value of the overhead-line voltage.

Diagrams D and E refer to regenerative-braking conditions at high and at low speed, respectively.

If the coefficients K_δ and K_ε had simply been taken equal to $\tfrac{1}{2}K_\beta$, then the resulting vector diagram of the brush voltages would have been distorted as Fig. 105 shows, diagram A corresponding to motoring and diagram B corresponding to a braking operation.

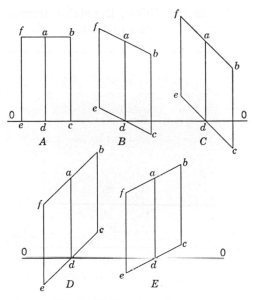

Fig. 104. Vector diagrams for the Trident transformer metadyne, applicable when the stator windings are chosen according to Equations 50.

Figures 106(a) and 106(b) give two views of the Trident metadyne before it was mounted on the locomotive. Figure 106(c) shows the

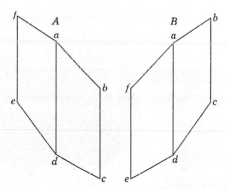

Fig. 105. Vector diagrams for a degree of compensation different from that of Fig. 104.

same machine located inside the locomotive, and it makes apparent the relatively small size of the Trident transformer metadyne.

Figures 106(d) and 106(e) give two views of the Trident transformer metadyne built for research work before the order for the regular equipment was accepted. In Fig. 106(e), the stator arrangement is clearly shown, the armature being dismounted; notice the small size of the

Fig. 106(a). View of the Trident transformer metadyne for the French switching locomotive. (*Courtesy of Als-Thom, Paris.*)

stator windings, taking into account that the machine is a single-cycle metadyne.

An important requirement that the French switching locomotive had to meet was to be able to haul and to maneuver a train in the

Fig. 106(b). The Trident metadyne and its blower. (*Courtesy of Als-Thom, Paris.*)

emergency that the overhead line would not be able to supply any electric power at all. The necessary power then would be supplied by a

Fig. 106(c).   The Trident metadyne mounted inside the French switching locomotive.
(*Courtesy of Als-Thom, Paris.*)

battery, carried by a tender attached to the locomotive, capable of giving direct current at 400 volts.

The metadyne must then transform the relatively low primary voltage, supplied to the primary brushes, a and d, by the battery, to a higher

Fig. 106(*d*).   An experimental Trident transformer metadyne.   (*Courtesy of Als-Thom, Paris.*)

voltage, up to 1000 volts, for the traction motors.   The vector diagrams of the brush voltages are then given by Fig. 106(*f*), diagram A for motoring and diagram B for braking.   It is obvious that current I_a is two to three times higher with the battery supply than with the overhead-line supply.   This requirement for battery operation is unfavorable to the solution using the Cross transformer metadyne with two commutators and favorable to the solution with the Trident transformer metadyne.

In order to make this point clear, it will be helpful to calculate the copper losses in the armature of the transformer metadyne in both cases, as these losses are a reasonable index of the size of the armature. Let R be the armature resistance measured between two diametrically

Fig. 106(e). Stator of the experimental Trident metadyne. (*Courtesy of Als-Thom, Paris.*)

opposite brushes. The angular distance between the two secondary brushes is 90 electrical degrees; the distribution of the currents is shown in Fig. 107. Thus the copper losses for the Trident transformer metadyne are

$$C_T = 4R\left[\frac{3}{4}\left(\frac{I_a}{2} - \frac{I_c}{4}\right)^2 + \frac{1}{4}\left(\frac{I_a}{2} + \frac{3I_c}{4}\right)^2\right] = \frac{1}{4}R[4I_a^2 + 3I_c^2] \quad (52)$$

For the comparison undertaken here, it will simplify the calculation to admit that the efficiency of the metadyne transformer is 100% and that the overhead-line voltage is 1500 volts while the maximum value

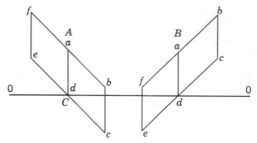

Fig. 106(*f*).   Vector diagram for battery operation of the Trident transformer metadyne.

of the voltage on the motors is 1000 volts [= 500 − (−500)].   Therefore, at full load,

$$I_c = 1.5I_a \qquad (53)$$

and then the copper losses C_T become

$$C_T = 2.69RI_a^2 \qquad (54)$$

Now consider a Cross transformer metadyne with two commutators, one commutator for the overhead-line current, I_a, and the other for the

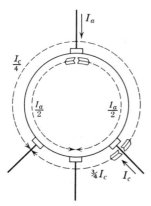

Fig. 107.   Armature current distribution in the Trident transformer metadyne.

motor current, I_m, and calculate the copper losses, with the assumption that the armature and the speed are the same as for the Trident. Then conductors must be provided in each slot for both commutators; that means that the available copper area for each commutator will be $\frac{1}{2}k$ of the copper area available for the single-commutator Trident transformer metadyne, k being a coefficient smaller than 1 which takes into account the major losses of available space because of the necessity of providing two distinct windings for two distinct commutators.

On the other hand, comparing the vector diagrams of Fig. 104 with those of Fig. 87 leads to the conclusion that the winding corresponding to the overhead-line current I_a must now have more peripheral conductors than that of the Trident, and that the ratio will be 3000/2500, whereas the winding corresponding

Fig. 108.   The first metadyne locomotive.   (*Courtesy of Als-Thom, Paris.*)

to motor current I_m must have fewer peripheral conductors, with the ratio equal to 2000/2500.   Therefore, the resistance between two diametrically opposite brushes for the former winding, the one carrying current I_a, will be $2kR(3000/2500)^2$, and for the latter winding will be $2kR(2000/2500)^2$.

Thus the losses, C_D, will be

$$C_D = 2kR[(\tfrac{30}{25})^2 I_a^2 + (\tfrac{20}{25})^2 I_m^2]$$ (55)

Fig. 109.   Another locomotive of the same type as that of Fig. 108.   (*Courtesy of Als-Thom, Paris.*)

If hypothesis 53 is applied to I_m, the following losses will occur at full load:

$$C_D = 2kR[(\tfrac{30}{25})^2 + (\tfrac{20}{25})^2 \times \overline{1.5^2}]I_a^2 = 5.68kRI_a^2 \qquad (56)$$

Even with $k = 1$, the copper losses will be much larger. The situation is worse when the Cross transformer metadyne is supplied by the battery at a comparatively low voltage. Thus the author chose the Trident

Fig. 110(a). A current model of the French metadyne locomotive. (*Courtesy of Als-Thom, Paris.*)

metadyne, which also happened to appease the anxiety of those engineers not familiar with the metadyne, with respect to commutation.

Finally, the locomotive also had to operate along any third-rail section of track, the third rail supplying current at 600 volts, at least as long as these old sections were still in service.

The exceptional flexibility of the Trident transformer metadyne to operate satisfactorily under line voltage varying from 1800 (= 1500 + 20%) volts to 400 volts is shared to a lesser extent by transformer metadynes of other kinds. This fact led to studies such as those of a colonial railway having an overhead line of 1500 volts in a densely populated area and 3000 volts in areas with small population. Similarly cases were considered with normal high voltage, say 1500 or 3000 volts, for the overhead along the main lines far from city stations and with a 750-volt overhead line in the large city stations.

Many such locomotives have been built; the test train was composed of the first metadyne locomotive constructed (shown in Fig. 108), five

Fig. 110(b).   The cab of the locomotive of Fig. 110(a).   (*Courtesy of Als-Thom, Paris.*)

standard rheostatic locomotives, and a variable number of coaches. Figure 109 shows another metadyne locomotive of the same type at work in the yards.   Figures 110(a) and 110(b) show external and internal views of a current type of these locomotives.

3. COMMUTATION IN THE TRIDENT TRANSFORMER METADYNE

Here is a typical example of commutation in a metadyne. Figure 111 shows six commutating poles for four brushes.

The design of the commutating-pole windings relative to the overhead-line current, I_a, shows no difference from the corresponding one of the Cross transformer metadyne, to which this design will be referred.

Fig. 111. Stator construction of the Trident transformer metadyne.

For the design of the windings interlinked with four commutating poles relative to the motor current I_c, the dotted integral path indicated in the figure will be considered, its positive sense being indicated by the arrow. The crosses and dots along the periphery of the armature indicate the sense of the armature currents for a positive value of I_a and I_c. Let a_e and a_b be the depth of the air gap under the commutating poles and H_e and H_b be the magnetic field required in the same air gaps for satisfactory commutation of the current I_c; with the same symbols as in Section 6 of Chapter 12, we obtain

$$-A_b + A_e + \frac{1}{8} NI_a + \frac{1}{8} NI_c = a_eH_e - a_bH_b + \int_S \frac{\bar{B}}{\mu} \cdot \overline{ds} \quad (57)$$

Application of the conditions

$$-a_bH_b = a_eH_e = -kI_c$$
$$-A_b = A_e$$

$$(58)$$

where k is a nondimensional coefficient (a number of turns), results in

$$-A_b = A_e = -kI_c - \frac{1}{16} NI_a - \frac{1}{16} NI_c + \frac{1}{2} \int_S \frac{\overline{B}}{\mu} \cdot \overline{ds} \qquad (59)$$

Note that the product $\overline{B} \cdot \overline{ds}$ is negative along a great part of the integral path S.

This equation shows that the commutating poles corresponding to current I_c must have two windings: one winding carrying current I_c,

Fig. 112. The clean appearance of this commutator is evidence of satisfactory commutation. (*Courtesy of Als-Thom, Paris.*)

and the other winding, somewhat smaller, carrying current I_a. It is important to note that for each brush c and e there are two commutating poles, and that the commutation of the current in the sections short-circuited by one of these two brushes takes place far from the interference of the commutating current in the sections short-circuited by the other brush. This arrangement has facilitated commutation of the current I_c. Figure 112 gives a view of the commutator of a Trident transformer metadyne after a long period of continuous operation, showing that the commutation has been satisfactory.

4. THE CADUCEUS TRANSFORMER METADYNE OPERATING AT CONSTANT VOLTAGE

The armature is provided with two distinct windings insulated from one another, and with two commutators. Figure 113 shows two variants

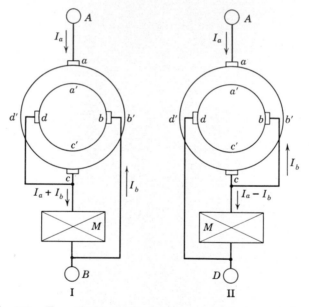

Fig. 113.   Two schemes for the Caduceus transformer metadyne.

of the general scheme. The two distinct armature windings are indicated by two concentric circles; on the exterior circuit are shown the primary brushes, a and c, and on the interior circuit, the secondary brushes, b and d.

Points a', b', c', d' indicate the points on one commutator corresponding to the angular location of the brushes bearing on the other commutator. The consumer is indicated by the rectangle M; and the terminals A and B for Fig. 113I, and A and D for Fig. 113II, are assumed to be connected to the feeder network.

Assume that the feeder network is a constant-voltage system, i.e., that between the terminals A and B (or A and D) a constant voltage, V, is maintained, whatever the value of current I_a may be, supplied or absorbed.

First, consider the scheme of Fig. 113I; if the losses are neglected, the fundamental equations may be written

$$\frac{1}{n} E_{ca} = K_b I_b + \sum_{\gamma=\alpha}^{\nu} K_{ca}^{\gamma} I_{\gamma}$$

$$\frac{1}{n} E_{bd} = K_a I_a + \sum_{\gamma=\alpha}^{\nu} K_{bd}^{\gamma} I_{\gamma} \tag{60}$$

Further,

$$V = E_{ca} + E_{bd} \tag{61}$$

Assume that the metadyne is provided with a regulator device that maintains the speed practically constant at the value n, and neglect the slight departures of the speed from its normal value, departures necessary for the normal operation of the regulator device. Then the regulator equation may be written

$$\sum_{\gamma=\alpha}^{\nu} (K_{ca}^{\gamma} I_a - K_{bd}^{\gamma} I_b) I_{\gamma} = 0 \tag{62}$$

where the regulator current, I_{ρ}, is included among the stator currents. Further, the following relations are established because the armature has two separate windings:

$$E_{b'd'} = \frac{N_1}{N_2} E_{bd}$$

$$E_{c'a'} = \frac{N_2}{N_1} E_{ca} \tag{63}$$

where N_1 and N_2 are the total peripheral conductors of the two distinct armature windings, the winding fed by brushes a and c and the winding fed by the other two brushes, respectively. For the sake of simplicity, the machine is assumed to have a single cycle and a winding of diametrical pitch. The action between the stator ampere-turns and the two armature currents I_a and I_b is the same as for the Cross transformer metadyne.

The current supplied to the consumer is $I_a + I_b$, and therefore the power, P_m, absorbed by it is

$$P_m = E_{db}(I_a + I_b) \tag{64}$$

It is important to determine the ratio τ of the power transformed by the metadyne to the power absorbed by the consumer:

$$\tau = \frac{E_{bd}(I_a + I_b)}{-E_{bd}I_b} = 1 + \frac{I_a}{I_b} = 1 + \frac{E_{bd}}{E_{ca}} \tag{65}$$

since

$$E_{ca}I_a - E_{bd}I_b = 0 \tag{66}$$

Now consider the scheme of Fig. 113II; fundamental Equations 60 are the same, regulator Equation 62 is the same, relations 63 hold, but Equations 61, 64, and 65 must be replaced, respectively, by

$$V = E_{ca} - E_{bd} \tag{67}$$

$$P_m = E_{bd}(I_a - I_b) \tag{68}$$

$$\tau = \frac{E_{bd}(I_a - I_b)}{-E_{bd}I_b} = 1 - \frac{I_a}{I_b} = 1 - \frac{E_{bd}}{E_{ca}} \tag{69}$$

Suppose that the secondary variator winding of the transformer metadyne creates a secondary current, I_b, that has the same direction

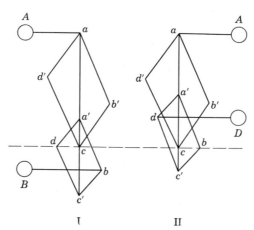

Fig. 114.   Vector diagrams for the schemes of Fig. 113.

as the secondary magnetizing current, $I_{b\mu}$; then scheme I is better suited for the motoring, and scheme II is better suited for the regenerating operation of the consumer. The converse holds when the secondary variator winding of the transformer metadyne creates a secondary current, I_b, in the opposite direction to the secondary magnetizing current, $I_{b\mu}$.

The Caduceus transformer metadyne is particularly suited for special operations of the consumer; for instance, for charging a battery, for continuous absorption of power, or for continuous regeneration of power.

Figure 114 shows two vector diagrams. Diagram I refers to scheme I of Fig. 113; the consumer is assumed to be motoring, the sum $I_a + I_b$ being positive; or the consumer is assumed to be regenerating, with the sum $I_a + I_b$ negative. Vector diagram II refers to scheme II of Fig. 113, with the consumer assumedly regenerating, the difference $I_a - I_b$ being negative; or the consumer may be assumed to be motoring, the difference $I_a - I_b$ being positive. In the vector diagrams, the potentials of the two terminals A and B, and A and D, have been pointed out, respectively.

5. THE CADUCEUS TRANSFORMER METADYNE OPERATING IN A LOOP OF A SERIES NETWORK

The terminals A and B and A and D, respectively, of schemes I and II of Fig. 113 are now assumed to belong to a series distribution system. The consumer M then becomes a section of the series network, in which the current is either $I_a + I_b$ or $I_a - I_b$, a current different from the current I_a of the series network.

Take, for instance, scheme I of Fig. 113 and assume that I_a and I_b both have the same sign. A current will flow in consumer M larger than the normal current of the series network and larger than the current supplied by the metadyne itself. The same may be said for scheme II of Fig. 113 when the currents I_a and I_b have opposite directions.

The equations, the vector diagrams, and most of the considerations developed in the previous section are still valid with this assumption that the Caduceus transformer metadyne is inserted into a series system with the value V of the voltage between the terminals being a variable and the value I_a of the current of the series network now being a constant or at least following a law independent of the characteristics of the Caduceus transformer metadyne.

When a Caduceus transformer metadyne is inserted into a series network carrying a constant current I_0, it is generally required that a consumer be supplied with a current I_s, different from I_0. The current I_s flowing in the consumer is either constant or a given function of the voltage of the consumer.

Suppose that it is desired to have I_s constant. Since $I_s = I_a \pm I_b$ and $I_a = I_0$, secondary current I_b must remain constant. The first Equation 60 shows that this result may be obtained, for n practically constant, with the use of only two stator windings, having their magnetic axes along the secondary commutating axis; the first winding carries a current I_α proportional to the primary voltage E_{ca} such that

$$E_{ca} = nK_{ca}^\alpha I_\alpha$$

and the second winding carries a constant current, I_β. Then the value of I_b results as follows:

$$I_b = -\frac{K_{ca}}{K_b} I_\beta \tag{70}$$

The desired value of I_s will thus be obtained by a proper setting of the value of stator current I_β.

In order to keep the speed n practically constant, a regulator device is needed, with a regulator winding having its magnetic axis along the primary commutating axis, in accordance with the limitation mentioned above for obtaining the result expressed by Equation 70. The correct location of the magnetic axis of the regulator winding also depends on the nature of the consumer; rules for checking the correct location of the magnetic axis of the regulator winding have been given in Section 3 ("Static Stability Regarding Speed") of Chapter 8. In practice, the device given above for the location of the magnetic axis of the regulator winding is generally satisfactory, provided that schemes I or II of Fig. 113 have been correctly chosen in connection with the particular type of consumer.

Thus the scheme of Fig. 115 is obtained. Secondary variator winding $W1$ is shunt-connected across the primary terminals A and C; secondary variator winding $W2$ creates some constant ampere-turns, set by the adjusting resistor, R; regulator winding RW has its magnetic axis along the primary commutating axis.

As a speed-regulating device, the regulator shunt dynamo, RD, in combination with the base dynamo, BD, has been chosen. The base dynamo also provides a suitable direct-current source at constant voltage for supplying variator winding $W2$. Thus the set is completely independent and does not require any auxiliary source when inserted into a loop of a series distribution system at the terminals $T1$ and $T2$.

The double dots at the terminals recall the existence of commutating-pole windings and of stabilizing windings not otherwise indicated on the scheme. A primary stabilizing winding may interfere with the shape of the main characteristic (current supplied to the consumer as a function of the voltage induced by it), and thus the current $I_s = I_a + I_b$ is only approximately constant. However, dynamic analysis yields a way to correct this undesired interference with the shape of the static characteristic.

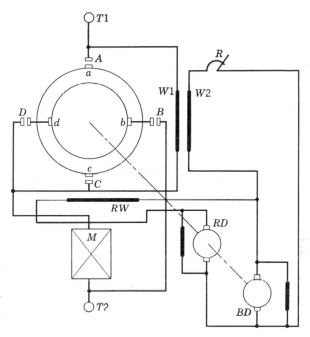

Fig. 115. Scheme of a Caduceus transformer metadyne for use in a series distribution system.

The Cross transformer metadyne with two commutators, the Trident transformer metadyne, and the Caduceus transformer metadyne may be considered three different solutions of the problem raised when the maximum voltage of the primary network and the maximum voltage of the consumer are very different from one another.

14 · Some Generator Metadynes of Degree $m = 4$

1. THE C GENERATOR METADYNE

Consider a transformer metadyne provided with a speed-regulator device. The regulator current will be zero only for a few exceptional values of load. Generally the regulator current will have a positive or a negative value different from zero; this means that for a general value of load there would be an accelerating torque or, correspondingly, a decelerating one if the regulator winding were not there. On the other hand, for a given general value of load, the primary current itself has a given positive or negative value; therefore, a transformation of electric power occurs.

Thus a generator metadyne may be derived from a transformer metadyne by

Removal of the speed-regulator device and the regulator winding.

Provision of means for reducing the primary current to a negligible value or, even better, to zero.

Figure 116 gives the scheme of a generator metadyne derived from the Cross transformer metadyne by means of the above-mentioned rule. The stator has two windings, a secondary variator winding, W, for regulating the value of the secondary current, I_b, supplied to consumer M, and a primary amplifying winding, S. There is no regulator winding, of course.

Let V_1 be the constant voltage of the primary source connected to the terminals A and C; denote by I_α the current flowing in variator winding W, and by K_{bd}^β the coefficient corresponding to amplifying winding S; finally, neglect the ohmic drops, and write the fundamental equations of the metadyne:

$$\frac{1}{n} V_1 = KI_b + K_{ca}^\alpha I_\alpha$$

$$\frac{1}{n} E_{bd} = KI_a + K_{bd}^\beta I_a \tag{71}$$

The first equation shows that secondary current I_b supplied to the consumer may easily be regulated by stator current I_α of secondary variator winding W, just as in the Cross transformer metadyne:

$$I_b = \frac{\frac{1}{n}V_1 - K_{ca}^\alpha I_\alpha}{K} \tag{72}$$

the term $K_{ca}^\alpha I_\alpha$ generally being negative. The second equation gives

$$I_a = \frac{\frac{1}{n}E_{bd}}{K + K_{bd}^\beta} \tag{73}$$

Multiply the numerator and the denominator of the second member by I_b and $[(1/n)V_1 - K_{ca}^\alpha I_\alpha]/K$, respectively, and, further, multiply

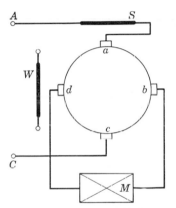

Fig. 116. Elementary scheme of the C generator metadyne.

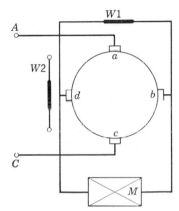

Fig. 117. A possible arrangement to reduce the primary current to zero.

both members of the equation by V_1. Thus the following relation is obtained:

$$V_1 I_a = \frac{E_{bd}I_b}{\left(1 + \frac{K_{bd}^\beta}{K}\right)\left[1 - \frac{K_{ca}^\alpha I_\alpha}{(1/n)V_1}\right]}$$

From this equation the ratio of primary to secondary power is obtained:

$$\frac{V_1 I_a}{E_{bd}I_b} = \frac{1}{\left(1 + \frac{K_{bd}^\beta}{K}\right)\left[1 - \frac{K_{ca}^\alpha I_\alpha}{(1/n)V_1}\right]} \tag{74}$$

If it is recalled that the product $K_{ca}^\alpha I_\alpha$ is generally negative, the conclusion is that the ratio between the primary and the secondary power becomes smaller as the absolute value of I_α becomes larger. In other words, (1) the ratio becomes smaller as the secondary current and the rotational speed n become larger; and (2), the ratio becomes smaller as the value of K_{bd}^β is made larger (by an increase in the number of turns of the amplifying winding).

It is important to note that, while the number of turns of the amplifying winding increases, the copper area decreases so nearly proportionally that finally the overall size of the stator coil remains approximately the same. By increasing the number of turns of the amplifying winding, one may reduce the ratio in Equation 74 to any desired value. From the dynamic point of view, a large number of turns of the amplifying winding is not desirable; a number of turns of the same order as the number of turns of the armature winding is generally adopted.

The metadyne generator derived from the Cross transformer metadyne is called the C generator metadyne. The stabilizing windings have not been mentioned, but they must comply with certain general rules for good dynamic behavior. Their interference with the static characteristics is generally small, and it may often be neglected.

A different arrangement of the stator windings of the C generator metadyne is indicated by the scheme of Fig. 117. The stator has two windings: A secondary variator winding, $W2$, allowing for the regulation of the value of secondary current I_b, and a primary variator winding, $W1$, shunt-connected across the secondary brushes.

The fundamental equations are now

$$\frac{1}{n} V_1 = KI_b + K_{ca}^\alpha I_\alpha$$

$$\frac{1}{n} E_{bd} = KI_a + K_{bd}^\beta I_\beta \tag{75}$$

where I_α and I_β are the currents flowing in variator windings $W2$ and $W1$, respectively.

Let R be the total resistance of the circuit of variator winding $W1$. The second Equation 75 may be written

$$\frac{1}{n} E_{bd} = KI_a + K_{bd}^\beta \frac{E_{bd}}{R} \tag{76}$$

If the relation

$$R - nK_{bd}^\beta = 0 \tag{77}$$

is satisfied, primary current I_a as derived from Equation 76 becomes zero. Relation 77 is called the relation of "astaticity," and the corresponding stator winding is said to be "astatically set" or, briefly, "astatic."

Under astatic conditions the primary source will generally supply no power, and only during rapid transient alteration of the conditions of operation will primary current I_a flow rapidly to and from the metadyne, provided that the stabilizing windings are correctly set for proper dynamic behavior of the metadyne. Otherwise, the stabilizing windings are not considered here but are tacitly assumed to be present.

The condition of astaticity given by Equation 77 may not be fulfilled if R has a larger value; then a primary amplifying winding may be

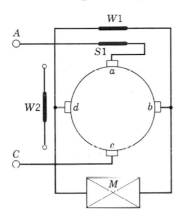

Fig. 118. The primary series winding helps to reduce the primary current.

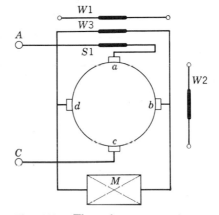

Fig. 119. The primary current can even be reversed with the proper excitation of winding $W1$.

provided with a moderate number of turns, in order to reduce further the primary current, which is already small. Thus the scheme of Fig. 118 is obtained.

The fulfillment of the condition of astaticity involves some danger of instability for certain types of consumer, if instead of Equation 77 the following relation is fulfilled:

$$nK_{bd}^\beta < R \tag{78}$$

Since the ampere-turns created by the winding shunt-connected across the secondary brushes is not sufficient for reducing the primary current to zero, another primary variator winding may be used, creating constant ampere-turns in the same sense as the shunt-connected primary winding. Thus the average value of the primary current may be reduced or brought to zero (or even made negative) without involving instability of operation. A primary amplifying winding may also be employed; this is the scheme of Fig. 119.

Another possible scheme is that indicated by Fig. 120; a single primary variator winding, $W2$, has its current I continuously set (for instance, by means of an adjusting resistor, R) in such a way as to keep the value of primary current I_a as near to zero as possible. The adjusting resistor may, for instance, be operated by a device sensitive to current I_a. With this scheme only peaks of current I_a will flow to and from the metadyne, tending to induce at any moment the right electromotive force, E_{bd}, required by the consumer. These peaks of current I_a will become smaller, the more rapidly the setting device operates the resistor R.

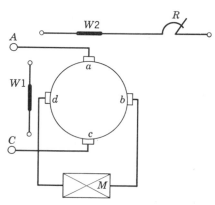

Fig. 120. Another circuit for effecting the transition from the Cross transformer to the C generator.

A variable depth of air gap is mentioned here as a means for obtaining the transition from a pure transformer metadyne to a transformer and generator metadyne or to a transformer and motor metadyne. Consider a Cross transformer metadyne without stator windings and with an air gap of constant depth; no regulator is needed. If the depth of the air gap is smaller along the primary commutating axis and larger along the secondary commutating axis as Fig. 121 shows, the machine operates as a transformer and as a generator simultaneously. If the depth of the air gap is smaller along the secondary commutating axis as Fig. 122 shows, the machine operates as a transformer and as a motor simultaneously.

The fundamental equations are

$$\frac{1}{n} E_{ca} = K_b I_b$$

$$\frac{1}{n} E_{bd} = K_a I_a$$

where $K_b < K_a$ for Fig. 121, whereas for Fig. 122 $K_a < K_b$.

The ratio of the primary and the secondary power is

$$\frac{E_{ca} I_a}{E_{bd} I_b} = \frac{K_b}{K_a}$$

This ratio is practically equal to the ratio of the depths of the air gap along the primary commutating axis and along the secondary commutating axis, respectively. The device mentioned here may be combined with the various arrangements of stator windings indicated in this chapter and in the following one.

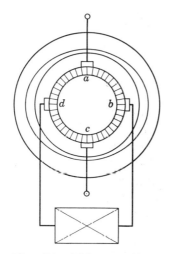

Fig. 121. This nonuniform air gap creates a simultaneous transformer and generator metadyne.

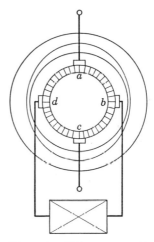

Fig. 122. This stator orientation creates a simultaneous transformer and motor metadyne.

The use of a secondary hypocompensating winding is another solution to the problem set forth at the beginning of this chapter. Figure 122(a) shows the corresponding diagram. The fundamental equations are

$$\frac{1}{n} E_{ca} = KI_b - K^\beta I_b$$

$$\frac{1}{n} E_{bd} = KI_a$$

where K^β is positive. In order to allow for a variable value of the intensity of current I_b, a movable contact member that inserts a variable number of turns of the hypocompensating winding is indicated in the figure. Instead of the sliding contact member, a shunt resistor may be

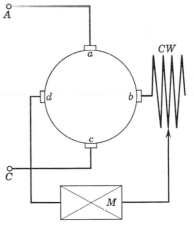

Fig. 122(a). Addition of a secondary hypocompensating winding to the Cross transformer metadyne.

used. However, the dynamic behavior of these two regulating means is
very different.   The real or virtual number of turns of the compensating winding may be kept constant, and regulation of the intensity of
secondary current I_b may be obtained with a secondary variator winding.
    The ratio between primary and secondary power is

$$\frac{E_{ca}I_a}{E_{bd}I_b} = 1 - \frac{K^\beta}{K}$$

For $K^\beta < K$, the winding being a hypocompensator, the primary source
supplies or absorbs power when the load absorbs or supplies power,
respectively.   The reverse occurs when $K^\beta > K$ and the winding is a
hypercompensator.
    The C generator metadyne has thus been derived from the Cross
transformer metadyne.   Similarly, an E generator metadyne may be
derived from the Eight transformer metadyne.   The latter is described
in Chapter 19.   Similarly, the U generator metadyne may be derived
from the Caduceus transformer metadyne.

2. THE S GENERATOR METADYNE

    The function of the primary source of constant voltage connected
to the primary brushes of the C generator metadyne, as pointed out in
the previous paragraph, may be obtained, whatever the value of the
voltage V_1 is of the primary source. The
necessary power at the primary brushes of
the C generator metadyne may be supplied
either by the primary source or by the
metadyne itself, or sometimes by the source
and sometimes by the metadyne, depending
on the specific setting of the primary variator windings.
    Therefore, voltage V_1 may be reduced to
zero, and the operation will still be satisfactory.   In this way the scheme of Fig. 123
is obtained, the primary brushes being short-
circuited; the metadyne is then called the
S generator metadyne.   No primary source
is required.

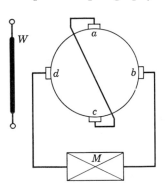

Fig. 123.   Elementary
scheme of the S generator
metadyne.

    The stator bears a single winding, the secondary variator winding W.
Call the current flowing through it I_α, neglect the ohmic drops, and write
the fundamental equations of the corresponding metadyne.

$$\frac{1}{n} E_{ca} = 0 = KI_b + K_{ca}^{\alpha} I_{\alpha}$$

$$\frac{1}{n} E_{bd} = KI_a$$

(79)

The first equation gives the value of the secondary current I_b proportional to the secondary variator winding current I_{α}; the second equation shows that the primary current I_a remains proportional to the secondary voltage, E_{bd}, supplied to the consumer. Thus if I_{α} is made constant,

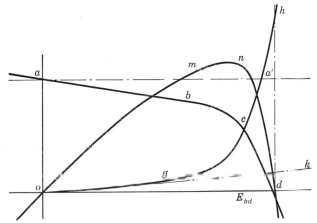

Fig. 124.   Some characteristics of the simple S generator metadyne.

the infinite, straight, horizontal line aa' on the diagram of Fig. 124 will represent the secondary current, I_b, supplied to the consumer as a function of the secondary voltage, E_{bd}, required by this consumer and plotted as abscissa. Primary current I_a is represented on the same diagram by the infinite, straight line ok, the rotational speed n being assumed constant.

3. CONSIDERATION OF OHMIC DROP AND IRON SATURATION

If ohmic drops are considered, Equations 79 are replaced by the following ones:

$$0 = KI_b + K_{ca}^{\alpha} I_{\alpha} + \frac{1}{n} R_a I_a$$

$$\frac{1}{n} E_{bd} = KI_a$$

(80)

where R_a is the resistance of the total primary circuit.

The corresponding diagram will again show two straight lines representing the currents I_a and I_b as a function of the secondary voltage E_{bd}, the line representing the current I_b being inclined in the opposite sense of the line representing I_a. Nevertheless, as the term $(1/n)R_aI_a$ is very small with respect to the other two terms of the first equation, the straight line representing I_b will be nearly horizontal.

From Equations 80 there results

$$I_b = \frac{1}{n^2}\frac{R_a}{K^2}E_{bd} - \frac{K_{ca}^\alpha}{K}I_\alpha \equiv I_{b\mu} + I_{bw} \tag{80a}$$

where $I_{b\mu}$ is the magnetizing component of current I_b and where I_{bw} is the remaining component. This definition is better understood when compared with the resolution of the secondary current in the Cross transformer metadyne. In the latter resolution, $I_{b\mu}$ appears even when the secondary variator winding current is zero, and the component I_{bw} appears when the secondary variator winding creates ampere-turns generally opposing the secondary armature ampere-turns. Thus I_{bw} in the Cross transformer metadyne compensates the variator ampere-turns completely, whereas the I_{bw} defined here compensates only a part of the secondary variator ampere-turns.

Equation 80a shows that the characteristic of secondary current versus secondary voltage is a drooping straight line. A more radical modification is obtained if iron saturation is considered. The fundamental equations must be written

$$0 = K_bI_b + K_{ca}^\alpha I_\alpha + \frac{1}{n}R_aI_a$$
$$\frac{1}{n}E_{bd} = K_aI_a \tag{81}$$

Not only will the coefficients K vary with iron saturation, but also the coefficients K_a and K_b will vary, generally in a different way from one another, and therefore they must be represented by different symbols.

It is laborious to follow analytically the variation of the coefficients K; a graphical representation of the primary and secondary currents as a function of the secondary induced electromotive force will here suffice for a clear understanding of the operation.

For small values of E_{bd}, small values of primary current are required. The iron saturation in both directions along the primary commutating axis and along the secondary commutating axis is negligible, and the corresponding segments of the characteristics approach the straight-line segments.

For high values of E_{bd}, the iron saturation along the primary commutating axis becomes more and more intense, and the required magnetizing current along this direction (the primary current I_a) becomes stronger and stronger, thus absorbing a larger part of the ampere-turns of the secondary variator winding W and leaving an ever smaller part of those ampere-turns for compensating the secondary current I_b. Thus the value of the secondary current decreases rapidly. This reduction will be more marked when iron saturation occurs along the secondary commutating axis as well.

The characteristics of the primary current, *ogch*, and of the secondary current, *abcd*, then show a sharp bend, as Fig. 124 indicates. Points *a* and *o* along the axis of the ordinates are the "short-circuit" points; points *h* and *d*, along the ordinate corresponding to the intersection *d* of the characteristic of secondary current with the axis of abscissas, are the "open-circuit" points.

The above-indicated features of the characteristics of the primary and the secondary currents are important for practical applications. If a short circuit occurs in the secondary circuit, i.e., in the load circuit, the secondary current will increase only slightly, and the primary current will decrease to zero. If the load circuit is accidentally interrupted, the secondary voltage will reach its "open-circuit" value, which is generally not much higher than the maximum value under normal operation; hence any danger due to overvoltage is avoided.

For normal operation the secondary current, I_b, supplied to the consumer is kept nearly constant over a very large range of values of secondary voltage. When the load reaches its maximum value, the secondary current begins to decrease rapidly, thus tending to reduce the load automatically.

It is impossible to overload the prime motor driving the S generator metadyne above the predetermined maximum value; in fact, if the power supplied to the load is plotted, the curve *omnd* is obtained, showing a flat maximum at *mn*, the value of which is independent of the operation of the load. Whatever mishandling may occur in controlling the operation, this maximum value cannot be exceeded.

If for some accidental reason a machine in the consumer group "runs away" and tends to require an ever higher voltage, the voltage cannot exceed its "open-circuit" value. Hence, before this value is reached, the supplied secondary current drops to such a low value that it cannot provide for torque sufficient to continue the acceleration of the runaway machine.

If it is desired not to exceed a value of secondary voltage E_{bd} smaller than the "open-circuit" value, the abrupt increase of primary current I_a

provides an easy means for applying an overload relay, operating under excellent conditions. When the overload relay is tripped, there is no need to interrupt the secondary or the primary circuit, but simply the circuit of the small current I_α of the secondary variator winding.

4. VARIANTS OF THE STATOR WINDINGS

Further consideration of the diagram of Fig. 124 shows that it is desirable to reduce the value of primary current I_a. For this purpose a primary amplifying winding may be used, as the scheme of Fig. 125

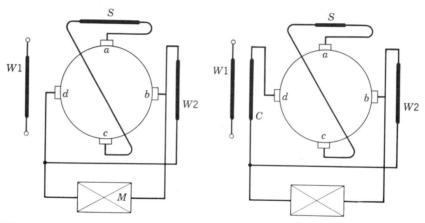

Fig. 125. Amplifying winding S helps to reduce the primary current.

Fig. 125(a). Circuit modification to reduce the control power of the S generator metadyne.

shows. If for the amplifying winding S a number of turns of the same order as the number of turns of the armature is chosen, the primary current is reduced to one-half or to one-third of its original value, and the corresponding losses become very small.

The slope of the segment of the characteristic of secondary current I_b, as a function of secondary voltage E_{bd} and corresponding to low and to moderate values of that voltage, generally has a stabilizing effect on the operation of the consumer; but for many practical applications, a constant value of secondary current I_b is preferred.

In order to obtain this result, a second member, $W2$, a secondary variator winding shunt-connected across the secondary brushes, may be used. The effect of this winding is clearly indicated in Fig. 126. Let $abcd$ be the original characteristic of the current I_b, the winding $W2$ being omitted.

In terms of ampere-turns, the ordinate of the horizontal line aa' represents the constant ampere-turns of the secondary variator winding $W1$ along the secondary commutating axis; the ordinates of the line $abcd$ represent the armature ampere-turns of the secondary current I_b along the same direction; the difference of the ordinates of the curve $abcd$ and the ordinate of the horizontal line aa' represents the ampere-turns necessary for creating the primary electromotive force required to overcome the ohmic drop in the whole primary circuit.

Now consider the ampere-turns created by variator winding $W2$. They may be represented by the ordinates of the inclined straight line

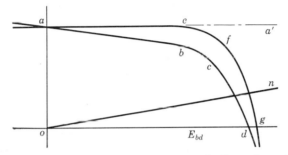

Fig. 126. The shunt variator winding can eliminate the linear droop in the characteristic.

on; these are added to the ampere-turns created by $W1$. Suppose that the resulting secondary current is represented by the ordinates of the curve $aefg$. Then its ordinates are the sum of the ordinates of the curve $abcd$ and of the corresponding ordinates of the straight line on, provided that the ratio of the ordinate of the horizontal line aa' to the ordinates of the straight line on is taken equal to the actual ratio of the ampere-turns of the corresponding variator windings, $W1$ and $W2$.

The simple graphical construction indicated above presupposes that the ampere-turns along the secondary commutating axis, necessary for inducing the electromotive force between the primary brushes needed for overcoming the ohmic drop in the whole primary circuit, are a function of the secondary electromotive force, E_{bd}, only. In fact, these ampere-turns depend also, to a lesser extent, on the saturation along the secondary commutating axis, i.e., they depend also on the value of the primary electromotive force; but this interference may be neglected for a first approximation. Such interference gives an even sharper bend to the curve $aefg$. Curve $aefg$ is more sharply bent then the magnetization curve of the magnetic circuit of the machine; this feature is of value in many practical applications.

The action of variator winding $W2$ may be increased, and from the original characteristic $abcd$ a curve efd may be obtained as indicated by Fig. 127, the inclination of the straight segment now being inverted.

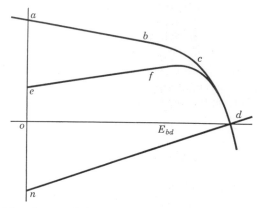

Fig. 127.   A rising characteristic is possible with increased ampere-turns in $W2$.

Such a characteristic is adequate for special applications requiring less torque at low speed.

Figure 128 shows another scheme allowing for a reduction of the primary current by the addition of a primary variator winding, $W1$, shunt-connected across the secondary brushes. If the condition of "astaticity" expressed by Equation 77 is fulfilled, the primary current

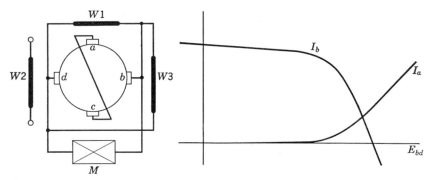

Fig. 128. The primary variator winding helps reduce the primary current.

Fig. 128(a). Effect of winding $W1$ of Fig. 128 on the S generator characteristics.

is practically zero all along the segment of the characteristic corresponding to a nonsaturated magnetic circuit, as Fig. 128(a) shows.

It is preferable to avoid astatic variator windings and instead fulfill relation 78. The primary current will not then be zero but it will be greatly reduced, and the use of a primary amplifying winding will further reduce the primary current. The scheme of Fig. 129 is obtained in this fashion.

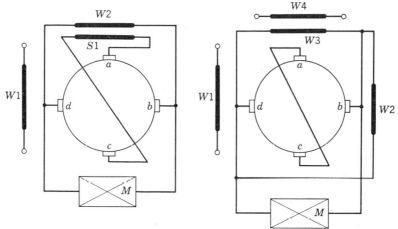

Fig. 129. Connection scheme when the primary variator winding is not astatic.

Fig. 130. A circuit for obtaining negative values of primary current.

Another variant is indicated by the scheme of Fig. 130. The primary variator winding $W3$ is intended to fulfill relation 78, and another primary variator winding, $W4$, is provided to create a constant number of ampere-turns. Primary current I_a may then take on negative values for low values of E_{bd}, as indicated by Fig. 131. A skillful setting will

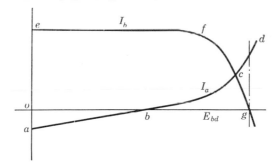

Fig. 131. Characteristics of the circuit of Fig. 130.

bring the point b, for which $I_a = 0$, near the point corresponding to the average value of electromotive force E_{bd}.

If primary current I_a has been greatly reduced, nearly to zero for the average of its variations, by means of the arrangement described above, a primary winding having a powerful stabilizing action may be used, as indicated by the scheme of Fig. 132. In this case the metadyne will create a large amount of "stabilizing power," i.e., it will have a strong stabilizing action although the corresponding copper losses are negligible. An exact definition of "stabilizing power" will not be given here, since this concept is a topic for dynamic analysis. Although the stabilizing windings are not mentioned often, they are generally assumed to exist.

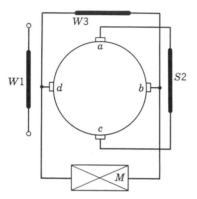

Fig. 132.   Addition of a stabilizing winding.

The control of the intensity of the secondary current requires little power, only the copper loss in the secondary variator winding. It may generally be taken equal to one-fourth of the power necessary for the excitation of a shunt dynamo of the same size. For some special applications it is desirable to reduce this power necessary for the control of the secondary current. Such a result may be obtained by means of a secondary compensating winding as indicated by Fig. 125(a), derived from Fig. 125, and the power absorbed by the secondary variator winding may be reduced practically to almost any desired value by a proper setting of the compensating winding. On the other hand, the dynamical behavior of the metadyne is then greatly modified.

5. SOME SIMPLE COMMENTS ON THE METADYNE GENERATORS

The C generator metadyne and the S generator metadyne are two examples of direct constant-current generators with satisfactory operation. Before the advent of the metadyne, a direct constant-current generator was well known under the name of "Craemer dynamo," having been named after its inventor. Figure 133 gives the scheme of this dynamo. The stator has three field windings: a series winding, A, connected in such a way to the brushes as to induce an electromotive force between the brushes which opposes the current; a winding, B, shunt-connected across the brushes; and finally, a third winding, C, separately excited and carrying a current, say I_α, arbitrarily defined. The induced electromotive force, E, may then be expressed as follows, if

secondary actions like copper loss and pole-shoe saturation by the armature ampere-turns are neglected:

$$\frac{1}{n} E = K_a I + K_b \frac{E}{R_b} + K_c I_\alpha$$

where I is the armature current and where R_b is the resistance of the
circuit comprising the shunt-connected winding; the coefficients K
remain constant as long as iron saturation
is not reached. If the shunt-connected coil
satisfies the condition of astaticity, we have

$$0 = K_a I + K_c I_\alpha$$

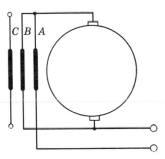

This equation shows that the armature
current remains constant if the current I_α
and the coefficients K remain constant.

    If iron saturation is considered, a char-
acteristic results that is similar to the one
obtained for the S generator metadyne.
Thus if the comparison is limited to static

Fig. 133.   Scheme of the
Craemer dynamo

operation, there are differences of quanti-
tative importance between the two machines, such as smaller weight for
the S generator metadyne, better commutation, and smaller excitation.

    If the comparison is extended to the dynamic behavior, then the
difference is an important one for practical applications. The dynamic
transient phenomena will not be discussed here; only some simple
considerations will be indicated, sufficient for pointing out the difference.

    Suppose that normal operation requires the sudden passage from full
load at normal voltage in the circuit of the consumer to a no-load or
short-circuit condition, a requirement often met in a series-circuit
distribution. Because of the large time constant of the shunt connected
field winding, the current in this winding will require a relatively long
time, say 30 seconds, to become practically zero; and during this time
the armature current will rise to a value about three to four times higher
than its normal value, depending on the construction of the machine.
With such overcurrent for, say, 5 seconds, heavy damage occurs.

    Now consider the simplest C generator metadyne of Fig. 134 under
the same conditions of operation. The primary current, I_a, must then
pass perhaps from one-fifth of the normal value of the secondary current, I_b, to the zero value. To obtain this result, the secondary current
must increase so as to induce a primary electromotive force, E_{ca}, equal
to the impressed primary voltage; this means that the secondary current

must increase by an amount ΔI_b sufficient to induce an increment ΔE_{ca} generally equal to

$$\Delta E_{ca} = \tfrac{1}{5}\,\tfrac{2}{100}E_{ca} = \tfrac{1}{250}E_{ca}$$

In fact the normal-current ohmic drop in the armature is about $\tfrac{2}{100}$ of the induced armature voltage.

Assume, further, that the normal value of secondary current I_b is about four times larger than the value of the secondary magnetizing current necessary for inducing the primary voltage, i.e., that the ampere-turns of the secondary variator winding are compensated by an armature current three times larger than the magnetizing current. Then the increase ΔI_b of the secondary current will have a ratio to the normal value of I_b as follows:

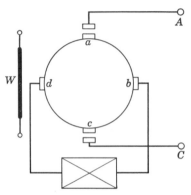

$$\frac{\Delta I_b}{I_b} = \frac{1}{4}\frac{1}{250} = \frac{1}{1000} \qquad (82)$$

Thus the increment of the load current, necessary to establish the new balance corresponding to short circuit, will be negligible.

Now reconsider a more general transient phenomenon for a series distribution system: the abrupt variation of the voltage in this system, a variation that may be represented by ΔE_{bd}. Following the same arguments as above yields the ratio

Fig. 134.   Scheme of a simple C generator metadyne.

$$\frac{\Delta I_b}{I_b} = \frac{1}{1000}\frac{\Delta E_{bd}}{E_{bd}} \qquad (83)$$

for the C generator metadyne of Fig. 134. For the Craemer dynamo, the current, i, in the shunt-connected field coil must be modified by Δi where

$$\frac{\Delta i}{i} = \frac{\Delta E}{E} \qquad (84)$$

if iron saturation is neglected. The variation Δi occurs very slowly because of the large value of the time constant of the circuit of the shunt-field coil and its interlinkage; further, the corresponding flux variation is even slower because of eddy currents, and during this time the armature current must increase to compensate for the ampere-turns $N_b\Delta i$, where N_b is the number of turns of the shunt-field coil.

Generally, it is admitted that the field-coil copper of a Craemer dynamo is about twice the normal amount, i.e., that the ampere-turns of the series coil A and the independently excited coil C are about half the ampere-turns of the shunt-connected coil B (which are the normal ampere-turns of a dynamo). In this case, the ratio $\Delta I/I$ during this transient period will reach the value

$$\frac{\Delta I}{I} = 2\frac{\Delta i}{i} = 2\frac{\Delta E_{bd}}{E_{bd}} \tag{85}$$

The comparison of the results indicated in Equations 83 and 85 give an idea of the difference in the dynamic behavior of the two machines. The consideration of any other C or S generator metadyne leads to similar results. In a similar way one may analyze the action of a metadyne provided with a secondary hypocompensator. The more the hypocompensator approaches full compensation, the more the metadyne loses its capacity for quick response.

6. GENERATOR AND TRANSFORMER METADYNES

In the first section of this chapter a transformer metadyne was considered, and means were indicated which tend to reduce the power supplied by the primary source towards zero and thus to turn the operation of a power-transforming metadyne into the operation of a power-generating metadyne. In particular, the Cross transformer metadyne was examined, but any other kind of transformer metadyne can be treated in a similar way. Take any of these metadynes and reduce the efficiency of the means for preventing electric power from flowing from the primary source; then the machine will operate simultaneously as a generator and as a transformer metadyne.

Consider, for instance, the scheme of Fig. 134. The primary current is not zero; rather, it is the primary magnetizing current, and the secondary current is four to five times larger. The value of this current is set by regulating the current I_α in the variator winding. If the iron is not saturated, the following fundamental equations may be written, the losses being neglected:

$$\frac{1}{n}E_{ca} = KI_b + K_{ca}^\alpha I_\alpha = K(I_{b\mu} + I_{bw}) + K_{ca}^\alpha I_\alpha$$

$$\frac{1}{n}E_{bd} = KI_a = KI_{a\mu} \tag{86}$$

where $I_{a\mu}$ and $I_{b\mu}$ are the magnetizing currents, and I_{bw} is the component of the secondary current due to the opposition of the secondary variator winding. Writing the fundamental equations for the case $I_\alpha = 0$ will yield the relation

$$E_{ca}I_{a\mu} = E_{bd}I_{b\mu} \tag{87}$$

and therefore the ratio τ between the power supplied to the consumer by the primary source and the power supplied by the machine moving the shaft of the metadyne will be

$$\tau = \frac{I_{b\mu}}{I_{bw}} \tag{88}$$

This ratio depends on the value of I_{bw}, i.e., on the value of the variator current I_α, which can easily be controlled, and on the value $I_{b\mu}$, i.e., on the value of the voltage of the primary source.

Now consider the more complete scheme of Fig. 120. Equation 87 still holds; further, there is:

$$I_a = I_{a\mu} + I_{aw}$$

$$I_b = I_{b\mu} + I_{bw}$$

The ratio τ may then be written

$$\tau = \frac{E_{ca}I_a}{E_{bd}I_b - E_{ca}I_a} = \frac{E_{ca}(I_{a\mu} + I_{aw})}{E_{bd}(I_{b\mu} + I_{bw}) - E_{ca}(I_{a\mu} + I_{aw})}$$

$$= \frac{E_{ca}(I_{a\mu} + I_{aw})}{E_{bd}I_{bw} - E_{ca}I_{aw}} = \frac{1 + (I_{aw}/I_{a\mu})}{(I_{bw}/I_{b\mu}) - (I_{aw}/I_{a\mu})} \tag{89}$$

The value of $I_{a\mu}$ depends on the voltage required by the consumer and generally cannot be modified; since the value of $I_{b\mu}$ depends on the voltage of the primary source, it is rather difficult to modify it; the values of I_{aw} and I_{bw}, on the contrary, may be very easily set by control of the currents of the two variator windings, the primary and the secondary variator winding, respectively. It is thus easy to obtain the desired distribution between power supplied electrically and power supplied mechanically.

Finally consider a metadyne mechanically coupled to a prime mover developing substantially constant torque, say a Diesel engine, and supplying current to a consumer that absorbs variable power, sometimes larger than the power that the prime mover can develop and sometimes smaller. It is required that the metadyne shall fully utilize the power of the Diesel engine whatever the power absorbed by the consumer may be, the difference of power being supplied or absorbed by a constant-voltage source. The metadyne must thus operate as a generator and as a transformer simultaneously.

The scheme of Fig. 120(a) meets the requirements; a Cross transformer metadyne is provided with a secondary variator winding, W, and a regulator winding, R, having its magnetic axis along the primary commutating axis. The regulator current is supplied by the shunt-excited regulator dynamo, RD, which is connected to a constant-voltage source by the terminals P and Q.

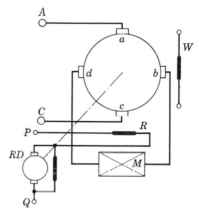

Fig. 120(a). Scheme of a Cross transformer metadyne capable of acting also as a C generator.

The current flowing in secondary variator winding W determines the secondary current. The regulator current is responsible for causing the metadyne to absorb or to supply the primary current, I_a, necessary to keep the power supplied by the prime mover constant in spite of the variations of the power absorbed by the consumer M, even if these variations are very rapid.

In a similar way one may derive a metadyne that operates simultaneously as a transformer and as a generator from any pure transformer metadyne.

15 · Some Motor Metadynes of Degree $m = 4$

1. OPERATION OF A DYNAMO IN A SERIES DISTRIBUTION SYSTEM

In the previous chapters many metadynes have been described which are able to operate satisfactorily as sources of electric power for a series distribution system; they may operate as transformer metadynes, as generator metadynes, or even as transformer and generator metadynes. This property opens a wide field of application for the series distribution system, which until now lacked a simple, statically and dynamically safe, and easily controlled source of energy; hence, the series distribution has remained undeveloped.

Now the operation of the various kinds of dynamos, when inserted into a series loop, will be investigated. For the sake of simplicity, it will be assumed in this chapter that the series network is conducting a current of constant intensity; then the power absorbed will be proportional to the voltage induced between the brushes of the load.

There are four kinds of dynamos: independently excited, series-excited, shunt-excited, and compound-excited dynamos. For a motor, the most important characteristic is the torque-speed characteristic; this is an expression of merit for the motor. For further simplification, losses and iron saturation will be neglected.

In a separately excited dynamo with its field winding creating a constant number of ampere-turns, the torque, T, remains constant for all values of speed n and may be represented by a straight line aa' as indicated by Fig. 135. Such a motor may be used to drive a machine which develops a resisting torque that increases quickly with speed, as the one represented in the same diagram by the dotted line oa'; a fan and a propeller are machines of this kind.

If for some reason the opposing torque vanishes, for instance, if the shaft breaks, the motor will accelerate dangerously and run away. Similar results are obtained with a series-excited dynamo.

Take a shunt-excited dynamo; the following relation holds:

$$\frac{1}{n} E = KE$$

which cannot be satisfied except for the critical speed, satisfying the relation

$$nK = 1 \tag{90}$$

Thus there will be no torque for values of speed n lower than the critical value, whereas for the critical speed any value of E may be obtained and therefore any value of the torque T; the characteristic will be the vertical straight line bb as indicated by Fig. 136. Such a motor cannot start; but, if the critical speed is somehow reached, the motor will tend to remain at this speed whatever the resisting torque may be.

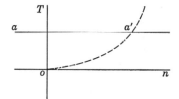

Fig. 135. Torque-speed charac- Fig. 136. Torque-speed
teristic of a separately excited characteristic for a shunt
dynamo. dynamo.

In a compound-excited motor provided with a series field and a shunt field, there is

$$\frac{1}{n} E = K'I + KE \tag{91}$$

The value of the torque T is given by

$$2\pi T = \frac{EI}{n} = K'I^2 + KEI = K'I^2 \frac{1}{1 - Kn} \tag{92}$$

where the value of E has been replaced by its expression as a function of n through Equation 91.

Thus, the characteristic is a hyperbola having its asymptotes parallel to the axes. If the constant K is positive and K' has the same sign, the hyperbola is oriented as indicated by Fig. 137; if these constants have opposite signs, K being positive, the arrangement of the diagram of Fig. 138 is obtained; if K is negative, the figures are folded around the axis of n. In both cases the segment of the hyperbola along which the motor may operate shows a torque slightly increasing or slightly decreasing with the speed n, with no substantial difference from the case of a simple series dynamo.

A combination of three field coils, one separately fed, one shunt-connected, and the third series-connected as indicated in Fig. 133, would again give hyperbolas. These hyperbolas have a convenient orientation only when the series winding is a stimulating winding, which is troublesome during transients and may produce instability.

If it is desired to have particular characteristics with an independently excited dynamo, it is necessary to excite this field winding with a current created by a special device and following some particular law suitable for each particular application. In the following chapters, many examples of such dynamos are given.

To summarize these results: Except for some particular applications, a dynamo separately excited by a constant voltage, a series dynamo, a shunt dynamo, a compound dynamo, and a dynamo having a series, a shunt field, and a field independently excited by a constant voltage— thus all the dynamos with standard excitation—are generally inadequate

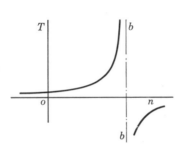

Fig. 137. Torque-speed characteristic of a compound dynamo.

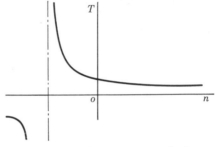

Fig. 138. Another torque-speed characteristic of a compound dynamo.

for operation when inserted in a loop of a series distribution system at constant current. Therefore, it is evident that the development of the direct-current series distribution network, based on the use of dynamos, has been handicapped not only because of the lack of suitable generators but also because of the very limited possibilities of the motors. On the contrary, there are members of the metadyne family which under the same conditions operate quite adequately as motors; in particular, the development of the Alpha motor metadyne made possible the successful construction of complete plants based on series distribution.

2. THE ALPHA MOTOR METADYNE

Figure 139 gives the simplest scheme of an Alpha motor metadyne. There are four equidistant brushes per cycle, the two nonconsecutive primary brushes, a and c, being inserted into the loop of the series distribution system. The secondary brushes b and d supply current to a secondary hypercompensator, H, having a relatively large resistance so as to allow for a secondary current having a maximum value relatively low with respect to the constant primary current, I_a. The stator further bears a secondary variator winding, W, independently fed, through which the current I_α flows, creating arbitrarily defined ampere-turns.

When losses are neglected, the fundamental equations of the metadyne may be written

$$\frac{1}{n}E_{ca} = K_bI_b + K^\alpha_{ca}I_\alpha + K^\beta_{ca}I_b = (K_b + K^\beta_{ca})I_b + K^\alpha_{ca}I_\alpha$$

$$\frac{1}{n}E_{bd} = K_aI_a$$

(93)

The coefficients K_a and K_b relative to the armature ampere-turns have been given different indices in order to take into account the difference in iron saturation along the two commutating axes. The coefficient K^β_{ca} is relative to hypercompensator H.

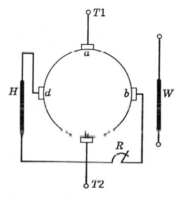

Fig. 139. Elementary scheme of the Alpha motor metadyne.

To the fundamental Equations 93 the following must be added because of the particular connections of the hypercompensator:

$$R_bI_b = E_{bd}$$

(94)

where R_b is the resistance of the whole secondary circuit.

It is now necessary to point out the signs of the coefficients appearing in the three equations. For this purpose recall the assumptions that the armature winding is a right-handed one with diametrical pitch, that the positive sense of rotation is the clockwise one, and that the coefficients K_a and K_b appearing in Equations 93 are positive.

Consider the metadyne at rest: The armature is carrying the constant primary current I_a; there is no secondary current I_b; and the only ampere-turns along the secondary commutating axis are due to the variator winding, W. On the assumption that the flux created by them is along the direction db, the machine will start to rotate in the clockwise direction. In other words, if the term $K^\alpha_{ca}I_\alpha$ is positive, n will be positive; if $K^\alpha_{ca}I_\alpha$ is negative, n will be negative. Notice, by the way, that the terms appearing in Equations 93 have the physical dimensions of a magnetic flux.

As soon as the metadyne rotates, the primary flux, having its magnetic axis along the primary commutating axis and being due exclusively to the primary armature ampere-turns, induces an electromotive force between the secondary brushes which creates a secondary current, I_b. This current causes armature ampere-turns having the same sense as the ampere-turns due to variator winding W, as may easily be checked by means of the corkscrew rule.

Write the expression for the torque T, the positive sense being the clockwise one:

$$2\pi T = \frac{1}{n} E_{ca} I_a = I_a[(K_b + K_{ca}^\beta)I_b + K_{ca}^\alpha I_a]$$

$$= I_a\left[(K_b + K_{ca}^\beta)\frac{K_a I_a}{R_b}n + K_{ca}^\alpha I_a\right] \quad (95)$$

Stator winding H being a hypercompensator, the value of K_{ca}^β is negative and

$$K_b + K_{ca}^\beta < 0$$

Taking into account the information regarding the sign of the coefficients and of the speed n readily demonstrates that, when the metadyne starts by its own means, the two terms appearing in the bracket of the last member of Equation 95 have opposite signs. Therefore, the torque-speed curve will be an inclined straight line as indicated by $pbqdg$ in Fig. 140, if the coefficients K are assumed constant at the same values

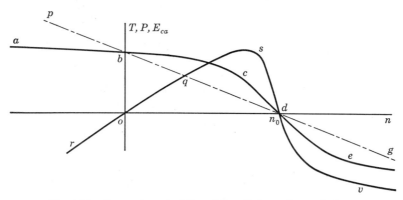

Fig. 140. Some characteristics of the Alpha motor metadyne.

they have when the machine is at rest. For positive increasing values of the speed n, the positive torque T decreases from its starting value ob to zero, which is reached at the so-called "no-load speed," $n_0 = od$; afterwards, it becomes negative, i.e., a braking torque. For negative values of speed, the torque remains positive, thus becoming a braking torque.

Now consider iron saturation and suppose that the ampere-turns of variator winding W cause intense iron saturation along the secondary commutating axis. Then the curve of the torque T will become the curve $abcde$, which has a nearly horizontal segment abc for negative values and for reduced positive values of the speed, and has a bend when the speed approaches the no-load value n_0, for which the ampere-turns of hypercompensator H, the ampere-turns of variator winding W, and the secondary armature ampere-turns compensate one another and leave the magnetic circuit free of saturation. The scales of the ordinates of the curves $pbqdg$ and $abcde$ are different. For increasing values of the speed, the resultant ampere-turns along the secondary commutating axis change sense, increase in value, and saturate the magnetic circuit again.

Such a characteristic is well suited for most practical applications since it allows very stable operation. The large torque at starting is nearly constant for small values of speed and permits good acceleration; when the normal speed is nearly reached, the torque diminishes quickly and thus allows a stable condition of running; if for some reason the load torque vanishes, the metadyne will not run away or even reach the no-load speed n_0; if for some reason the opposing torque becomes an accelerating one, the metadyne will brake above the no-load speed and will resist overspeed with its maximum torque; if, on the other hand, the opposing torque changes direction and tries to drive the metadyne into negative values of speed, the metadyne will resist with a torque greater than its starting torque.

The curve $rosdv$ is the diagram of the developed power, P, or of the electromotive force, E_{ca}, induced between the primary brushes. Although zero at starting, it increases almost proportionally to the speed for low values of speed, shows a flat maximum at a value generally lower than the normal operating speed, and then decreases quickly to zero at the no-load speed. Beyond this speed, it becomes negative and larger in absolute value.

In the previous section, in the investigation of the operation of dynamos, instability has been pointed out around the intersection of the speed axis and the asymptote of the hyperbolas of Figs. 137 and 138. At this point no practical steady-state operation is possible, and the equations show a division by zero.

In Fig. 140 there is also an intersection of the torque-speed characteristic and the axis of speed n at the "no-load" speed, but this point does not correspond to a mathematical singularity; the operation is then stable and can continue indefinitely. In fact, at the no-load speed the primary flux, created by the constant primary current, induces between the secondary brushes an electromotive force high enough to give a secondary current, I_b, that creates armature and hypercompensator ampere-turns nearly compensating the ampere-turns of the variator winding. Then along the secondary commutating axis there will be just a small flux that, with the primary current, I_a, creates a component torque due to the primary flux acting upon secondary current I_b, which compensates the component torque due to the secondary flux acting upon the primary current. Thus the resultant torque and the primary electromotive force, E_{ca}, are then zero.

If for some reason the speed increases, the metadyne brakes; and, if the speed decreases, the metadyne develops an accelerating torque, thus keeping the operation very stable.

No matter how satisfactory a characteristic may be, it is always desirable to allow the operator to modify it at will by some easy control. Suppose that the operator, by reducing current I_a, modifies the value of the constant ampere-turns created by the variator winding, the balance of the ampere-turns along the secondary axis will take place at a lower speed and thus the whole characteristic is shifted towards the left, from the curve $abcd$ of Fig. 141, to a curve efg, the no-load speed now being reduced to the abscissa of point f.

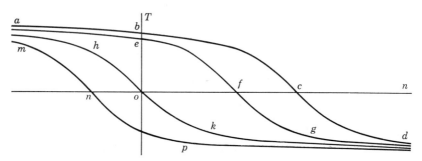

Fig. 141.   The speed intercept of the torque-speed characteristic of the Alpha motor can be changed through control of the variator current.

If variator current I_α is interrupted, the characteristic will be represented by the curve hok. This characteristic shows that if the variator current is purposely or accidentally interrupted the metadyne will resist rotation no matter what the sense is, and it will tend to keep the whole mechanism motionless or at least running only very slowly although primary current I_a flows in its armature. This is a valuable property for practical application.

Further, if current I_α is inverted by the operator, the sense of the ampere-turns created by W thus being inverted, the characteristic is further shifted to the left as the curve *mnp* shows; the no-load speed has a negative value, and exactly the same torque-speed characteristic is obtained with respect to the counterclockwise direction. Thus, to reverse the direction of rotation, it is sufficient to invert the variator current.

For some important applications the operator must work from a family of characteristics with shiftable "no-load" speed, but always with the same value of starting torque. This adjustment is easily

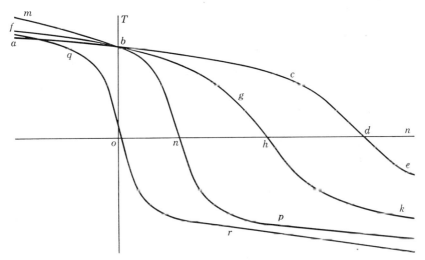

Fig. 142.   Family of characteristics having the same starting torque.

obtained by means of a rheostat, R, in the secondary circuit as Fig. 139 shows. In fact, the no-load speed n_0, and the starting torque T_s are determined by the equations

$$(K_b + K_{ca}^{\beta})K_a I_a n_0 + R_b K_{ca}^{\alpha} I_a = 0$$

$$2\pi T_s = K_{ca}^{\alpha} I_\alpha I_a \tag{96}$$

which may be satisfied for any desired value of no-load speed n_0 and starting torque T_s within the possibilities allowed by the size of the machine. Figure 142 shows some members of the family thus obtained. The curve *qor* corresponds to $I_\alpha = 0$ and $R_b = 0$, and it shows how under these conditions the metadyne opposes any movement. The larger the ratio between the maximum and minimum values of the no-load speed, the more valuable the machine is.

3. VARIANTS OF THE ALPHA MOTOR METADYNE

Figure 143 shows an Alpha motor metadyne provided with a primary amplifying winding A. This winding allows a wider range of the no-load speeds, since the induced electromotive force, E_{bd}, between the secondary brushes is now higher for a given value of speed.

Figure 144 shows another variant. To the secondary hypercompensator, H, and the secondary variator winding, $W2$, a primary variator winding, $W1$, is added. Control of the current in $W1$ controls the value

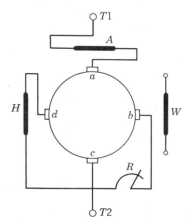

Fig. 143. Addition of a primary amplifying winding to the scheme of Fig. 139.

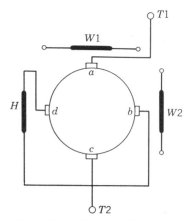

Fig. 144. Rheostat R may be eliminated when a primary variator winding is added.

of secondary current I_b for a given value of the speed; therefore, control of the current in $W1$ makes possible control of the value of the no-load speed without modifying the secondary circuit. The rheostat in the secondary circuit may thus be eliminated as Fig. 144 shows.

Since rheostat R of the schemes of Figs. 139 and 143 is indirectly inserted into the main loop of the series distribution system, it may be brought to a relatively high potential and it must be insulated accordingly. Since variator windings $W1$ and $W2$ may instead be inserted into a low-voltage auxiliary network, they do not need heavy insulation.

The fundamental equations of the Alpha motor metadyne corresponding to Fig. 144 are

$$\frac{1}{n} E_{ca} = K_b I_b + K_{ca}^\alpha I_\alpha + K_{ca}^\gamma I_b$$

$$\frac{1}{n} E_{bd} = K_a I_a + K_{bd}^\beta I_\beta$$

(97)

where I_α and I_β are the currents passing through secondary variator winding $W2$ and primary variator winding $W1$, respectively. If R_b is the resistance of the entire secondary circuit, there is, further,

$$E_{bd} = R_b I_b \qquad (98)$$

From Equations 98 and 97 the expression of torque T is obtained by neglecting the copper losses in the secondary circuit:

$$2\pi T = I_a^2 \frac{nK_a}{R_b} (K_b - K_a + K_{ca}^\alpha) + I_a I_\alpha K_{ca}^\alpha$$

$$+ I_a I_\beta (K_b - 2K_a + K_{ca}^\gamma) \frac{K_{bd}^\beta n}{R_b} - I_\beta^2 (K_{bd}^\beta)^2 \frac{n}{R_b} \qquad (99)$$

This expression, being algebraic with respect to parameters I_α and I_β, allows the determination of these parameters in such a way as to make

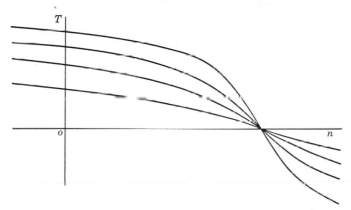

Fig. 145. Torque-speed characteristics of an Alpha motor metadyne with simultaneous variation of primary and secondary parameters.

the torque-speed characteristic pass through two arbitrarily chosen points. Thus, a great variety of families of characteristics may be obtained if the resistors regulating stator currents I_α and I_β are combined and controlled simultaneously by a single handle.

Similar statements may be made for the schemes of Figs. 139 and 143 with the limitation, however, that R_b must remain positive and be equal to or larger than the resistance of the armature plus the resistance of the hypercompensator. The family of characteristics of Fig. 141 requires the regulation of current I_α only; the family of Fig. 142 requires the regulation only of resistor R or only of current I_β; the family of Fig. 145 requires instead the simultaneous regulation of current I_α and of resistance R_b, or of current I_α and of current I_β, respectively. All curves of the family of Fig. 145 have the same no-load speed, but they show different values of torque T for a given value of speed n.

4. THE THETA MOTOR METADYNE

In its simplest form, this metadyne has four equidistant brushes per cycle, a, b, c, d, as Fig. 146 shows, primary brushes a and c being connected to terminals $T1$ and $T2$ of the machine, secondary brushes b and d being essentially short-circuited. The stator is provided with a primary variator winding, 2, and a secondary variator winding, 3, both receiving excitation from a separate source.

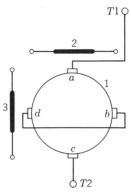

Let I_α and I_β be the currents in the primary and the secondary variator windings, respectively; let R be the total resistance of the secondary circuit. The fundamental equations may be written

$$\frac{1}{n} E_{ca} = K I_b + K_{ca}^\beta I_\beta$$

$$\frac{1}{n} R I_b = K I_a + K_{bd}^\alpha I_\alpha \tag{100}$$

Fig. 146. Elementary scheme of the Theta motor metadyne.

From the second equation is obtained the value of the primary current, which may be resolved as follows:

$$I_a = \frac{1}{n}\frac{R}{K} I_b - \frac{K_{bd}^\alpha}{K} I_\alpha = I_{a\mu} + I_{aw} \tag{101}$$

The first component, $I_{a\mu}$, may be termed the magnetizing component of the primary current; and the second one, I_{aw}, the variator component. Since the magnetizing component is relatively very small with respect to the variator component, and since the variator component is determined at some arbitrary value by parameter I_α, it may be stated that primary current I_a of the Theta motor metadyne depends essentially on the value of current I_α of the primary variator winding. If current I_α is held constant, primary current I_a will be substantially constant, whatever may be the speed and the voltage at terminals $T1$ and $T2$. This is the chief static characteristic of the Theta motor metadyne.

To start the machine, a current, I_β, must be sent through the secondary variator winding, and the direction of this current determines the direction of rotation. When speed n exceeds a given minimum value, say the value n_m, current I_β may be cut off and the Theta motor metadyne will operate with only its primary variator windings and it will show all its special static and dynamic characteristics.

The fundamental equations are then simplified:

$$\frac{1}{n} E_{ca} = KI_b$$

$$\frac{1}{n} RI_b = KI_a + K_{bd}^\alpha I_\alpha \tag{102}$$

$$
\left.
\begin{array}{c}
I_{aw} = -\dfrac{K_{bd}^\alpha}{K} I_\alpha \\[2mm]
I_a \equiv I_{a\mu} + I_{aw} \\[2mm]
I_{a\mu} = -\dfrac{1}{n}\dfrac{R}{K} I_b = \dfrac{1}{n^2}\dfrac{R}{K^2} E_{ca}
\end{array}
\right\} \tag{103}
$$

The torque T may be calculated as follows:

$$2\pi T - K_{bd}^\alpha I_\alpha I_b = -\frac{1}{n}\frac{K_{bd}^\alpha}{K} I_\alpha E_{ca} \tag{103a}$$

Formulas 103 show that for $n > n_m$ the primary current remains practically independent of speed n and of primary voltage E_{ca}, and it is constant if parameter I_α is kept constant. Equations 103 also show that

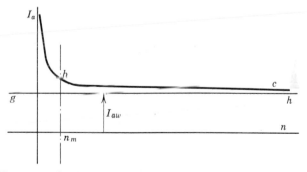

Fig. 147. Characteristic of the Theta motor metadyne at constant primary voltage.

the magnetizing component, $I_{a\mu}$, diminishes very quickly when the speed increases, even if primary voltage E_{ca} increases proportionally to speed n. Figure 147 gives primary current I_a as a function of speed n when primary voltage E_{ca} is kept constant. For very small values of speed, current I_a shows large variations; but for $n > n_m$, this current remains practically constant.   The two components of I_a are separated by the straight horizontal line gh, which has as its ordinate the value of the variator component.   Magnetizing component $I_{a\mu}$ is relatively small and diminishes with speed.

Figure 148 again shows current I_a as a function of primary voltage E_{ca} for a given constant speed.   For very small values of voltage E_{ca}, there are large variations of current I_a due to secondary causes (ohmic drop for instance); but, when E_{ca} exceeds a minimum value (the abscissa of point a), the primary current remains practically constant.   The magnetizing component increases with voltage E_{ca} but remains relatively small until iron saturation is reached (part bc of the curve).

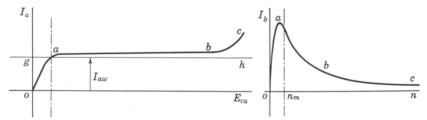

Fig. 148.   Constant-speed characteristic of the Theta motor metadyne.

Fig. 149.   Behavior of secondary current for constant primary voltage of the Theta motor metadyne.

With a change of the sign of current I_α, component I_{aw} also changes sign, and the Theta motor metadyne is then made to regenerate a substantially constant current.   The magnetizing component keeps its sign; therefore, when the Theta motor metadyne is regenerating, the absolute value of primary current I_a is smaller than that of component I_{aw} by the amount of the magnetizing component $I_{a\mu}$.

Figure 149 gives a diagram of current I_b as a function of the speed n for a constant value of primary voltage E_{ca}; for values of speed $n > n_m$ the curve is a hyperbola as the first of Equations 102 indicates.

It has been shown that the value of primary current I_a remains substantially independent of the value of the primary voltage E_{ca} within wide limits.   This special characteristic property holds even when the primary voltage varies very quickly from one value to another; this result is due to secondary current I_b, which adjusts itself very quickly and creates the right secondary flux for inducing the primary voltage at its new values.

5. VARIANTS OF THE THETA MOTOR METADYNE

The purpose of the variants indicated by the schemes of Figs. 150 and 151 is to reduce current I_b. The diagram of Fig. 150 shows the addition of a secondary variator winding, 4, shunt-connected across the primary brushes.

The ampere-turns of secondary variator windings 3 and 4 constitute the most important part of the necessary magnetizing ampere-turns, and secondary current I_b creates only the remaining part of the ampere-turns. Current I_b provides for the sudden peaks of magnetizing ampere-turns when the primary voltage varies quickly.

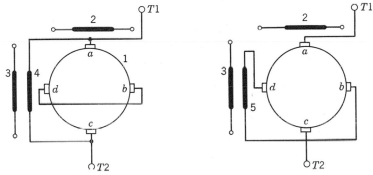

Figs. 150 and 151. Two schemes for reducing the value of the secondary current of the Theta motor metadyne.

The diagram of Fig. 151 shows a secondary amplifier winding, 5, connected in series with the secondary brushes. Thus, for a given value of current I_b, a larger number of ampere-turns is created.

For many applications, it is required that around some arbitrarily defined no-load speed n_0 the torque shall drop very quickly, become zero, and even change sign when the speed increases above the given value. This result is obtained by the arrangement of Fig. 152; a regulator dynamo, 7, is mechanically coupled with the Theta motor metadyne and feeds a primary variator winding, 6. The regulator dynamo indicated in the figure is shunt-connected; to the shunt-field winding, 8, a biasing independent field winding, 9, is added.

Figure 153 gives a diagram of current I_a as a function of the speed n, primary voltage E_{ca} being assumed constant. When the speed n is smaller than the critical speed n_0 of regulator dynamo 7, the regulator current is practically zero. Current I_a flowing in primary variator winding 2 is the only one affecting primary current I_a of the Theta motor metadyne. If I_a is kept constant, current I_a will remain substantially constant. When the critical speed n_0 is approached, a regulator current builds up and creates ampere-turns in a direction opposite to the ampere-turns of variator winding 2, and the characteristic shows the sharp bend

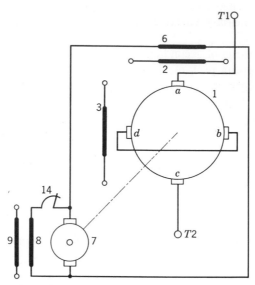

Fig. 152. The regulator dynamo makes possible more flexible control of the Theta motor metadyne.

$cn_0 f$. When saturation of regulator dynamo 7 occurs, the segment fd is obtained. The value of n_0 may be arbitrarily determined by the operator of the motor if he adjusts rheostat 14 inserted in the circuit of the shunt-field winding. Instead of a shunt-excited regulator dynamo, any other kind of regulator dynamo may be used, as described in Chapter 5.

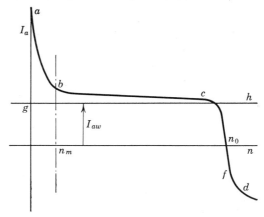

Fig. 153. Characteristic of the Theta motor metadyne with regulator dynamo.

The variants corresponding to the diagrams of Figs. 154 and 155 are meant to correct the reduction of torque that occurs when the speed increases, as formula 103a indicates.

The diagram of Fig. 154 shows the addition of a primary variator winding, 10, shunt-connected across the primary brushes of the Theta motor metadyne. The ampere-turns created by this winding 10 increase

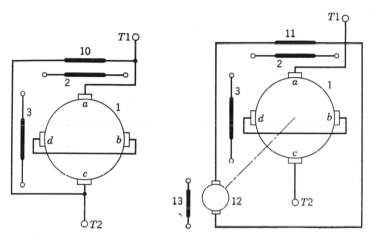

Figs. 154 and 155. Schemes of Theta motor metadynes that possess torque-droop compensation.

the value of current I_a in proportion to the primary voltage to give a supplementary component of torque, increasing with the primary voltage.

The scheme of Fig. 155 is more effective, but it requires an auxiliary dynamo, 12, coupled with the Theta motor metadyne. The auxiliary dynamo is provided with a separately excited field winding, 13, and it feeds primary variator winding 11 with a current proportional to the speed n. The supplementary ampere-turns created by 11 give rise to a component of current I_a proportional to speed, and to a component torque substantially independent of speed. Interesting characteristics are also obtained when the Theta motor metadyne is inserted in a constant-current loop.

6. THE GAMMA MOTOR METADYNE

Whereas the Theta motor metadyne is more suitable for operation in a shunt network where the voltage either may be kept constant or may vary rapidly within wide limits, and whereas the Alpha motor metadyne is suitable for operation in a series network, the Gamma motor metadyne will operate satisfactorily either in a shunt or in a series network. Inserted into a series network, the Gamma motor metadyne has an advantage over the Alpha motor metadyne.

Consider the arrangement of two similar Alpha motor metadynes, connected in parallel and mechanically coupled, inserted into a loop of a series distribution system at constant current I. It is desired that the two Alpha motor metadynes share this current I equally.

From the fundamental Equations 93 and the equation

$$E_{bd} = R_2 I_b$$

is obtained

$$\frac{1}{n} E_{ca} = I_a \frac{nK_a}{R_2} (K_b + K_{ca}^\beta) + K_{ca}^\alpha I_\alpha$$

where n and $K_{ca}^\alpha I_\alpha$ have the same sign, K_a is essentially positive, and $K_b + K_{ca}^\beta$ is essentially negative. Therefore, the first term of the second member is negative and acts as an ohmic drop through a negative resistance. If, therefore, there is a slight difference in the construction of the two Alpha motor metadynes, the primary current in one of them becomes very different from the primary current in the other.

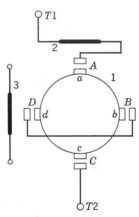

Fig. 156. Elementary form of the Gamma motor metadyne.

The Alpha motor metadyne thus cannot operate satisfactorily under these conditions unless some stator correcting windings are added. For instance, such correcting windings may be stabilizing windings carrying the primary current and having their magnetic axes along the secondary commutating axis. It will be shown in this section that the Gamma motor metadyne permits a satisfactory distribution of the primary current under the same conditions of operation.

Figure 156 gives the schematic arrangement in its simplest form: The armature bears four equidistant brushes per cycle, primary brushes a and c are connected to terminals $T1$ and $T2$; secondary brushes b and d are essentially short-circuited. The figure shows the four terminals A, B, C, and D. It is assumed that a series stator winding, for instance a commutating-pole winding, is inserted between the brush indicated by a small letter and the corresponding dot indicated by the homonymous capital letter. The stator bears a primary hypocompensator, 2, and a secondary variator winding, 3.

Primary hypocompensator 2 is designed to bring about resultant ampere-turns, in the direction of the primary commutating axis and in the sense of the primary armature ampere-turns, such that the induced electromotive force between secondary brushes b and d creates a secondary current, I_b, that is small compared with the normal value of the primary current, even when speed n and primary current I_a reach their maximum operating values, respectively. Thus any value of primary current, within the range of normal operation, is allowed to enter the Gamma motor metadyne without excessive reaction due to secondary current I_b; the increased secondary current I_b will concur with secondary variator winding 3 to create the proper secondary flux necessary for inducing the primary electromotive force, but it does not prevent the primary current from reaching its full value. Quick variations of the primary voltage will give rise to sudden increases of the secondary current I_b. Thus, since peaks of primary current are eliminated, the operation gains stability.

The fundamental equations may be written

$$\frac{1}{n} E_{ca} - KI_b + K_{ca}^{\beta} I_{\beta}$$

$$\frac{1}{n} RI_b = KI_a + K_{bd}^{\alpha} I_a \qquad (104)$$

where I_{β} is the current flowing through variator winding 3, where the constant K_{bd}^{α} refers to hypocompensator 2, and where R is the total resistance of the secondary circuit. The value of the torque T may be expressed by

$$2\pi T = K_{ca}^{\beta} I_{\beta} I_a - K_{bd}^{\alpha} I_a I_b = (K_{ca}^{\beta} I_{\beta} - K_{bd}^{\alpha} I_b) I_a \qquad (105)$$

Assume that the Gamma motor metadyne is inserted into a loop of a series power network having a constant-current intensity. Then I_a is a constant; I_b increases with speed n, parameter I_{β} being assumed constant as the second Equation 104 shows. Then the torque increases when speed n increases, as the diagram of Fig. 157 shows, for a constant value of I_{β}. This increasing of the torque, proportionally to speed, is due to the second term of formula 105, because the sign of K_{bd}^{α} is negative and because I_b is proportional to speed n as the second Equation 104 indicates.

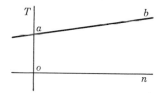

Fig. 157. Torque-speed characteristic of a Gamma motor metadyne in a constant-current system.

The design of the hypocompensator requires skill, and the amount of partial compensation depends on the special application for which the

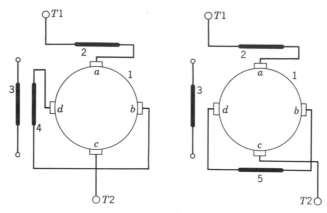

Figs. 158 and 159. Two schemes for controlling the variation of secondary current in the Gamma motor metadyne.

Gamma motor metadyne is intended. The scheme of Fig. 158 may be used for adjusting the effect of secondary current I_b; the secondary series winding, 4, is inserted into the secondary circuit and its action may be the action of an amplifying winding or of a hypocompensator, depending on the particular application considered.

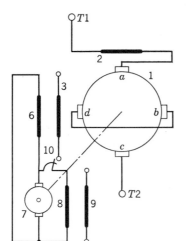

Fig. 160. Gamma motor metadyne with a regulator dynamo.

The diagram of Fig. 159 gives another means for adjusting the stabilizing action of the secondary current I_b: A stabilizing winding, 5, having its magnetic axis along the primary commutating axis, is inserted into the secondary circuit; the electromotive force that it induces opposes secondary current I_b.

Often, it is desired that the torque shall decrease very quickly around an arbitrarily defined no-load speed n_0. Such a result may be obtained with the Gamma motor metadyne by the use of a regulator dynamo connected as indicated by the scheme of Fig. 160.

By means of the regulator current, the regulator dynamo, 7, feeds winding 6, having its magnetic axis along the secondary commutating axis. As the metadyne approaches the critical speed, the regulator current builds up very quickly and creates, in winding 6, ampere-turns in a direction opposite to the ampere-turns of secondary variator winding 3. The resulting characteristic of the torque T is then given by the diagram of Fig. 161. The value of the no-load speed n_0, which is also the

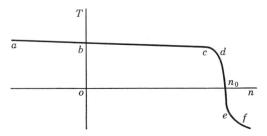

Fig. 161.   Torque-speed characteristic of the metadyne of Fig. 160.

critical speed of the regulator dynamo, 7, is arbitrarily determined by adjustment of the rheostat, 10, inserted into the circuit of the shunt-connected field winding, 8. Field winding 9, fed from a separate source,

creates a small amount of constant biasing ampere-turns. In Fig. 160, a shunt-excited regulator dynamo is shown, but any other kind of regulator dynamo may be used instead.

The primary hypocompensator of the Gamma motor metadyne in the schemes so far considered only partially compensates the primary armature ampere-turns and allows for a resultant primary flux having the same direction as the flux due to the primary armature ampere-turns exclusively. The dynamic stabilizing action of such an arrangement has already been pointed out. It is possible to obtain such a dynamic stabilizing action, even when the static compensation of the primary armature ampere-turns is complete, by means of the scheme of Fig. 162. Stator winding 2 is shunted by a resistor, 11, which is so designed that the component of primary current, say I_{a1}, that passes through winding 2 creates ampere-turns which completely compensate the action of the primary armature ampere-turns; then the resulting primary flux is zero. Let I_{a2} be the

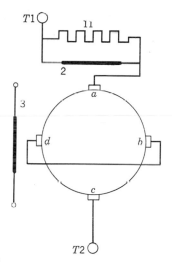

Fig. 162. Scheme of a Gamma motor metadyne having dynamic stabilization and primary compensation.

component of primary current flowing in resistor 11:

$$I_a = I_{a1} + I_{a2}$$

in the steady state; then any primary steady-state current may pass through the machine without causing any reaction.

When a rapid transient variation of the primary current occurs, the primary current is divided, between winding 2 and resistor 11, into two components, say I'_{a1} and I'_{a2}, having a different ratio, which will be

$$\frac{I'_{a2}}{I'_{a1}} > \frac{I_{a2}}{I_{a1}}$$

where the inequality is greater the quicker the transient considered. During this transient, the primary armature ampere-turns will not be compensated. A primary flux will result, creating a peak of secondary current I_b that will develop a temporary dynamic stabilizing action.

For such an arrangement secondary current I_b is zero during steady-state operation; of the two fundamental Equations 104 only the first one is left. The torque is expressed by

$$2\pi T = K_{ca}^{\beta} I_{\beta} I_a \tag{106}$$

If, then, primary current I_a is constant and the parameter I_{β} is held constant, the torque will remain constant as shown by the diagram of Fig. 163.

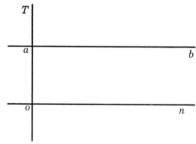

Fig. 163.   Constant-torque characteristic of the scheme of Fig. 162.

Now consider an arrangement of two similar Gamma motor metadynes mechanically coupled and connected in parallel, the pair being inserted into a loop through which a constant current I flows. It is desired that the two machines share the current equally.

From the fundamental Equations 104 is obtained

$$\frac{1}{n} E_{ca} = I_a \frac{K(K + K_{ba}^{\alpha})n}{R} + K_{ca}^{\beta} I_{\beta}$$

The signs of n and K_{ca}^{β} are the same; the sign of $n[K(K + K_{ba}^{\alpha})/R]$ is then also positive, because K_{ba}^{α}, although negative, is smaller in absolute value than K. Therefore, the first term of the second member acts as an ohmic drop, having a rather large resistance, and it tends to distribute the primary current equally between the two machines. The two Gamma motor metadynes will therefore operate satisfactorily even under the conditions indicated above.

To investigate the operation of the Gamma motor metadyne connected to a constant-voltage system, one may consider the three Equations 104 and 105. Elimination of currents I_b and I_a gives the expression of the torque T as a function of the speed n in the form

$$2\pi T = \frac{A}{n} + \frac{B}{n^2} + \frac{C}{n^3}$$

the constants A, B, and C being functions of the voltage of the shunt distribution system and of stator current I_β. The family of the characteristics thus obtained is statically stable, and some of them are similar to the well-known characteristics of the compound dynamo. Note that the formula gives an infinite torque at $n = 0$ because no resistance in the primary circuit has been considered.

16 · Some Applications Using Metadynes Previously Described

1. DECK AUXILIARIES

The application of the metadyne system to deck auxiliaries has been contemplated since the advent of the Alpha motor metadyne, for its torque-speed characteristic has been recognized as being very well adapted for anchor hoists and for capstans. The first ship to be equipped was the French liner *Colombie*, of 15,000 tons. Later came the Italian cruiser *Duca degli Abruzzi*, of 10,000 tons. After successful tests on the latter, two other, similar cruisers were also equipped.

Soon, nine destroyers of the Italian Navy were equipped with metadynes. These last-mentioned plants comprise metadyne motors of a type to be considered later on. Therefore, the description given here applies only to the metadynes on the first four ships mentioned above. Since each of the plants on the three cruisers was designed after the tests of the preceding deck auxiliary plant, some improvements were added each time. The diagram shown in Fig. 164 corresponds to the first plant, and it can show only the main features.

Figure 164 gives the scheme of a loop, showing the most essential parts. The ships were equipped with a direct-current constant-voltage (240 volts) network, indicated by 32. A Cross transformer metadyne, 1, has its primary brushes, *a* and *c*, connected to the constant-voltage line, 32, by means of a starting rheostat, 9, and a contactor, 8. The secondary brushes, *b* and *d*, of the machine feed the main loop. The stator of the Cross transformer metadyne bears the secondary variator winding, 2, shunt-connected across the primary brushes, and the regulator winding, 3, having its magnetic axis along the primary commutating axis.

The regulator dynamo, 4, is mechanically coupled to the shaft of the transformer metadyne; it is shunt-excited and connected to the constant voltage of the shunt network 32. The Cross transformer metadyne starts by itself through starting rheostat 9; when it approaches its normal speed, regulator dynamo 4 builds up and keeps the speed at the normal value. The value of the current in the main loop is determined by the current flowing in secondary variator winding 2 and is controlled by the rheostat, 10.

The motors are Alpha motor metadynes. They are represented in Fig. 164 by a rectangle with two diagonals, such as 12, 13, 22, 23, 24, 25, and 26, except for motor 14 indicated with all its main features. Alpha

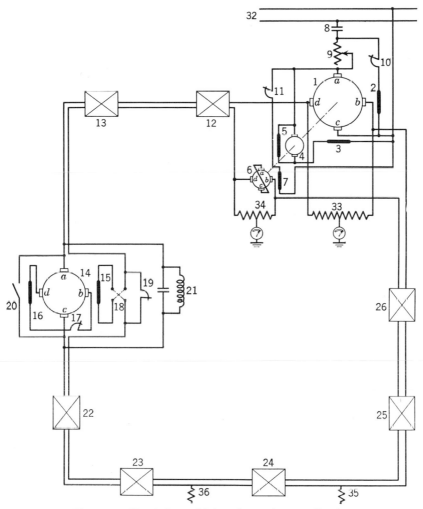

Fig. 164.   Circuit for a shipboard metadyne application.

motor metadyne 14 has its primary brushes *a* and *c* connected to the main loop, and its secondary brushes *b* and *d* connected to a hypercompensator, 16. The value and the direction of its starting torque is determined by the value and the direction of the current flowing in the secondary variator winding, 15.

The armatures of the Alpha motor metadynes are supplied with power by the Cross transformer metadyne, 1, and the secondary variator windings of these motors are supplied with current from a small S generator metadyne, 6, coupled to the shaft of the Cross transformer metadyne. S generator metadyne 6 has its primary brushes, c and a,

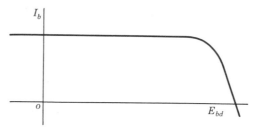

Fig. 165.   No overload is possible with this characteristic.

short-circuited, whereas its secondary brushes, b and d, feed an auxiliary loop represented by the inner line following the main loop, which is represented by the outer line.

The arrangement of two loops, a main loop for the armatures and an auxiliary loop for the variator windings, is an improvement over the first system of using the constant-voltage network to supply the variator windings, and a second system of using the current of the main loop for the variator windings, as well. For the main loop the standard value of 400 amperes was chosen, and the auxiliary loop was standardized at 50 amperes.

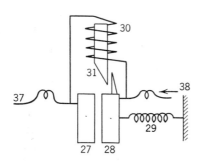

Fig. 166.   This device prevents interruption of the series loop.

The maximum permissible secondary voltage of the Cross transformer metadyne is 600 volts, which gives a maximum output of 240 kilowatts. Consider the curve $osdv$ of Fig. 140 representing the power absorbed by the Alpha motor metadyne as a function of the speed n; this curve shows only one peak at s because there is no starting rheostat. The probability of operating just at this peak for one hoist or capstan is small, and the probability of operating just at this peak for all winches, hoists, and capstans simultaneously is practically zero. Therefore the sum of the nominal power of all the installed motors is much higher than the nominal power of the transformer metadyne. Tests were made and a ratio of 3 to 1 was found safe. Thus the main loop may feed $3 \times 240 = 720$ kilowatts of Alpha motor metadynes without exceeding 600 volts as peak voltage. For the auxiliary loop, a peak of 60 volts was found sufficient; this gives a peak power of 50 × 60 = 3000 watts.

The amount of switchgear is reduced. Although it must carry a reasonably large current, 50 amperes, which makes feasible physically strong wires, this current is low enough to permit simple contact members. Further, insulation of the switchgear is very simple, as it has to withstand a peak of only 60 volts.

The switchgear of each Alpha motor metadyne consists essentially of a switch, 20, that short-circuits the armature when the motor is not

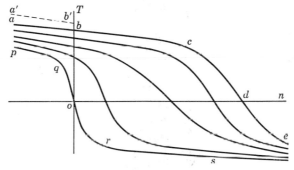

Fig. 167. Torque-speed characteristics of the shipboard motor metadynes.

operating; of an inverter, 18; of a rheostat, 19, for controlling the current in the variator winding, 15; and of a rheostat, 17, for controlling the current of the secondary circuit.

Figure 167 is a diagram of the family of characteristics selected; the no-load speed is modified simultaneously with the starting torque. This requires the simultaneous control of the two rheostats 19 and 17. These rheostats, inverter 18, and switch 20 are operated by the single handle of a relatively small controller.

Switch 20 does not need to dissipate energy when it opens because it does not interrupt a circuit but merely diverts the current from one short branch to another short branch. Therefore, this switch is a simple one and is often called a "diverter" in order to differentiate it from the usual circuit breakers or contactors in which provision must be made for the dissipation of a relatively large amount of electromagnetic energy.

Consider the torque-speed characteristic *abcde* of Fig. 167 of the Alpha motor metadyne in connection with the operation of an anchor hoist. The anchor hoist must develop a tractive effort larger at lower speed and smaller at higher speed. If stalled, when the anchor for some reason becomes entangled, however, the tractive effort must not exceed a safe value, say 67% of the effort that would break the chains.

When the anchor cannot be disentangled for some reason and there is a heavy sea, the ship may be shifted by a sudden wave; and, if the hoist does not slacken, the chain may break. To prevent this serious accident, it is desirable to have the hoist pay out the chain while still developing a high tractive effort compatible with the strength of the chain. As the thrust of the wave ceases, the hoist must automatically wind up the chain again and keep it taut. When the anchor is lifted freely, the speed must not exceed a given maximum safe value. Therefore, the tractive effort must tend towards zero near this speed.

All these desired conditions of operation are satisfactorily met by the Alpha motor metadyne: Segment bc corresponds to low-speed operation and it provides for a high tractive effort; segment cd corresponds to high values of speed and shows a quick reduction of the tractive effort towards zero; if the machine is stalled, the tractive effort becomes the starting effort; finally, segment ab corresponds to rotation of the motor in the reverse sense when the hoist pays out the chain. In the event of the hoist's paying out the chain the friction losses of the mechanical transmission add their effect to the effort of the Alpha motor metadyne, and the tractive effort on the chain increases abruptly from the ordinates of segment ab to the ordinates of segment $b'a'$. Such an increase, conveniently limited by reasonable construction of the mechanical transmission, is welcome.

The curve $pqors$, corresponding to zero current in the variator winding and to the zero position of the controller, shows that, when the operator is at the zero position, the chain is prevented from moving in either direction with a resisting effort that increases very quickly even for small values of speed.

A simple device on the controller allows for a time delay in closing switch 20 when the operator brings the handle of the controller to its zero position. Thus, while using the controller, the operator may remain at the zero position for a short time or may pass from one direction to the opposite while switch 20 remains open.

Although the shunt network of the ship is insulated for 240 volts, a peak voltage of 600 volts for the main loop is possible. However, although a short circuit on the shunt network may have very serious consequences, a short circuit on the loop fed by the metadyne has no harmful consequences. The main current remains the same; at the fault, the current is divided between two branches, the normal branch and the accidental one created by the short circuit. Thus the latter branch generally carries only a rather small current that will not have the destructive effect of a current due to short circuit of a shunt network. For the same reason, a short circuit in the armature of a load machine inserted into a metadyne loop does not have the same destructive effect as in a shunt network.

Although the electric stress on the insulating material is continuous and has its maximum value everywhere on a cable forming part of a shunt network, in a series network this stress corresponds to the maximum value only near the source of supply and it lasts only a few seconds when the peak of voltage is attained. The larger part of the distribution system remains at an average voltage much lower than the peak voltage, and even this voltage appears only while relatively large power is supplied to the loads. When the loads in the loop are idle or require relatively small power, the electric stress on the insulating material is negligible. This is particularly favorable on ships, where the decay of the insulating qualities of the cables is rather rapid.

The author advocates a grounded neutral for the metadyne plants. For this purpose the middle point of a resistor, of relatively high resistance, is grounded through an ammeter. In Fig. 164 such an arrangement is shown, in 33 for the main loop, and in 34 for the auxiliary loop. The peak difference of potential thus becomes 300 volts for the main loop and 30 volts for the auxiliary loop.

The ammeter inserted in the grounding connection is a good detector of incipient failures of the insulation. Suppose that a short circuit occurs at point 35. Operation will go on as normal because the leakage current is comparatively very small, but the grounded ammeter will detect the fault in the insulation. This failure may be easily located by comparison of the readings of ammeters inserted along the line.

If a second short circuit occurs at point 36, the grounded ammeter will detect it as well, and the ammeter on load 24 will locate it. If the insulating material in 35 and 36 becomes somewhat deteriorated, as it generally does, the current through the failure will generally be only a small part of the current in the main loop and all motors will operate normally. Only when the deterioration of the insulating material at both points 35 and 36 is severe will the leakage current be a large part of the normal current. Motor 24 will then operate with low torque, and this evidence immediately locates the defect; the other motors will operate normally. A comparison of the effects of the same faults on a shunt network points out the safety of operation of the metadyne network.

In order to prevent a dangerous overload, the characteristic of secondary current I_b versus secondary voltage E_{bd} of the transformer metadyne shows a bend when the maximum voltage in the loop is reached, as Fig. 165 shows. When maximum voltage is approached, the intensity of the current in the loop decreases and the whole load is reduced.

The intersection of current I_b with the axis of abscissas E_{bd} corresponds to open-circuit operation. The primary current then has a small value corresponding to the losses. Thus, when the loop is accidentally opened, there will be no overcurrent in the primary circuit and the metadyne will run quietly.

To obtain the shape of the characteristic of Fig. 165, many methods may be employed. Usually, it is obtained by supplying the secondary variator winding with a modulator dynamo provided with two field windings, the first creating constant ampere-turns and the second one shunt-connected across the secondary brushes of the metadyne to create opposing ampere-turns. The sharp bend is obtained through severe iron saturation of the modulator dynamo. Figure 164 does not show this machine.

The accidental interruption of the loop will not provoke any destructive effect, but it stops the operation. Although it has been observed on damaged naval ships that the conductors of the electric network easily get short-circuited, they are not interrupted but simply stretched. It is nevertheless necessary to take some steps toward reestablishing the accidentally interrupted loop, particularly for navy ships where the fighting capacity must be maintained at all costs during the short time of a battle during which damage is highly probable.

Figure 166 shows a simplified scheme of an apparatus to protect against interruption of the loop: Two contact members, 27 and 28, are connected to two points of the loop by means of the conductors 37 and 38. One contact member, 27, is fixed; the other, 28, is movable and is compelled by the spring, 29, to contact fixed member 27, but a very small air gap is kept between the two contact members through a mechanical interlock. When interruption of the loop occurs, the voltage between the terminals increases quickly, owing to the sudden reaction of the metadyne. The winding, 30, of a magnet attracts the iron pole piece, 31, and unlatches the mechanical interlock that restrains contact member 28, and 28 comes into contact with 27. The air gap is very small, of the order of one millimeter, and spring 29 is strong enough that the circuit is reestablished in a small fraction of a second. Tests made do not reveal any operating difficulties when an interruption of the loop occurs at a segment protected by this apparatus.

Such a protective device is indicated schematically at 21, connected between the terminals of the Alpha motor metadyne and protecting the loop against interruption due to a fault in the motor. This appara-

tus is very small, has very little energy consumption, and may be connected across any two points of the circuit.

In the event of emergency, it is very easy to connect the two terminals
of the interrupted loop; it suffices to ground them through a heavy
metallic piece. On the contrary, in the event of short circuit on a shunt
network, the reestablishment of proper insulation is a rather long and
difficult operation.

For reasons of safety, at least two loops are provided on a ship, each
loop having its own metadyne for supplying power. The two loops
normally operate independently of one another. If a fault occurs in
one metadyne supplying power, the two loops are connected so that the
unit still in order may supply power to the two loops interconnected into

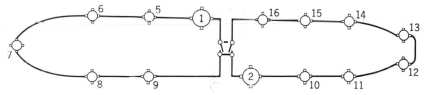

Fig. 108. Two loops, with arrangement for interconnection, afford reliable operation
even in an emergency.

a single loop. Figure 168 gives an example of this arrangement; one
loop extends from the middle of the ship to the bow; the other loop
extends from the middle to the stern. The two loops have a common
point. When the switches (simple "diverters") are in the vertical position, the loops operate independently; when the switches are in the
horizontal position, the two loops form a single one, and a single metadyne may supply power to all motors. Metadynes 1 and 2, supplying
the power, are generally located near one another at the middle of the
ship in the machine room. All other units indicated on Fig. 168 (5, 6,
7, 8, 9, 10, 11, 12, 13, 14, 15, and 16) are supposed to be Alpha motor
metadynes.

Figures 169, 170, and 171 give views of a Cross transformer metadyne,
of an Alpha motor metadyne, and of an anchor winch of the liner
Colombie.

A common objection against the metadyne plant is raised because of
the copper losses along the loop due to the constant current that flows
through the loop continuously even when all the motors are idle. The
copper losses along a distribution line are important, say 5% of the
transmitted power, when the transmission line is a relatively long line,
say 500 kilometers. But for compact plants like the one considered
here, the copper losses along the loop are negligible, a fraction of 1%.

Nevertheless, some arrangements are used to reduce the current in the loop when all the motors are idle. One means for this purpose con-

Fig. 169. Cross transformer metadyne for the liner *Colombie*. (*Courtesy of Als-Thom, Paris.*)

sists essentially of a voltage relay shunt-connected across the secondary brushes of the auxiliary S generator metadyne. When any of the

Fig. 170. One of the Alpha motor metadynes for the *Colombie*. (*Courtesy of Als-Thom, Paris.*)

motors are put into operation, the corresponding secondary variator winding is excited, and therefore the secondary brushes of the S generator metadyne rise to a definite voltage. This voltage energizes the relay, which in its turn controls the energizing of the secondary variator winding of the Cross transformer metadyne.

When no motor is operating, the relay cuts off the current from the secondary variator winding of the Cross transformer metadyne and the secondary current drops to the value corresponding to the magnetizing component, about one-fifth of the normal current. The copper losses are then reduced to $\frac{1}{25}$ of the normal losses. Regarding copper losses, one may point out a large saving due to the absence of starting rheostats and due also to the regeneration of power every time the motors brake, no matter what their speed.

There were hopes for a reduction of the weight of the cables of a metadyne plant analogous to the reduction of switchgear. Two reasons

Fig. 171.   An anchor winch on the *Colombie*.   (*Courtesy of Als-Thom, Paris.*)

may be stated for this desirable reduction: (1) the single cable connecting one load to another and to the supply source; (2) the high value of the peak voltage.

On the first plants such a reduction was not apparent, mainly because the plants were relatively small and superimposed on shunt networks already existing. Having acquired experience, the author planned metadyne plants for large ships, which would take advantage of all the characteristics of the metadyne and exclude any useless superposition with other systems. Numerical comparisons of the cable weight then show a clear advantage in favor of the metadyne system.

The application of the metadyne system is not restricted to naval ships by the facts that the system offers safety, reliability, and fighting capacity because it operates even when damaged. All these advantages are just as valuable on merchant ships.

2. A SYSTEM OF CRANES FOR PIERS

The torque-speed characteristic of the Alpha motor metadyne is suited for hoists and cranes, particularly in places where many similar lifting machines operate simultaneously.

The piers of the Mediterranean harbors are often equipped with a large number of cranes that move along a section of the waterside of the pier above a pair of railway tracks. The ports of Genoa and Venice were enlarged just before the outbreak of the war, and two large projects were prepared for a general metadyne plant. Figure 172 gives the scheme with the main features. At the foot of the pier a small substation, 1, is provided, essentially comprising an alternating-current three-phase 3000-volt motor, 3, driving an S generator metadyne, 2, that supplies the power to a loop feeding the cranes of that pier. On each pier there are sometimes twelve cranes. In Fig. 172 six such cranes are represented schematically by a rectangle with diagonal, the cranes 4, 5, 14, 15, and 16, and also the crane 6, the latter being indicated with its main elements: a hoisting motor, 7; a motor, 8, for swinging the arm of the crane; a motor, 10, for the movement of the crane along the waterside of the pier above the railway tracks; and an auxiliary motor, 9, for general control. All motors are Alpha motor metadynes; motor 7 delivers about 100 kilowatts, the two motors 8 and 10 about 50 kilowatts, and the auxiliary motor 9 about 10 kilowatts. Motor 9 drives an auxiliary S generator metadyne, 12, and a small dynamo, 13; S generator metadyne 12 supplies the control current to an auxiliary loop circulating only in the corresponding crane. The same auxiliary loop also supplies small motors for internal service on the crane, such as pumps and ventilators, not indicated in the figure.

The standard value of the current was chosen at 500 amperes in the main loop and 50 amperes in the auxiliary loop. A ratio of 4 to 1 was considered possible between the sum of the nominal power of the motors and the nominal power of the main metadyne generator. For twelve cranes, this choice gives a peak voltage in the main loop of 1200 volts. With a grounded neutral at the substation, the insulation corresponds to 600 volts, which is a standard value. For a smaller number of cranes, the current intensity in the main loop was lowered to 400 amperes. The peak voltage in the auxiliary loop in each crane was 140 volts, reduced to 70 volts by the grounded neutral.

The main loop in each crane is cut off by switch 11 when the crane is idle. Switch 11 is represented as a knife switch in the figure for the sake of simplicity, but it actually short-circuits the conductors of the two trolleys and cuts off and isolates the main loop of the crane. If the

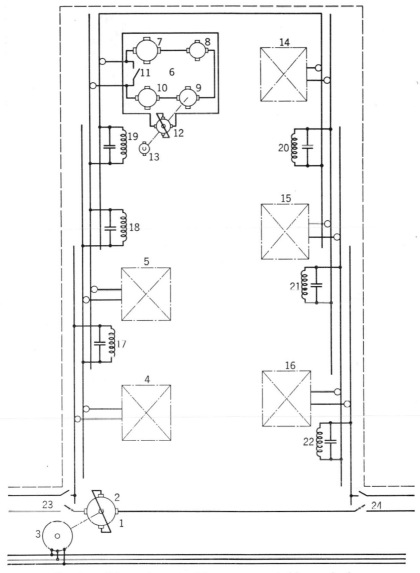

Fig. 172.   Scheme for waterside cranes operated in a series loop.

number of cranes is m, the number of isolated segments of lines for the trolleys is $m - 1$.

A protective device is connected to each pair of the trolley lines, and there are as many pairs as there are separate cranes.   The numerals 17, 18, 19, 20, 21, and 22 indicate this apparatus.   These protective devices are closed when the crane is idle. Before entering the cab, the operator uses a key to separate the contact members of the corresponding protective apparatus, and he brings them into contact again with the same key when he comes down from the crane at the end of his work.

In order to prevent overloads, the secondary current-voltage characteristic of the S generator metadyne, 1, has the shape indicated by Fig. 165.

If substation 1 goes out of service, switches 23 interconnect the main loop of the pier under consideration with the main loop of the pier immediately to the left; then the substation of the latter pier supplies power to both piers. Similarly switches 24 interconnect the loop of the first pier with the loop at its right. Such an arrangement also permits supplying power to two or even more piers from a single substation if only a few cranes are operating on each pier.

Large cranes for factories have been constructed in England.

3. THE SHIP *ORLANDO*

The *Orlando* was constructed for rapid transportation between the continent and the island Sardinia, and she is driven by Diesel engines. She is equipped with a complete metadyne plant for all auxiliary machines, anchor winches, capstans, hoists, compressors, pumps, ventilators, and even for the steering gear.

Similarly to the plants for deck auxiliaries already described, two main loops and two auxiliary loops are provided, each main loop and each auxiliary loop being fed by S generator metadynes, which form a single set driven by a separate oil engine. The motors are all Alpha motor metadynes, except for the ventilators, which are simple series dynamos inserted into the auxiliary loop.

The secondary current-voltage characteristics of the S generator metadyne have the shape indicated by Fig. 165, for the same reasons given in Section 1. The same protections have been taken for short-circuiting a segment of the main loop when it is accidentally opened and for interconnecting the two loops into a single one.

Figure 173 shows a set composed of an oil engine and two S generator metadynes, one for the main loop and another for the auxiliary loop. The photograph also shows the control board with the measuring apparatus.

This installation was very satisfactory. When the engineers took charge of it, they did not know the new system. After operating it for an hour, however, they mastered it. The numerous faulty maneuvers they made during the first hour did no harm and allowed them to get a proper understanding of the characteristics of the plant.

Fig. 173. Metadyne-Diesel set for the *Orlando*. (*Courtesy of the San Giorgio Co.,*
Genoa.)

4. CHEMICAL PLANTS. TEST BED FOR OIL ENGINES

In many chemical plants, a large number of compressors are needed.
The nature of the compressed fluid may lead to frequent stalling of the
pump, or danger may arise if the pressure is increased above a given
limit. In such cases a metadyne plant with Alpha motor metadynes
permits frequent stalling with no trouble and prevents the pressure,
which depends on the torque of the motor, from ever exceeding a safe
value arbitrarily determined. Such applications were carried out in
Italy during the war. Figure 174 shows an Alpha motor metadyne
directly coupled to a compressor.

In sugar factories there are a large number of centrifugal machines
which must reach a maximum speed for a short time and then slow
down to standstill. The Alpha motor metadyne very easily brakes re-
generatively, no matter what the speed. Figure 175 shows two typical
torque-speed characteristics of an Alpha motor metadyne, the curve
$abcdn_0e$ corresponding to a large, say positive, value of ampere-turns of
the secondary variator winding, and the curve $fghk$ corresponding to a
moderate negative value of ampere-turns of the same secondary variator
winding. In starting, the operator brings the handle of the controller
to the position corresponding to the curve $abcdn_0e$, and the centrifugal
apparatus reaches the maximum speed, corresponding to the abscissa

of the point d. He waits there a few seconds, and then he brings the handle to the position corresponding to the curve $fghk$, the point representing the operation jumps from d to k, and regenerative braking begins and lasts with a practically invariable torque until the centrifugal apparatus is brought to standstill. The accelerating and decelerating

Fig. 174. Air compressor driven by an Alpha motor metadyne. (*Courtesy of the San Giorgio Co., Genoa.*)

periods last the shortest possible time because the accelerating or braking torque keeps its maximum value throughout all the corresponding period, no matter what the speed is. The ordinates of points b and k have been calculated from the maximum safe value permitted by the mechanical transmission.

For similar reasons, and also because of the facility with which the no-load speed can be shifted between limits of speed as wide as 20 to 1, a very large metadyne plant was planned for the test bed of the automobile motors of the Fiat. The saving in energy consumption would easily pay for the capital expenses.

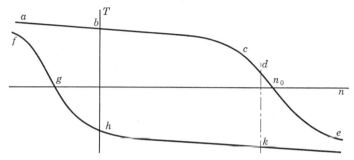

Fig. 175.   Particular torque-speed characteristics of an Alpha motor driving a centrifuge.

5. SPECIAL APPLICATIONS

In this section certain important applications of several different forms of the metadyne are described briefly. These examples show the versatility of the metadyne in its adaptation to functions ranging from special generating problems for large power to delicate control of large power through low-power devices.

A. Mine Locomotives.   Since mine locomotives must haul a train of cars filled with ore through the mine galleries, these locomotives are small, their height rarely exceeding four feet. They are generally supplied with electric power from an overhead line or from a battery. With either source, though particularly with a battery, the electric equipment must be as simple and as compact as possible. Since most of the time these locomotives maneuver rather than run steadily, energy saving is important, especially with a battery as the source of power.

A transformer metadyne is employed for supplying the motors with current. Usually the secondary current-voltage characteristic is a hyperbola, such as *abc* in Fig. 176I. The conic *def* shown in the same figure is the corresponding characteristic of regulator current versus secondary voltage.

It is shown in Chapter 8 that a transformer metadyne without a regulator winding and operating with constant voltages at its brushes has a finite steady-state speed. Thus with load variation the speed will vary between two finite limits. These limit values of speed may be made very close to one another through the agency of a primary shunt winding connected across the secondary brushes. This shunt winding has its resistance set so that its current, I_δ, is a particular linear function of E_{bd}, as represented by the straight segment *hk* of Fig. 176I, almost overlapping the curved segment *def*. It is assumed that the number of turns of the shunt winding is the same as the number of turns of the regulator winding. Under these conditions the speed remains practically constant even without a regulator dynamo. Figure 176II shows the simplified diagram of such a circuit with a Cross transformer metadyne, *TM*. Locomotives of this type that have been constructed by the author in Italy operate satisfactorily.

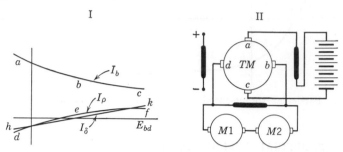

Fig. 176. I. Some current-voltage characteristics of the mine-locomotive transformer, which show the relationship of the shunt-winding current to the equivalent regulator current. II. Transformer metadyne *TM* supplies power to the two traction motors of the mine locomotive; note that the shunt winding essentially replaces the usual regulator dynamo.

B. Mine Hoist at Luossavaara-Kiirunavaara, Sweden. Figure 177 shows a diagram of the system, comprising a mine hoist driven by motor *M*, which is separately excited and supplied with electric power from generator *G*. The generator is excited by an S generator (see page 247) metadyne, *AM*, which acts as an amplifier and is controlled by three

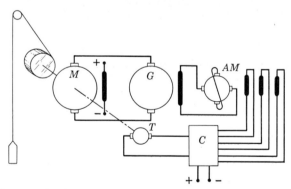

Fig. 177. Diagram of a feedback-controlled Ward Leonard system employing an S generator metadyne, as applied to drive a mine hoist.

secondary variator windings. The first one gives the "signal" or order from the operator, and the second is excited by a feedback current derived essentially from the difference between a preset constant voltage and the voltage of tachometer *T*. This second winding determines the ultimate steady-state speed of the hoist. The acceleration is further limited by the third variator winding, which is made sensitive to the derivative of the speed with respect to time. Controller C combines and distributes the three variator currents. It is in turn supplied from a source of direct current at constant voltage.

When the hoist is either lifting or lowering, the speed of the car reaches a maximum value of 16 meters per second. Motor M is a 2800-kilowatt dynamo having a maximum speed of 44 revolutions per minute. Generator G is driven at a constant speed of 540 revolutions per minute.

Fig. 178. Hoist motor and drum for the mine equipment shown in Fig. 177. (*Courtesy of ASEA, Sweden.*)

The nominal power of the amplifier metadyne is 5 kilowatts. Figure 178 shows the motor coupled to the hoisting drum, and Fig. 179 shows the amplifier metadyne. This equipment is made by ASEA (Allmänna Svenska Elektriska Aktiebolaget) in Sweden.

C. Reversible Cold-Strip Mill at Surahammar, Sweden. As Fig. 180 shows, the steel to be worked is rolled between the two cylinders, Y and Y', driven by motor $M5$ in opposite directions. The resulting strip is reeled back and forth between drums D and D'. Motor $M5$ determines the linear speed of the strip, and drums D and D' must maintain the proper tension in the strip. While the thickness of the strip is being altered by cylinders Y and Y', the peripheral speeds of the cylinders and of both drums D and D' differ from each other. Motor $M5$ is separately

Fig. 179. Amplifier metadyne for the mine-hoist system. (*Courtesy of ASEA, Sweden.*)

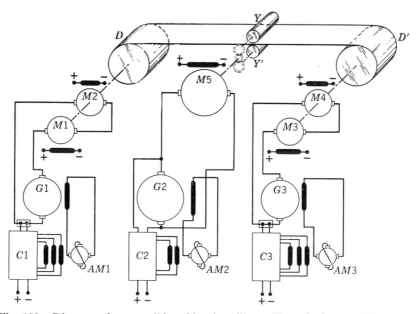

Fig. 180. Diagram of a reversible cold-strip rolling mill employing amplifier-metadyne control on each of three separate drives.

excited and is supplied with electric power by generator $G2$. The excitation of $G2$ is in turn controlled by amplifier metadyne $AM2$, which has two variator windings. One of these is excited by a signal current, determined by the operating engineer, and the other winding is excited

Fig. 181. Over-all views of the mill equipment shown schematically in Fig. 180. (*Courtesy of ASEA, Sweden.*)

by a feedback current determined essentially by the voltage supplied by generator $G2$, and conveniently corrected in order to take into account the maximum safe limits of speed, acceleration, and power. Controller $C2$, supplied with direct current at constant voltage, combines and distributes the appropriate currents to the variator windings.

Drum D is driven by the twin motors $M1$ and $M2$, which are connected in series and supplied with electric power by generator $G1$. These motors are separately excited, and generator $G1$ is in turn excited by amplifier metadyne $AM1$. Among the eight variator windings of $AM1$, the three most important are: (1) the winding excited by the signal current determined by the operating engineer; (2) the winding carrying a feedback current proportional to the output current of generator $G1$; and (3), the winding excited by a current that is a measure of friction losses. Controller $C1$, supplied with direct current at constant voltage, provides the desired currents for the variator windings, with limits on

Fig. 182.   View of the drive equipment for one drum of a large reversible cold-strip mill.   (*Courtesy of ASEA, Sweden.*)

acceleration, peaks of current, drum-speed variation, and other secondary factors.   There is a similar arrangement for drum D'.

Figure 181 shows an overall view of one of these cold-strip plants constructed by ASEA in Sweden.   The mill motor is rated at 200 kilowatts, with a variable-speed rating between 890 and 1780 revolutions per minute.   The strip speed is 34 meters per second when the mill motor is turning at 890 revolutions per minute.

A more important plant constructed by the same company comprises a mill motor, which is rated at 1850 kilowatts, 232 revolutions per minute, and 650 volts, and a pair of twin motors as drive machines for each drum.   These twin motors are rated at 735 kilowatts and 875 revolutions per minute for each pair.   Since the mill proper and the driving sets for the individual drums are all located in separate rooms, it is impossible to obtain an overall view of the equipment. Figure 182 shows a generator and one pair of motors that comprise the driving equipment for one of the mill drums.

D. Miscellaneous. Figure 183 shows a complete set for a deck auxiliary under test in the factory before delivery. From left to right the

Fig. 183. A deck winch and its metadyne drive equipment, under operating test. (*Courtesy of ASEA, Sweden.*)

machines are a transformer metadyne, a motor metadyne, and a deck winch actually in operation. This equipment is constructed by ASEA in Sweden.

Figure 184 shows an amplifying transformer metadyne of the Cross type, built by AEG (Allgemeine Elektrische Gesellschaft) in Berlin. The refinements of this particular type of amplifier metadyne endow it with the most exact response of any amplifier metadyne yet built. A drive motor coupled to the transformer metadyne helps to keep the regulator current almost constant. Therefore, since the speed is quite constant, the exactitude of response is increased.

Figure 185 gives an overall view of the complete metadyne equipment of a turret for the Italian Navy as set up on the factory test floor for checking the complete simultaneous operation of all the elements of the

Fig. 184. Example of a Cross metadyne that is simultaneously a transformer and an amplifying generator. (*Courtesy of AEG, Berlin.*)

Fig. 185. A test set-up for shipboard turret-drive equipment having precision metadyne control. (*Courtesy of the San Giorgio Co., Genoa.*)

equipment. Other metadyne equipment has been used successfully on minesweepers. The constructor of the turret equipment is the San Giorgio Company of Genoa.

6. A HIGH-VOLTAGE METADYNE FOR A PRECIPITATOR

In a precipitator, small solid particles of chemicals carried by a gaseous stream flowing through a metallic chamber are electrically charged by a central, insulated conductor brought to a potential high enough to create corona. Then the particles are attracted by the metallic cover of the chamber and are collected.

An arc short-circuiting the central conductor with the external metallic cover is frequent, and it is generally due to the irregular density

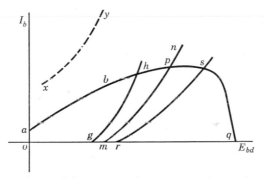

Fig. 186. Characteristics of the metadyne constructed for an electric precipitator.

of the solid particles in suspension. For the same reason, a continuous adjustment of the potential of the central conductor becomes necessary.

A metadyne is suitable for the electric source for such a device and gives a satisfactory operation because of its inherent characteristics. One may use an S generator metadyne or a Cross transformer metadyne. One secondary brush is connected to the metallic cover of the precipitation chamber, and the other secondary brush is connected to the central conductor. The secondary voltage increases very quickly until the corona effect starts and reaches the radius necessary to draw a current corresponding to a point on the static characteristic of secondary voltage versus secondary current of the metadyne.

Let p be this point on the characteristic $abpq$ shown in Fig. 186. The corona will have a stable radius if the density of the gaseous stream and the density of the suspended particles are unaltered, because point p must be the intersection of the metadyne characteristic and of the characteristic mpn peculiar to the corona effect.

If the density varies, the characteristic of the corona moves between two limits, *rs* and *gh,* corresponding to the practical limits of density, and the operating point will then slide along segment *sph.* Thus the metadyne continuously sets the proper potential in the precipitation chamber according to the continuously varying density.

Suppose that the conditions of a flashover occur. The arc may start, but it vanishes immediately because a flashover requires a current much larger than the metadyne could supply.

Fig. 187.   A high-voltage metadyne designed as a power supply for a precipitator. (*Courtesy of the Metropolitan-Vickers Co., Ltd., Sheffield.*)

It is very difficult to record the characteristic of a flashover. It may be represented very roughly by the dotted line *xy,* which shows no possible intersection with the metadyne characteristic. Thus when a flashover starts, the resistance between the central conductor and the metallic cover of the precipitation chamber drops abruptly, the representative point of the operation slides along segment *ba* of the metadyne characteristic, and the flashover dies out before it can become dangerous.

As soon as the flashover vanishes, the secondary voltage of the metadyne rises quickly to set itself at the proper value. Then the operation continues regularly.

Figure 187 gives a view of an S generator metadyne constructed in England for application in a precipitator, at 25,000 volts. This voltage is induced by two identical armature windings, each winding being associated with a separate commutator. Each winding can supply 15,000 volts as a maximum value. The secondary brushes of the two commutators are connected in series; the commutation is black.

17 · Special Metadynes of Degree $m = 4$

1. AMPLIFIER METADYNES

Since the early days of the development of electric machines, the dynamo has often been used as an amplifier. Thus the voltage regulator of an alternator acts upon the current i of the field excitation of the exciter dynamo and controls the armature current I, which in turn flows through the field coils of the inductor of the alternator. The author suggested rotating amplifier machinery for equally varying alternating currents as early as 1916.[*]

In these cases the amplification ratio has an average value of $\eta = 20$. The amplification ratio may be defined for a rapid transient as the ratio

$$\eta = \frac{(\Delta I) \text{ max}}{(\Delta i) \text{ max}} \tag{107}$$

between the maximum value of the variation ΔI of, say, the amplified current and the maximum value of the variation Δi of, say, the pilot current.

The quality of amplification also depends on the distortion of the function of time $I(t)$ with respect to the function of time $i(t)$ and on the time lag. The time lag may be defined as the time elapsing from the instant at which the pilot current i has reached $Q/100$ of its final steady value to the instant at which the amplified current I reaches the same percentage of its final steady value; the constant Q is obviously smaller than 100.

Figure 188A shows the diagram of the increase $\Delta i(t)$ of the field current i due to a sudden increase of the voltage impressed on the field winding of a dynamo. Diagram B shows the variation of the electromotive force $\Delta e(t)$ of the dynamo; it is assumed that the magnetic circuit is completely laminated, free from short-circuiting bolts and from any other short-circuited field winding; this diagram is similar to diagram A. Diagram C gives the increase $\Delta I(t)$ of amplified current I; the tangent at point 0 is horizontal, and its inclination increases slowly. The difference $t_2 - t_1$ is the time lag for $Q = 95$. The distortion is clearly apparent.

Now consider the S generator metadyne of Fig. 189. Its stator bears two windings: winding 3 shunt-connected across the secondary brushes

---

[*] See *L'Elettrotecnica*, August 15, 1919, pp. 481–487.

b and d, and winding 4 carrying pilot current I_γ. Diagrams D, E, and F of Fig. 188 refer to a sudden increase of voltage impressed upon the terminals of variator winding 4, the same per cent increase as the one relative to the diagrams A, B, and C previously mentioned; the armature is assumed to be the same.

The power absorbed by variator winding 4 is about one-fifth of the power absorbed by the field winding of the dynamo considered above. Thus, if a resistance is connected in series with variator winding 4 so that the same total loss of power is obtained as in the field winding of

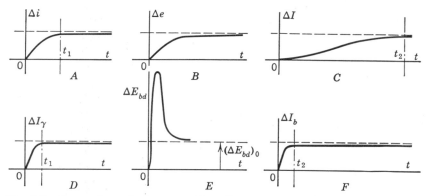

Fig. 188.   Comparison of a dynamo with an S generator metadyne relative to amplification.

the dynamo, the tangent at the origin 0 becomes about five times steeper. The exponential curve of diagram D is obtained in this way.

The voltage E_{bd} induced between the secondary brushes, b and d, of the S generator metadyne shows a sudden peak as indicated by diagram E. The ratio of the peak value of ΔE_{bd} to the steady-state increase $(\Delta E_{bd})_0$ depends on the initial value of the voltage between the secondary brushes. It becomes larger, however, the larger is the discrepancy between the actual instantaneous value of secondary current I_b, the amplified current, and the value of that current statically balancing the corresponding actual instantaneous value of the pilot current I_γ. In fact, this discrepancy of currents yields resultant ampereturns along the secondary commutating axis that give rise to a peak of primary current, which in turn induces the peak of voltage between the secondary brushes. The relative size of the peak has been investigated roughly in Section 5 of Chapter 14. An oscillogram is given in a later chapter.

The resulting variation, $\Delta I_b(t)$, of the secondary current is represented by diagram F. The amplification ratio η depends, of course, on the construction of the metadyne. The value $\eta = 500$ can easily be reached. The distortion of the corresponding increments is relatively small. The time lag $t_2 - t_1$ is much smaller than for the corresponding dynamo, say fifty times smaller.

In order to obtain little distortion between the entire pilot current, I_γ, and the entire secondary current, I_b, and not only between their corresponding increments as indicated above, some further precautions are necessary:

Secondary current I_b may be resolved into two parts as follows:

$$I_b = I_{b\mu} + I_{bw}$$

where $I_{b\mu}$ is the magnetizing component and I_{bw} is the component due to the reaction of the secondary armature ampere-turns to the ampere-turns of secondary variator winding 4. The component $I_{b\mu}$ must be compensated some other way than by the ampere-turns created by the pilot current.

For this purpose the shunt variator winding 3 has been used in the scheme of Fig. 189. Write the fundamental equations:

$$-\frac{1}{n} R_a I_a = \frac{1}{n} E_{ca} = K I_b + K_{ca}^\alpha \frac{E_{bd}}{R_1} + K_{ca}^\gamma I_\gamma$$

$$\frac{1}{n} E_{bd} = K I_a \tag{108}$$

where R_a is the resistance of the primary circuit and R_1 the resistance of shunt variator winding 3.

From these equations is obtained

$$-\frac{1}{n^2} \frac{R_a}{K} E_{bd} = K I_b + \frac{K_{ca}^\alpha}{R_1} E_{bd} + K_{ca}^\gamma I_\gamma \tag{109}$$

The resistance R_1 is made to satisfy the relation

$$-R_1 = \frac{1}{R_a} K K_{ca}^\alpha n^2 \tag{110}$$

and Equation 109 is then simplified as follows:

$$I_b = -\frac{K_{ca}^\gamma}{K} I_\gamma \tag{111}$$

which shows that, if the instantaneous transient values of I_b do not depart very much from the static values, the distortion of the amplified current with respect to the pilot current will be small. Further improvements to reduce distortion can be found through appropriate dynamic analysis.

The S generator metadyne thus constitutes a good current-amplifying device, and as such it was first used by the author for the gun-control plant for the Italian Navy and for the excitation of alternators. Later on, he suggested it for the gun control of the British and the United States Navy in 1936, with the permission of the Italian government.

Compared with the electronic tube, the amplifier metadyne is slow and distorting. It can handle large amounts of power, however, whereas

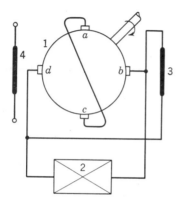

Fig. 189. The shunt winding eliminates the distortion of the magnetizing component of secondary current.

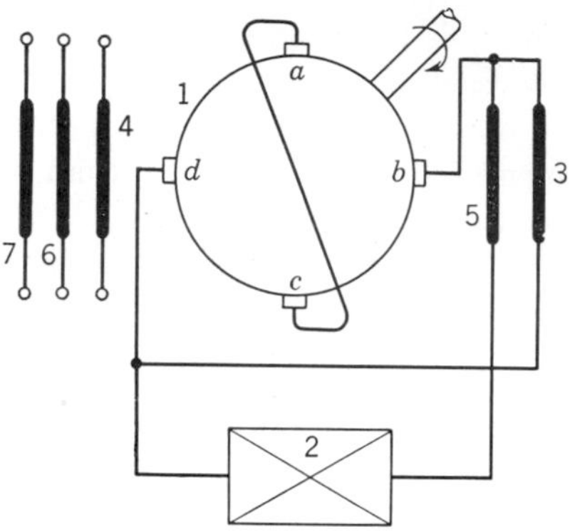

Fig. 190. The series winding of this S generator provides a degree of compensation for armature reaction.

the power handled directly by the tube is comparatively very small. In Italy, the author has constructed amplifier metadynes of 300 kilowatts.

Consider the scheme of Fig. 190. The stator of the S generator metadyne has a secondary compensator, 5, and four secondary variator windings: winding 3 shunt-connected across the secondary brushes, and the three windings 4, 6, and 7 carrying three independent pilot currents. Instead of three pilot currents, consider ν of them, $I_\gamma, I_\delta, \cdots, I_{\nu+2}$.

The fundamental equations may be written

$$-\frac{1}{n} R_a I_a = \frac{1}{n} E_{ca} = K I_b + K_{ca}^\beta I_b + K_{ca}^\alpha \frac{E_{bd}}{R_1} + \sum_{\delta=\gamma}^{\nu+2} K_{ca}^\delta I_\delta$$

$$\frac{1}{n} E_{bd} = K I_a$$

(112)

Let the resistance R_1 satisfy Equation 110. Then from Equation 112 there is

$$I_b = -\frac{1}{K + K_{ca}^\beta} \sum_{\delta=\gamma}^{\nu+2} K_{ca}^\delta I_\delta \qquad (113)$$

The last equation shows that

1. The amplified current can be made equal to any linear function of ν independent pilot currents.

2. The ratio of amplification with respect to the pilot current I_δ

$$\eta_\delta = -\frac{K_{ca}^\delta}{K + K_{ca}^\beta} \qquad (114)$$

can be made arbitrarily large by reduction of the value of the denominator appearing in relation 114 without increase in the distortion.

In fact, to increase η_δ, one may increase the value of K_{ca}^δ by suitable increase in the number of turns of the variator winding carrying the pilot current I_δ, but this involves an increased resistance of that winding and an increased self-induction, both increasing with the square of the number of turns.

The denominator $K + K_{ca}^\beta$ may be reduced at will and thus provide for a large value of η_δ with a relatively small value of K_{ca}^δ, as a more and more complete compensation of the flux due to the secondary armature ampere-turns is achieved. Such a compensation of flux may be made optimum even with concentrated stator coils interlinked with a whole polar segment; we say, then, that the compensating winding is a "total compensating winding" as defined clearly in Part I.

It is important to note that, the more nearly complete flux compensation is approached, the less the metadyne is reactive; and for $K + K_{ca}^\beta = 0$ the capacity of the armature currents to react upon one another is also zero. Winding 5 is often a hypocompensator. When it is made a full compensator, the reactivity of the metadyne may be obtained with devices indicated by the results of dynamic analysis.

In this way values as high as $\eta = 10,000$ are reached. It should be noted that the possibilities 1 and 2 are special characteristics of the metadyne; electronic tubes, strictly speaking, do not offer the equivalent.

The use of the compensating winding 5 also involves the advantage of reducing the self-induction of the secondary circuit. In order to get the greatest benefit from it, a distributed compensator may be constructed.

Under the abridged designation of Amplidyne, this form was used in a very large number of applications. Improvements in the constructional details and in particular operational characteristics were made by the cooperation of highly skilled engineers.

There is an optimum value for the depth of the air gap if a distributed compensating winding is used. If the air gap is too small, the leakage flux around the teeth of the armature and the teeth of the stator becomes too important and increases the self-induction of the secondary circuit; for the optimum value of air gap, the self-induction of the secondary circuit passes through its minimum.

Figure 191 gives a variant of the scheme of Fig. 190. The stator windings shown are a compensator, 5, a secondary variator winding, 4,

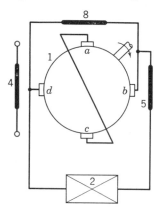 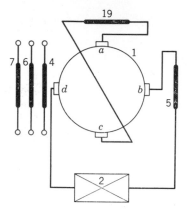

Fig. 191.　Note that the shunt winding is in the primary circuit of this arrangement.

Fig. 191(a).　The primary amplifying winding reduces the primary current.

assumed to be carrying a pilot current, and a primary variator winding, 8, having its magnetic axis along the commutating axis of primary brushes a and c and shunt-connected across secondary brushes b and d. This replaces the secondary variator winding 3 of the previous schemes.

The fundamental equations are

$$-\frac{1}{n} R_a I_a = \frac{1}{n} E_{ca} = K I_b + K_{ca}^\beta I_b + K_{ca}^\gamma I_\gamma$$

$$\frac{1}{n} E_{bd} = K I_a + K_{ca}^\alpha \frac{E_{bd}}{R_1} \tag{114a}$$

Resistance R_1 of shunt variator winding 8 satisfies the relation

$$R_1 = n K_{ca}^\alpha \tag{114b}$$

Thus we obtain

$$I_a = 0$$

$$I_b = -\frac{K_{ca}^\gamma}{K + K_{ca}^\beta} I_\gamma \tag{114c}$$

It is important to note that, although the static value of current I_a is zero, its transient or dynamic value is different from zero. But condition 114b corresponds to instability of operation.

Figure 191(a) shows a further variant comprising a primary amplifying winding, 19, for reducing the magnitude of the primary current. Such an arrangement, however, decreases the quick response of the amplifier metadyne.

2. OTHER AMPLIFIER METADYNES

The amplifier metadynes described in the previous section are generators and need a machine to drive them, preferably at constant speed. In this chapter amplifier metadynes are described which run at fairly constant speed from their internal torque.

Figure 192 gives the scheme of an amplifier metadyne having the external connections of a Cross transformer metadyne. Primary brushes

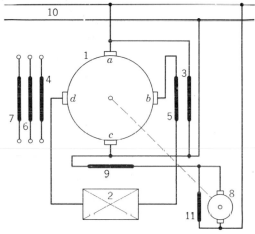

Fig. 192. An amplifier metadyne derived from the Cross transformer connections.

a and c are connected to a constant-voltage line 10. The secondary brushes feed a consumer 2. The stator is provided with the following windings: a secondary compensator winding, 5; four secondary variator windings (winding 3 is shunt-connected across the primary brushes, and windings 4, 6, and 7 carry the pilot currents); and, finally, a regulator winding, 9, which has its magnetic axis along the primary commutating axis. The regulator dynamo 8 coupled on the same shaft as the amplifier metadyne, 1, is shown shunt-excited, operating under voltage V of line 10.

Write the fundamental equations:

$$\frac{1}{n} E_{ca} = K I_b + K_{ca}^\beta I_b + K_{ca}^\alpha \frac{E_{ca}}{R_1} + \sum_{\delta=\gamma}^{\varepsilon} K_{ca}^\delta I_\delta$$

$$\frac{1}{n} E_{bd} = K I_a + K_{bd}^\rho I_\rho$$

(115)

$$2\pi T = K_{ca}^\beta I_b I_a + K_{ca}^\alpha \frac{E_{ca}}{R_1} I_a + I_a \sum_{\delta=\gamma}^{\varepsilon} K_{ca}^\delta I_\delta + K_{bd}^\rho I_\rho I_b$$

$$I_\rho = K_\rho (n - n_0)$$

To simplify, choose $V = E_{ca}$, and $n = n_0$. The number of equations of the simplified system 115 is reduced to three. Then for a given value of voltage E_{bd} the first two equations of the simplified system determine current I_b.

Let the resistance R_1 satisfy the equation

$$R_1 = n K_{ca}^\alpha \tag{116}$$

The secondary current is then made equal to the desired value,

$$I_b = - \frac{1}{K + K_{ca}^\beta} \sum_{\delta=\gamma}^{\varepsilon} K_{ca}^\delta I_\delta \tag{117}$$

as in Equation 113. The two remaining equations of the simplified system 115 determine the values of I_a and I_ρ for any given value of E_{bd}. It is important to note that the regulator current I_ρ does not interfere with the value of the amplified current I_b.

Figure 193 shows the scheme of another amplifier transformer metadyne. The external connections correspond to the Eight transformer metadyne investigated in Chapter 19. Primary brushes a and c are connected to the line, 10, supplying a constant voltage, say V; secondary brush b is connected to one terminal of a consumer, 12, the other terminal of which is connected to the same line as brush a; secondary brush d is connected to one terminal of another consumer, 2, the other terminal of which is connected to the same line as brush c. The stator windings are the same as in Fig. 192 and are indicated by the same numerals except that there is only one pilot current, for the sake of simplicity. The operation and the equations are similar to those of the previous case. The difference lies in the fact that the metadyne of Fig. 193 supplies two consumers of the same size as the single consumer supplied by the metadyne of Fig. 192, although the metadyne itself is the same size in both cases. This is because the consumers are partially supplied with power by the line indirectly through the metadyne, and partially by the line directly. The metadyne, therefore, transforms only a part of the total power supplied to the consumers, generally no more than one-half, as will be shown in Chapter 19.

The commutator of the metadyne of Fig. 193 has half the length of the commutator of a metadyne connected as indicated by scheme 192 and supplying the two consumers 2 and 12, which are connected in

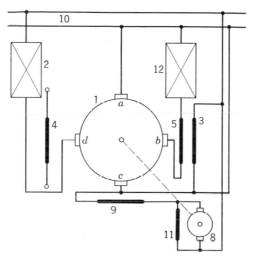

Fig. 193. This amplifier metadyne is related to the Eight transformer metadyne.

parallel. Correspondingly, there are also twice as many carbon blocks for the brushes of Fig. 192 with this connection of the consumers.

The scheme of the amplifier generator metadyne of Fig. 194 is derived from the scheme of Fig. 191 in the same way as the scheme of the amplifier transformer metadyne of Fig. 193 is derived from the scheme of Fig. 192. The same arguments as those developed above will explain the increased capacity of the metadyne of Fig. 194 as compared with the metadyne of Fig. 190. The generator metadyne of Fig. 194 may be referred to as an F generator metadyne.

Sometimes the opposite problem arises: From a large current, difficult to handle, a much smaller current is desired which will be proportional to the larger one and will follow its variations as closely as possible. With the small current, a relatively large voltage is generally desired.

The metadyne offers a good solution to this problem. The large current is now the pilot current; it flows in a stator coil, say of one single turn; this constitutes the secondary variator winding. The secondary brushes supply the desired small current at a relatively large voltage. The other stator windings and the other connections may follow any of the schemes indicated above for the amplifier metadyne.

Notice that during transient operations, which are most important for an amplifier metadyne, the current in the shunt variator winding 3 of the schemes of Figs. 189, 190, and 194 and the current in the variator winding 8 of Fig. 191 are continuously varying. Since this variation is rather slow, the compensation for which this current is used is incom-

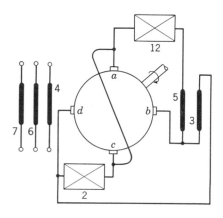

Fig. 194. The F generator metadyne.   Fig. 194(a). The S generator metadyne with series windings in both loops.

plete.   On the contrary, the current in the shunt winding 3 of the schemes of Figs. 192 and 193 remains practically constant during rapid transients, and the compensation for which these windings were constructed remains complete during these transients.

This fixed compensation shows that the amplifier transformer metadynes give a less-distorted amplified current and more accurate results than the amplifier generator metadynes. The former are therefore preferred for applications where precision and accuracy are required.

3. COMMENTS ON AMPLIFIER METADYNES

The last two sections show that many forms of metadynes may be adapted to operate as amplifiers. The S generator metadyne has been chosen for the comments developed in this section; similar comments may be made for the other forms of amplifier metadynes.

An amplifying apparatus is particularly interesting when the quantity to be amplified varies rapidly. Therefore, for complete judgment of the operation, it is necessary to investigate the dynamic behavior of the apparatus concerned. Amplifier metadynes have found extensive application, particularly as a result of careful dynamic analysis. Here, more information on their static operation is given, limited to such forms of metadyne as readily appear to have dynamical characteristics very close to their static ones. Thus shunt-connected variator windings will be omitted. The nature of the consumer supplied with current by the amplifier metadyne, although very important for a dynamic investigation, will be considered here only occasionally.

Consider the metadyne of Fig. 191(a). Its fundamental equations are

$$\frac{1}{n} E_{ca} = -\frac{1}{n} I_a R_a = (K + K_{ca}^\beta) I_b + \sum_{\delta=\gamma}^{\varepsilon} K_{ca}^\delta I_\delta$$

$$\frac{1}{n} E_{bd} = (K + K_{bd}^\alpha) I_a \tag{117a}$$

from which we derive the amplification ratio η_δ of current I_b with respect to the pilot current I_δ, assuming that all other pilot currents are zero, as follows:

$$\frac{I_b}{I_\delta} = \eta_\delta = -\frac{K_{ca}^\delta}{K + K_{ca}^\beta} - \frac{E_{bd}}{n^2} \frac{R_a}{I_\delta} \frac{1}{(K + K_{bd}^\alpha)(K + K_{ca}^\beta)} \tag{117b}$$

Compared with Equation 114, the amplification ratio (Equation 117b) has a smaller absolute value for the same value of $K + K_{ca}^\beta$. Further, whereas Equation 114 is constant, Equation 117b is a function of secondary electromotive force E_{bd} and pilot current I_δ.

When $K + K_{ca}^\beta$ tends toward zero, the absolute value of the two terms of Equation 117b increases towards infinity; I_δ and E_{bd} are of opposite signs. In order to obtain the limiting value of Equation 117b when $K_{ca}^\beta + K$ tends toward zero, go back again to Equations 117a, set $K + K_{ca}^\beta = 0$, and obtain

$$\lim \eta_\delta = -\frac{n^2(K + K_{bd}^\alpha)}{R_a R_b} K_{ca}^\delta \tag{117c}$$

where R_b is the resistance of the total secondary circuit: $E_{bd} = R_b I_b$. This limit has a constant, finite value.

The S generator metadyne operates as a power amplifier simultaneously modifying current and voltage. Consideration has already been given to the current amplification ratio η. Now consider the voltage amplification ratio ρ, defined as the ratio of the secondary voltage E_{bd} to the voltage V_δ impressed on the pilot variator winding of index δ where $V_\delta = I_\delta R_\delta$, R_δ being the resistance of this variator winding.

$$\frac{E_{bd}}{V_\delta} = \rho_\delta = - \frac{n^2(K + K_{bd}^\alpha)}{R_a}\left[\frac{K_{ca}^\delta}{R_\delta} + \frac{K + K_{ca}^\beta}{V_\delta}I_b\right] \qquad (117d)$$

The voltage amplification ratio is thus a function of the secondary current I_b. It becomes a constant when $K + K_{ca}^\beta = 0$, and it is then

$$\lim \rho_\delta = - \frac{n^2(K + K_{bd}^\alpha)K_{ca}^\delta}{R_a R_\delta} \qquad (117e)$$

The power amplification ratio σ is the product of the current amplification ratio and the voltage amplification ratio when the latter two ratios are constants:

$$\sigma = \eta\rho$$

Thus, for $K + K_{ca}^\beta = 0$, the constant limit value is

$$\lim \sigma_\delta = \frac{n^4(K + K_{bd}^\alpha)^2}{R_a^2 R R_b}(K_{ca}^\delta)^2 \qquad (117f)$$

This value points out the importance of using a high rotational speed n.

This consideration of the variation of the amplification ratios while K_{ca}^β is given values increasing in magnitude from 0 to $-K$ makes apparent the gradual change of the S generator metadyne from a reactive metadyne to a nonreactive one. It has been pointed out many times that the reactive metadynes generally possess the ability to force the current supplied by the metadyne to its consumer to reach a desired value very rapidly by temporarily impressing on the consumer an electromotive force much higher than that necessary for steady-state operation. This forcing action of the reactive metadyne is the main reason for its quick response. However, the forcing action vanishes for $K_{ca}^\beta = -K$, the metadyne then being partially nonreactive.

Shunt-connected stator windings have been avoided in order to obtain values of amplification ratio derived from the equations of static operation, which would then hold approximately even for operation with rapidly varying pilot currents. Figures 194(a) and 194(b) show two further stator arrangements of the S generator metadyne comprising only series-connected stator windings.

Consider the arrangement of Fig. 194(a). It comprises three secondary variator windings, 4, 6, 7, for three pilot currents; a secondary compensator winding, 5; and a winding, 17, having its magnetic axis coincident with the secondary commutating axis and carrying primary current I_a. The fundamental equations are

$$-\frac{1}{n} R_a I_a = \frac{1}{n} E_{ca} = (K + K_{ca}^{\beta}) I_b + K_{ca}^{\alpha} I_a + \sum_{\delta=\gamma}^{\varepsilon} K_{ca}^{\delta} I_\delta$$

(117g)

$$\frac{1}{n} E_{bd} = K I_a = \frac{1}{n} R_b I_b$$

From these equations one may derive the current amplification ratio as follows:

$$\eta_\delta \equiv \frac{I_b}{I_\delta} = -\frac{K_{ca}^{\delta}}{K + K_{ca}^{\beta}} - \frac{E_{bd}}{I_\delta} \frac{R_a + n K_{ca}^{\alpha}}{n^2 K (K + K_{ca}^{\beta})}$$

(117h)

which may be compared to the value of formula 117b; and similar comments apply.

If

$$R_a + n K_{ca}^{\alpha} = 0$$

(117i)

the current amplification ratio is a constant, independent of the secondary voltage E_{bd}, and its value may be made equal to any predetermined value when $K + K_{ca}^{\beta}$ approaches zero; on the other hand, the stability of operation is impaired.

From the same equations, the voltage amplification ratio is obtained as follows:

$$\rho_\delta = \frac{E_{bd}}{V_\delta} = -\frac{n^2 K}{R_a + n K_c^{\alpha}} \left[\frac{K_{ca}^{\delta}}{R_\delta} + \frac{K + K_{ca}^{\beta}}{V_\delta} I_b \right]$$

(117j)

This equation may be compared to Equation 117d. It gives, for $K + K_{ca}^{\beta} = 0$,

$$\rho_\delta = -\frac{n^2 K K_{ca}^{\delta}}{R_\delta (R_a + n K_{ca}^{\alpha})}$$

(117k)

The coefficient K_{ca}^{α} may be given a positive or a negative value. Positive values increase stability; negative values increase the amplification ratios to any desired value but decrease stability.

The fundamental equations corresponding to the arrangement of Fig. 194(b) are

$$\frac{1}{n} E_{ca} = -\frac{1}{n} R_a I_a = (K + K_{ca}^{\beta}) I_b + \sum_{\delta=\gamma}^{\varepsilon} K_{ca}^{\delta} I_\delta$$

(117l)

$$\frac{1}{n} E_{bd} = K I_a + K_{bd}^{\beta} I_b = \frac{1}{n} R_b I_b$$

from which is derived

$$\eta_\delta = \frac{-1}{K + K_{ca}^\beta - (R_a K_{bd}^\beta / nK)} \left[K_{ca}^\delta + \frac{E_{bd}}{I_\delta} \frac{R_a}{n^2 K} \right]$$

(117m)

$$\rho_\delta = -\frac{n^2 K K_{ca}^\delta}{R_a R_\delta} - \frac{I_b}{V_\delta} \frac{n^2 K}{R_a} \left[K + K_{ca}^\beta - \frac{K_{bd}^\beta R_a}{nK} \right]$$

These formulas may be compared to the similar ones commented upon previously. In formulas $117m$ the quantity $K + K_{ca}^\beta - (R_a K_{bd}^\beta / nK)$,

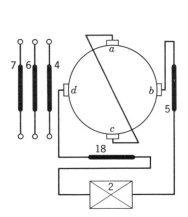

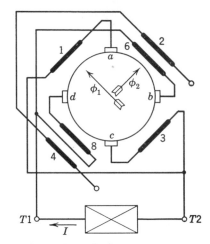

Fig. 194(b). Both series windings carry the secondary current.

Fig. 194(c). The B generator metadyne.

having the dimensions of self-induction, may approach zero without requiring complete compensation of the secondary armature ampere-turns, in other words allowing the metadyne to keep its forcing capacity.

Now consider formulas 114, 114c, 117, and 117k. The corresponding arrangements are those of Figs. 190, 191, 192, and 194(a). These formulas show that the value of the corresponding current or voltage amplification ratio may take any predetermined value, no matter how high. But this implies that a shunt stator winding of the arrangements of Figs. 190, 191, and 192 satisfy the condition of astaticity or that in the arrangement of Fig. 194(a) the resistance of the primary circuit is set to its critical value at the operating speed. Either of these implications involves instability of operation for all arrangements mentioned except for the arrangement of Fig. 192, which remains stable.

The amplifier metadyne may be considered as a current to voltage transducer, in other words, as an apparatus transforming a given current into a predetermined voltage, the amplification factor being no longer nondimensional but having the dimensions of a resistance. The action of the amplifier metadyne may thus be represented by a very low negative resistance, which may be referred to as the resistance amplification factor, R_ϕ.

Similarly, the amplifier metadyne may be considered as a voltage to current transducer, in other words, as an apparatus transforming a given voltage into a predetermined current, the amplification factor having the dimensions of a conductance which may be referred to as the amplification conductance factor: $1/R_\phi$.

In both cases the analysis may be made along the same lines as shown in the preceding sections.

4. THE B GENERATOR METADYNE OPERATING AS AN AMPLIFIER METADYNE

Next, consider the metadyne class indicated by o in Fig. 36; obviously this letter refers to a generator metadyne or to a motor metadyne. Let the four brushes be equidistant and the pitch of the armature winding be 90 electrical degrees. The B generator metadyne thus obtained is represented by Fig. 194(c).

As a result of the half-diametrical pitch, the flux ϕ_1, created by a canonical current I_{ac} flowing through the armature, is located at 45 electrical degrees from the electrical diameter ac, the locus of the external commutating axis of brushes a and c. Similarly, a canonical current I_{bd} flowing through the armature creates a flux ϕ_2 displaced 90 electrical degrees with respect to the flux ϕ_1.

The stator windings used are a secondary variator winding comprising two identical coils, 4 and 2, for the arbitrary pilot current I_γ, a secondary compensating winding comprising two identical coils 6 and 8, and two identical primary coils 1 and 3 carrying the canonical current I_{ac}.

The output current I is related to the brush currents as follows:

$$I = -I_a - I_c = I_b + I_d \qquad (117n)$$

To establish the fundamental equations, select the following system of canonical currents:

$$I_{ac}, I_{bd}, I_{ba} = I_{dc}$$

In order to prove that this system is a system equivalent to the brush currents of the metadyne, examine the correlated equations

$$I_a = I_{ac} - I_{ba}$$

$$I_b = I_{bd} + I_{ba} \hspace{4cm} (117o)$$

$$I_c = -I_{ac} - I_{dc} = -I_{ac} - I_{ba}$$

$$I_d = -I_{bd} + I_{dc} = -I_{bd} + I_{ba}$$

Since only three of these equations are independent, choose the first three for consideration. The determinant of the coefficients is equal to -2. Therefore, the system selected is an equivalent one, and the values of the canonical currents are obtained as follows:

$$I_{ac} = \tfrac{1}{2}(I_a - I_c)$$

$$I_{bd} = \tfrac{1}{2}(I_b - I_d)$$

$$I_{ba} = -\tfrac{1}{2}(I_a + I_c)$$

Hence, $2I_{ba} = I$.

Before the equations are written, it is necessary to note that:

The two coils 6 and 8 of the secondary compensating winding have the same number of turns and are connected so that they create a flux opposite to the secondary armature flux when they carry current I_{bd}.

Coils 1 and 3 have the same number of turns, and both of them together, when excited by the canonical current I_{ac}, create either a centrifugal or a centripetal flux.

Coils 2 and 4 have the same number of turns; when excited by the variator current I_γ, one coil creates a centrifugal flux and the other coil a centripetal flux.

Note further that:

The active peripheral conductors of the armature for inducing the electromotive force E_{ca} are only those along segments ab and cd.

The active peripheral conductors for E_{bd} are only those along segments bc and da.

The active conductors for E_{ba} are only those along segment ac, for it should be recalled that segments are counted only in the clockwise direction.

Coils 6 and 8, when excited by the canonical current I_{bd}, are assumed to compensate, either partially or completely, the secondary flux ϕ_2. However, for the sake of generality, these coils may also be considered to be secondary amplifying windings. It is important to notice that, if these coils form a secondary compensating winding, they are stabilizing windings when excited by $I_{ba} = I_{dc} = \frac{1}{2}I$, with respect to the circuit through which I flows. Conversely, the coils will be stimulating windings with respect to the circuit just mentioned, if they form a secondary amplifying winding with respect to the secondary circuit carrying I_{bd}. Similarly, coils 1 and 3, when excited by $I/2$, create a flux that may be in the same direction as ϕ_1, or in the opposite direction, according to the connection chosen.

The analysis developed below will show that when the B generator metadyne acts as an amplifier it yields a higher amplification factor when coils 6 and 8 are connected as a secondary compensating winding. Careful analysis of the dynamic operation will show which connection of the coils 1 and 3 is preferable.

The canonical currents I_{ba} and I_{dc} induce no electromotive force between the brushes when they pass through the armature. When they flow in windings 6 and 8, they induce an electromotive force between any two consecutive brushes, but none between two diametrically opposite brushes. When they flow in windings 1 and 3, they induce an electromotive force between brushes b and d.

Thus the fundamental equations are simplified as follows:

$$-\frac{1}{n}R_a I_{ac} = \frac{1}{n}E_{ca} = K_{ca}^{bd}I_{bd} + K_{ca}^{\beta}I_{bd} + K_{ca}^{\gamma}I_{\gamma}$$

$$\frac{1}{n}R_b I_{bd} = \frac{1}{n}E_{bd} = K_{bd}^{ac}I_{ac} + K_{bd}^{\alpha}I_{ba} \tag{117p}$$

$$\frac{1}{n}E_{12} = K_{ba}^{\alpha}I_{ac} + K_{ba}^{\beta'}I_{ba} + K_{ba}^{\beta''}I_{ba} = K_{ba}^{\alpha}I_{ac} + K_{ba}^{\beta}I_{ba}$$

where E_{12} is the electromotive force induced in the circuit beginning at $T1$ and ending at $T2$, where K_{ca}^{β} and $K_{ba}^{\beta'}$ refer to windings 6 and 8, where K_{bd}^{α} refers to windings 1 and 3, where K_{ba}^{α} and $K_{ba}^{\beta''}$ refer to windings 1 and 3, and where R_a and R_b are the resistances of the primary and secondary circuits, respectively.

To the relations 117p, the following may be added:

$$E_{12} = R_e I = 2R_e I_{ba} \tag{117q}$$

This equation is valid if the circuit carrying I has a constant resistance, R_e.

The first two Equations 117p may be solved for I_{ac} and I_{bd}. In Fig. 194(c) only one secondary variator winding, 2 and 4, is represented, excited by just one pilot current, I_{γ}, for the sake of simplicity, but many similar secondary variator windings can be used, each carrying an independent pilot current I_γ, I_δ, I_ε. Then the last term of the first equation may be replaced by the familiar symbol $\sum\limits_{\delta=\gamma}^{\varepsilon} K_{ca}^\delta I_\delta$. Upon substitution in the third equation, the following formula is obtained:

$$E_{12} = \frac{-n^2 K_{ba}^\alpha R_b}{D_1} \sum_\delta K_{ca}^\delta I_\delta + \frac{D_1 n K_{ba}^\beta - n^3 K_{bd}^\alpha K_{ba}^\alpha (K_{ca}^{bd} + K_{ca}^\beta)}{2D_1} I \quad (117r)$$

where $D_1 = R_a R_b + n^2 K_{bd}^{ac}(K_{ca}^{bd} + K_{ca}^\beta)$.

By solving system 117p for $I_{ba} = \frac{1}{2}I$, one obtains the output current I:

$$I = \frac{2n^2 R_b K_{ba}^\alpha}{D_2} \sum_\delta K_{ca}^\delta I_\delta + 2\frac{R_a R_b + n^2 K_{bd}^\alpha (K_{ca}^{bd} + K_{ca}^\beta)}{D_2} E_{12} \quad (117s)$$

where $D_2 = n R_a R_b K_{ba}^\beta + n^3 (K_{ca}^{bd} + K_{ca}^\beta)(K_{bd}^{ac} K_{ba}^\beta - K_{bd}^\alpha K_{ba}^\alpha)$.

Formulas 117r and 117s may easily be discussed in the same manner as was done for the S generator metadyne.

If the resistance R_e of the circuit in which I flows is constant, the last formulas, combined with Equation 117q, give

$$E_{12} = \frac{-2n^2 K_{ba}^\alpha R_b R_e}{D_1(2R_e - nK_{ba}^\beta) - n^3 K_{bd}^\alpha K_{ba}^\alpha (K_{ca}^{bd} + K_{ca}^\beta)} \sum_\delta K_{ca}^\delta I_\delta$$

$$(117t)$$

$$I = \frac{2n^2 R_b K_{ba}^\alpha}{\left\{ \begin{array}{l} n^2[K_{ca}^{bd} + K_{ca}^\beta][K_{bd}^{ac}(nK_{ba}^\beta - 2R_e) - nK_{bd}^\alpha K_{ba}^\alpha] \\ \quad + R_a R_b(nK_{ba}^\beta - 2R_e) \end{array} \right\}} \sum_\delta K_{ca}^\delta I_\delta$$

Differentiating both members of Equations 117r, 117s, and 117t gives the corresponding voltage and current amplification factors. All these formulas simplify if $K_{ca}^{bd} + K_{ca}^\beta = 0$, i.e., if the secondary compensation is complete. The corresponding amplification factors then have the following high values:

$$\frac{\partial E_{12}}{\partial V_\gamma} = \rho_\gamma = \frac{2n^2 R_e K_{ba}^\alpha K_{ca}^\gamma}{R_a R_\gamma (nK_{ba}^\beta - 2R_e)}$$

$$(117u)$$

$$\frac{\partial I}{\partial I_\gamma} = \eta_\gamma = \frac{2n^2 K_{ba}^\alpha K_{ca}^\gamma}{R_a (nK_{ba}^\beta - 2R_e)}$$

One may easily compare these values with the corresponding values obtained for the S generator metadyne. Other stator windings than those indicated in Fig. 194(c) may be considered and discussed as in the case of the S generator metadyne used as an amplifier.

Although the analysis outlined above must be completed with the investigation of operation under transient voltages and currents, it is apparent that many forms of metadynes may be used as rotating amplifiers with extremely flexible operation.

5. THE D GENERATOR METADYNE

This machine was constructed for supplying electric power to two distinct consumers independently of one another, the supplied power having the characteristic appropriate for a metadyne generator. The essential parts of the scheme are indicated by Fig. 195. The D generator metadyne has four equidistant brushes per cycle: the nonconsecutive brushes a and c are connected to consumer 3; and the other two brushes, b and d, are connected to consumer 2. The stator has four windings:

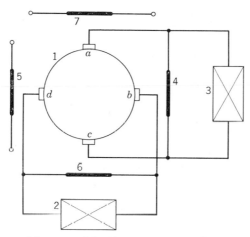

Fig. 195.   The D generator metadyne.

windings 4 and 5 have their magnetic axis along the commutating axis of the brushes b and d; winding 4 is shunt-connected across the brushes a and c, and winding 5 is excited by an independent current I_β. Windings 6 and 7 have their magnetic axis along the commutating axis of the brushes a and c; winding 6 is shunt-connected across the brushes b and d, and winding 7 is excited by an independent current I_α.

Write the fundamental equations:

$$\frac{1}{n} E_{ca} = K I_b + K_{ca}^\beta I_\beta + K_{ca}^\delta \frac{E_{ca}}{R_2}$$

$$\frac{1}{n} E_{bd} = K I_a + K_{bd}^\alpha I_\alpha + K_{bd}^\gamma \frac{E_{bd}}{R_1}$$

(118)

where R_1 and R_2 are the total resistances of the shunt windings. These resistances satisfy the relations

$$R_2 = nK_{ca}^{\delta}$$

$$R_1 = nK_{bd}^{\gamma} \tag{119}$$

Therefore,

$$I_b = -\frac{K_{ca}^{\beta}}{K} I_{\beta}$$

$$I_a = -\frac{K_{bd}^{\alpha}}{K} I_{\alpha} \tag{120}$$

The currents I_{α} and I_{β} control the two armature currents I_a and I_b independently of one another and independently of the brush voltages.

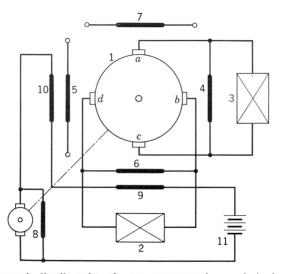

Fig. 196.   Power is distributed to the two consumers in any desired relationship.

This independence holds for the steady-state values of the armature currents.   During rapid transients, the instantaneous value of these armature currents may be resolved into two parts: the steady-state value, say I_{as} and I_{bs}, which may be briefly called the "static component"; and the remaining part, say I_{ay} and I_{by}, which may be called the "dynamic component."

$$I_a = I_{as} + I_{ay}$$

$$I_b = I_{bs} + I_{by} \tag{121}$$

The dynamic components occur only temporarily and vanish when the voltage or current variations are relatively slow.   They are responsible for the stability of operation, characteristic of the metadyne during rapid transients.

It is often desired to utilize the full torque of the prime mover and to keep the speed, n, constant; this is always desired when the prime mover is a Diesel engine. In this event the scheme of Fig. 196 or of Fig. 197 is often used.

The scheme of Fig. 196 is applied when the whole power supplied by the prime mover is to be distributed to both consumers according to an arbitrarily determined law. A shunt-excited regulator dynamo, 8, is mechanically coupled to the shaft of the metadyne, and the regulator current, I_ρ, flows through two regulator windings, a winding 9, having its magnetic axis along the commutating axis of brushes a and c, and a winding 10, having its magnetic axis along the commutating axis of brushes b and d.

The fundamental equations are

$$\frac{1}{n} E_{ca} = KI_b + K^\beta_{ca}I_\beta + K^\delta_{ca}\frac{E_{ca}}{R_2} + K^\rho_{ca}I_\rho$$

$$\frac{1}{n} E_{bd} = KI_a + K^\alpha_{bd}I_\alpha + K^\gamma_{bd}\frac{E_{bd}}{R_1} + K^\rho_{bd}I_\rho$$

(122)

Let the resistances R_1 and R_2 satisfy relations 119. Then

$$I_b = -\frac{K^\beta_{ca}}{K} I_\beta - \frac{K^\rho_{ca}}{K} I_\rho$$

$$I_a = -\frac{K^\alpha_{bd}}{K} I_\alpha - \frac{K^\rho_{bd}}{K} I_\rho$$

(123)

In order to have the currents I_a and I_b proportional to one another in the ratio η, the currents I_α and I_β are chosen so as to satisfy the equation

$$\eta = \frac{K^\rho_{bd}}{K^\rho_{ca}} + \frac{K^\alpha_{bd} I_\alpha}{K^\beta_{ca} I_\beta}$$

In particular, currents I_α and I_β may be made zero, and the number of turns of regulator windings 10 and 9 are chosen with a ratio η. In this way

$$\frac{I_a}{I_b} = \frac{K^\rho_{bd}}{K^\rho_{ca}} = \eta$$

It may happen that one of the consumers, say consumer 2, must operate with a current rigidly predetermined, and that it is desired that the other consumer absorb the remaining power until the prime mover is fully loaded at the speed _n_. Then the scheme of Fig. 197 is chosen,

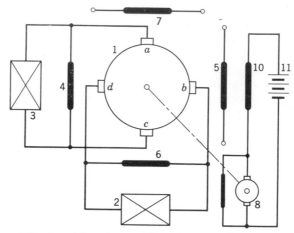

Fig. 197. A modification of the scheme of Fig. 196 to permit one consumer to operate at a fixed current value.

with only one regulator winding, 10, having its magnetic axis along the commutating axis of brushes _b_ and _d_, which supply consumer 2.

6. THE BETA MOTOR METADYNE

Dynamos that are coupled mechanically and are operating in parallel easily give a current distribution very different from the desired one.

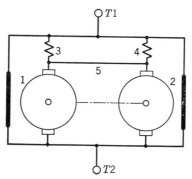

Fig. 198. Connections for two shunt dynamos operating in parallel.

Consider, for instance, the two similar shunt-excited dynamos 1 and 2 of Fig. 198, mechanically coupled together. Even with the very slight differences in their construction, within the limits of factory tolerances, the currents easily show a ratio ranging from 1 to 5.

In order to reduce such a large difference between the currents, a heavy copper conductor 5 is used to connect the homonymous brushes in parallel and leave the coils of the commutating poles outside the circuits of the armature. The etiology lies in the dynamic behavior of this equipment.

Even so, the currents may have a ratio ranging from 1 to 2. In fact, let V be the voltage between bar 5 and terminal $T2$, let R_1 and R_2 be the armature resistances, let I_1 and I_2 be the armature currents, and let $K_{(1)}(V/R_3)$ and $K_{(2)}(V/R_4)$ be the volts per revolution induced by the shunt windings. Then

$$R_1 I_1 = V - K_{(1)} \frac{V}{R_3} n$$

$$R_2 I_2 = V - K_{(2)} \frac{V}{R_4} n$$

(124)

The first member of these equations is about 1/100 of each term of the second member. Unavoidable differences in construction result in

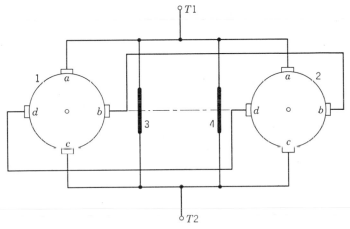

Fig. 199. Two Beta motor metadynes in parallel.

differences in the second term of the second member of the order of several per cent; the air gap depth, for instance, may have differences of 5% to 10% even with accurate construction; temperature may also cause 1% to 2% difference in the field-winding resistance. Therefore, in spite of the moderating effect of the local armature reaction on saturated pole segments, one of the armature currents may be two times larger than the other. For a better balance, a frequent setting of resistances R_3 and R_4 is needed.

By an appropriate choice of stator windings, the Beta motor metadyne may be made to have any of the current-voltage characteristics suitable for a dynamo, yet it operates in parallel satisfactorily, permitting any desired distribution of the currents. Figure 199 shows the scheme of two Beta motor metadynes connected in parallel and coupled mechanically. They have four equidistant brushes. All homonymous brushes are connected in parallel, and the nonconsecutive brushes a and c are connected to terminals $T1$ and $T2$ of the set. Each metadyne is provided with a stator winding that has its magnetic axis along the commutating axis of brushes b and d and is shunt-connected across brushes a and c.

Now write the fundamental equations of the two metadynes:

$$\frac{1}{n}(V - R_{a1}I_{a1}) = \frac{1}{n}E_{ca1} = K_1 I_{b1} + K_{ca1}^\alpha \frac{V}{R_3}$$

$$\frac{1}{n}E_{bd1} = K_1 I_{a1} \tag{125}$$

for the Beta motor metadyne 1; and

$$\frac{1}{n}(V - R_{a2}I_{a2}) = \frac{1}{n}E_{ca2} = K_2 I_{b2} + K_{ca2}^\alpha \frac{V}{R_4}$$

$$\frac{1}{n}E_{bd2} = K_2 I_{a2} \tag{126}$$

for the Beta motor metadyne 2.

Notice that

$$I_{b1} = -I_{b2}$$

$$I_{d1} = -I_{d2}$$

Admit that

$$I_{b1} = -I_{d1}$$

$$I_{b2} = -I_{d2} \tag{127}$$

and call R_b the total resistance of the circuit going from brush $b1$ to brush $d1$, then from brush $d2$ to brush $b2$, and closing at brush $b1$.

From the two second equations of systems 125 and 126 is obtained

$$E_{bd1} - E_{bd2} = R_b I_{b1} = n(K_1 I_{a1} - K_2 I_{a2}) \tag{128}$$

The term $R_b I_{b1}$ is very small compared with the term $nK_1 I_{a1}$ or with $nK_2 I_{a2}$; their average ratio is about $1/500$. Therefore, Equation 128 may be simplified as follows:

$$K_1 I_{a1} = K_2 I_{a2} \tag{128a}$$

K_1 and K_2 may differ by 1% to 5%, and therefore I_{a1} and I_{a2} will differ only by the same amount; hence, they may be considered practically equal.

In view of the relation $I_{b1} = -I_{b2}$, one obtains from the first equations of the systems 125 and 126

$$R_{a1}I_{a1} = V - nK_1I_{b1} - n\frac{K_{ca1}^\alpha}{R_3}V$$

$$\text{(129)}$$

$$R_{a2}I_{a2} = V + nK_2I_{b1} - n\frac{K_{ca2}^\alpha}{R_4}V$$

These equations show how the corrective terms $-nK_1I_{b1}$ and $+nK_2I_{b1}$ act to render the very small terms $R_{a1}I_{a1}$ and $R_{a2}I_{a2}$ very nearly equal

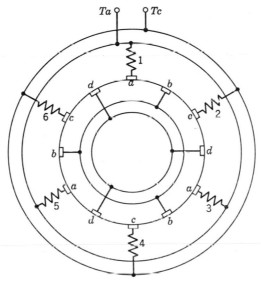

Fig. 200.   A three-cycle Beta motor metadyne.

in spite of a possible discrepancy in the large terms $n(K_{ca1}^\alpha/R_3)V$ and $n(K_{ca2}^\alpha/R_4)V$ of, say, 10% from one another.   With the Beta motor metadynes the construction may be much less accurate without harm.

Now consider a Beta motor metadyne having more than one cycle, say three cycles, as shown by Fig. 200.   The machine may be synthesized with an assembly of three elementary Beta motor metadynes connected in parallel and rotating at the same speed.   Then the same arguments may be applied that were developed for the scheme of Fig. 199, and it may be deduced that the currents in brushes a, a, a and c, c, c are practically equal in spite of unavoidable imperfections in the construction.   The corrective action of the currents of brushes b, b, b and d, d, d is so effective that the current of each brush a, a, a or c, c, c may be allowed to flow in the coil of the corresponding commutating pole as Fig. 200 shows, the coils being indicated by the numerals 1, 2, 3, 4, 5, and 6.

In the scheme of Fig. 201, to the two Beta motor metadynes coupled mechanically and electrically in parallel, a primary variator winding, 5, has been added for metadyne 1 and a similar winding, 6, for metadyne 2. Let $I_{\alpha 1}$ and $I_{\alpha 2}$ be the currents flowing in these windings.

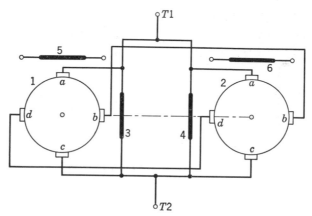

Fig. 201.   Current division may be controlled with the primary variator windings.

Instead of Equation 128a, there is now the following one:

$$K_1 I_{a1} + K_{bd1}^{\alpha} I_{\alpha 1} = K_2 I_{a2} + K_{bd2}^{\alpha} I_{\alpha 2} \qquad (130)$$

This equation shows that the ratio of currents I_{a1} and I_{a2} may be controlled by controlling the independent currents, $I_{\alpha 1}$ and $I_{\alpha 2}$, of the primary variator windings (or even only one of them).

In general, the resisting torque on the shaft is definite in value, very often a function of the speed n; therefore, the sum of the currents I_{a1} and I_{a2} is determined. In fact, the relation must then be

$$V(I_{a1} + I_{a2}) = 2\pi n T \qquad (131)$$

where T is the resisting torque, the losses being neglected. Equation 131 is obviously valid for the previously examined cases as well.

The system of Equations 129 remains unaltered, and it must be interpreted with comments similar to those given above: The corrective current I_{b1} allows currents I_{a1} and I_{a2} to remain substantially at the values determined by Equations 130 and 131 even if the third term of the second members of Equations 129 differ from one another by several per cent.

If it is desired to have the ratio I_{a1}/I_{a2} remain constant throughout the operating period, currents I_{a1} and I_{a2} are made to be the brush currents I_{a1} and I_{a2}, respectively; stator windings 5 and 6 then become series windings. Equation 130 is in this case modified as follows:

$$\frac{I_{a1}}{I_{a2}} = \frac{K_2 + K_{bd2}^{\alpha}}{K_1 + K_{bd1}^{\alpha}} \tag{132}$$

With the proper sense and number of turns of the two series windings, any desired value of the ratio of the brush currents may be obtained and kept constant whatever the load may be.

7. THE K TRANSFORMER OR GENERATOR METADYNE

The great majority of metadynes considered so far are reactive metadynes; the machine described in this section is a nonreactive metadyne.

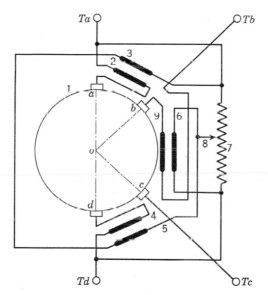

Fig. 202.   The K metadyne.

The K transformer metadyne schematically shown by Fig. 202 has four brushes per cycle, say a, b, c, d. Two of the brushes, a and d, are diametrically opposite, and the other two, b and c, are located symmetrically with respect to the same diameter to which brushes a and d are symmetrically located. Terminals Ta and Td corresponding to brushes a and d are assumed to be connected to one electrical source or consumer; terminals Tb and Tc are assumed to be connected to a second source or consumer. Thus there are only two distinct canonical currents, current $I_a = -I_d$ and current $I_b = -I_c$.

Since $K_{ad}^b = K_{bc}^a = 0$, the armature currents do not react upon one another. The stator has six different windings: windings 2 and 3, with their magnetic axis along the bisectrix of the radii oa and ob to brushes a and b, and interlinked with the pole pieces covering segment ab (and its symmetric one with respect to the center, as usual); windings 6 and 9, with their magnetic axis along the diameter of symmetry, and interlinked with the pole pieces having the same diameter of symmetry as their geometrical axis; and, finally, windings 4 and 5, with their magnetic axis along the bisectrix of the radii oc and od to brushes c and d, and interlinked with the pole pieces comprised between the same radii.

The shunt windings 3 and 5 are connected in series between terminal Ta and the sliding contact member 8 of rheostat 7. Winding 6 is shunt-connected across contact member 8 and terminal Td. The series windings 2 and 4 are excited by current I_a. The series winding 9 is excited by current I_b.

The fundamental equations are

$$\frac{1}{n}(V_1 - 2R_{ab}I_a - R_{bc}I_b) = \frac{1}{n}E_{da}$$

$$= 2K_{ba}^\alpha I_a + K_{cb}^\beta I_b + 2K_{ba}^\gamma I_\gamma + K_{cb}^\delta I_\delta \quad (133)$$

$$\frac{1}{n}(V_2 - R_{bc}I_b) = \frac{1}{n}E_{cb} = K_{cb}^\beta I_b + K_{cb}^\delta I_\delta$$

where V_1 and V_2 are the voltages between terminals Td and Ta and terminals Tc and Tb, respectively. If the adjustments

$$\frac{1}{n}R_{ab}I_a = K_{ba}^\alpha I_a$$

$$\frac{1}{n}R_{bc}I_b = K_{cb}^\beta I_b$$

$$(134)$$

are made, the equations are then simplified as follows:

$$\frac{1}{n}V_1 = 2K_{ba}^\gamma I_\gamma + K_{cb}^\delta I_\delta$$

$$\frac{1}{n}V_2 = K_{cb}^\delta I_\delta$$

$$(135)$$

These equations show that brush currents I_a and I_b have no interaction either with one another or with the brush voltages; the metadyne is completely nonreactive. Currents I_a and I_b may have any value, whereas voltages V_1 and V_2 remain constant.

Suppose that terminals Ta and Td are connected to a source of constant voltage, while terminals Tb and Tc are connected to a consumer. Further, assume that the currents I_γ and I_δ are varied by moving con-

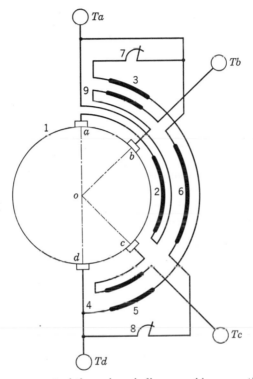

Fig. 203. The arrangement of the series windings provides a reactive K metadyne.

tact member 8 along rheostat 7, which operates as a potentiometer, so that the second member of the first equation of the system remains constant. The metadyne will then run at constant speed and will operate as a transformer, transforming power at the constant voltage V_1 into power at a variable voltage V_2.

If it is required that voltage V_2 vary from 0 to V_1, the angular distance between radii oa and ob and between radii oc and od must be taken equal to 45° to obtain the highest efficiency. The copper losses in the armature then become minimum.

If the K metadyne is instead driven by a motor at a constant speed n, with terminals Ta and Td now connected to one consumer and with the terminals Tb and Tc connected to a second consumer, and if stator currents I_γ and I_δ vary in such a way as to keep the second member of the first equation of system 135 constant, the machine will operate as a double generator supplying the first consumer with any current at constant voltage V_1, and the second consumer with any current at variable voltage V_2.

Figure 203 gives the scheme of a K motor metadyne with the same arrangement of the brushes, external connections, and shunt stator windings but with a different arrangement of the series stator windings. Stator windings 9 and 4 interlinked with the pole pieces comprised between the radii oa and ob and oc and od, respectively, are excited by current I_b; stator winding 2, interlinked with the polar segment comprised between the radii ob and oc, is excited by current I_a. By this arrangement of the series stator windings, the K metadyne becomes a reactive one. The machine may operate either as a transformer or as a generator.

The currents in the shunt stator windings are controlled by two separate rheostats, 7 and 8. These two rheostats may be operated by a single handle, and the resistance between segments may be so arranged as to obtain any desired law of variation of currents I_α and I_β.

8. THE A GENERATOR METADYNE

In the previous section an otherwise nonreactive metadyne is described, which becomes a reactive one by means of a special arrangement of its stator windings. In this section an otherwise reactive metadyne is described which becomes nonreactive through its special stator windings.

The metadyne shown by Fig. 203(a) is provided with four equidistant brushes and with four stator windings, 1, 2, 3, 4. Windings 1 and 2 are fully compensating windings; 3 is a shunt-connected variator winding, and 4 is an independently excited variator winding.

Fig. 203(a). The fully compensating windings make this metadyne nonreactive.

The voltage and the current corresponding to terminals $T1$, $T2$ are completely independent of the voltage and the current corresponding to terminals $T3$, $T4$. Thus this metadyne may operate as two generators, one shunt-excited and the other independently excited. It may operate as a motor generator; for instance, as a constant-speed motor with its terminals $T1$, $T2$ connected to a constant-voltage line and as a variable-voltage generator inducing a variable voltage at its terminals $T3$, $T4$, controlled by the ampere-turns of variator winding 4.

The arrangement given by Fig. 203(a) is illustrative of the possibilities of such a metadyne, which may be referred to as the A generator metadyne. Many other arrangements of its stator windings may be selected to adapt this metadyne to special purposes.

18 · Some Applications of the Metadynes Already Described

1. ALTERNATOR VOLTAGE CONTROL

The control of the voltage of alternators is generally obtained by a voltage regulator, substantially a relay very sensitive to voltage, acting upon the field excitation of the exciter dynamo supplying current to the field of the alternator. For satisfactory operation of a voltage regulator the electric circuit directly controlled by it must absorb as little power and store as little electromagnetic energy as possible.

The substitution of an amplifier metadyne for the exciter dynamo substantially improves the voltage control. The main reasons for this result are the following:

(a) The circuit directly controlled by the voltage regulator is a secondary variator winding which absorbs, say, five times less power and stores, say, twenty times less electromagnetic energy than the field winding of the corresponding dynamo.

(b) For a given voltage variation, say $k/100$, in percentage of the normal voltage, created by the voltage regulator, the transient voltage variation impressed on the field of the large generator, expressed also in percentage of the normal voltage, is perhaps ten times to a hundred times larger ($10k/100$ to $100k/100$), whereas with the corresponding dynamo it would be only $k/100$. The metadyne is assumed to be a reactive type. In some cases a nonreactive metadyne may be chosen and property (b) renounced.

Figure 204 gives the simplified schematic of an alternator, 7, excited from an amplifier metadyne, 1. The voltage regulator indicated in the figure consists essentially of a magnetic core, 3, interlinked with a coil connected across two wires of the main line and of a movable armature, 4, acted upon by a spring opening and closing the contact, 5, by which a resistor, in series with variator winding 2, is short-circuited. Any other voltage regulator may be used, such as a static magnetic regulator.

Only the secondary variator winding, 2, carrying the pilot current is indicated in the figure, for the sake of simplicity. The amplifier metadyne, 1, indicated is derived from an S generator metadyne, but one may employ any other form of amplifier metadyne.

For very large alternators, two and sometimes three exciter dynamos are used in cascade. The arrangement of many exciter dynamos in cascade is adopted only when the voltage regulator is unable to control directly the field excitation of the largest exciter dynamo. Such an arrangement involves a very large time lag between the voltage variation created by the voltage regulator and the voltage variation imposed on the inductor of the alternator.

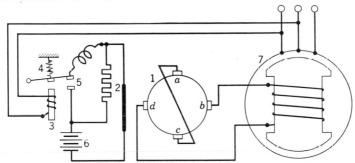

Fig. 204. Excitation for an alternator may be supplied from an amplifier metadyne.

Figure 205 gives the scheme of an amplifier metadyne, 1, in cascade with an exciter dynamo, 10. The voltage regulator is indicated by 8; metadyne 1 supplies its current to the field winding, 9, of dynamo 10.

A further arrangement is indicated by the scheme of Fig. 206, where the amplifier metadyne, 1, is shown supplying current to the secondary

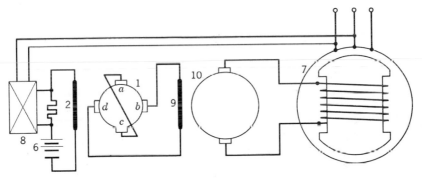

Fig. 205. For large alternators, additional amplification may be inserted with a dynamo.

variator winding, 9, of the amplifier metadyne, 11, which in its turn supplies current to the field of the alternator.

The time lag between the voltage variation created by the voltage regulator, 8, and the voltage variation impressed on the exciting field of the alternator, 7, is, say, twenty to one hundred times shorter than the time lag corresponding to the arrangement of two exciter dynamos

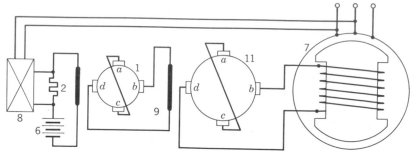

Fig. 206. A cascade of metadyne exciters has a much shorter time lag than a cascade of dynamos.

Fig. 207. This amplifier metadyne is the exciter for a water-driven alternator. (*Courtesy of Brown, Boveri and Co., Ltd., Milan.*)

in cascade. The voltage variation created by the voltage regulator is conveyed to the exciting field of the alternator as a voltage variation, say, one hundred times larger than the voltage variation conveyed with the arrangement of two exciter dynamos in cascade. The amplification ratio between the pilot current supplied by the regulator dynamo and the current in the field excitation of the alternator is, say, 1000 times larger than with the arrangement of the two dynamos in cascade. For all these reasons, a single amplifier metadyne may supplant two exciter dynamos arranged in cascade, and two amplifier metadynes may replace three exciter dynamos in cascade.

Fig. 208. The metadyne of Fig. 207 is shown mounted vertically on the shaft extension above the alternator. (*Courtesy of Brown, Boveri and Co., Ltd., Milan.*)

Notice that the amplifier metadynes of Figs. 204, 205, and 206 have been indicated in a simplified way; they are generally constructed with all or with some of the stator windings described in the first and second sections of Chapter 17. Figures 207 and 208 are views of an amplifier metadyne installed in a hydroelectric plant.

Particularly interesting is the combination of electronic tubes controlled by an apparatus, which is sensitive to the selected variable to be controlled, and an amplifier metadyne, the pilot current of which consists of the relatively weak current obtained from the electronic tubes. Such arrangements are used for the regulation not only of the alternator voltage but also of its load and its power factor, or of the reactive power of a transmission line in the case of a synchronous condenser. Similar arrangements are also used for speed regulation.

Servomechanisms of any kind may use metadynes extensively, generally as their amplifying element. Comments on the operation of the amplifier metadynes in servomechanisms and in regulating devices will not be given here, since these applications require a careful study of the dynamic behavior of the metadynes.

2. AN AMPLIFIER METADYNE CONTROLLING THE CURRENT OF LARGE DIRECT-CURRENT GENERATORS

The arrangement schematically represented by Fig. 209 is used for controlling the current of large dynamos by an amplifier metadyne. The amplifier metadyne, 1, is provided with several, say ν, variator windings carrying the pilot currents (two windings are represented in

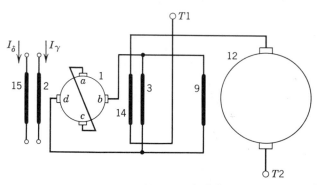

Fig. 209. Circuit arrangement to provide control of the output current of a dynamo through an amplifier metadyne.

the figure, windings 2 and 15). There is another secondary variator winding, 14, which carries the current I of the armature of the large dynamo, 12; in addition, there may be any of the windings indicated in Chapter 17, Sections 1 and 2. The distortion of the amplified current with respect to the pilot current is of little importance for amplifier metadynes controlling the voltage of large generators. On the contrary, when the amplifier metadyne is used for the control of current, the distortion must be reduced as much as possible; in other words, the fidelity of the amplification must now be the best attainable. In order to emphasize this point, Fig. 209 shows secondary variator winding 3 shunt-connected across secondary brushes b and d, according to the scheme developed in the first sections of the previous chapters.

The fundamental equations are

$$\frac{1}{n} R_a I_a = \frac{1}{n} E_{ca} = K I_b + K_{ca}^\alpha I + K_{ca}^\beta \frac{E_{bd}}{R_1} + \sum_{\delta=\gamma}^{\nu+2} K_{ca}^\delta I_\delta$$

(136)

$$\frac{1}{n} E_{bd} = K I_a$$

Resistance R_1 of shunt variator winding 3 is adjusted to satisfy the relation

$$R_1 = K_{ca}^\beta K \frac{n^2}{R_a}$$

(137)

The first of the Equations 136 may then be simplified as follows:

$$0 = K I_b + K_{ca}^\alpha I + \sum_{\delta=\gamma}^{\nu+2} K_{ca}^\delta I_\delta$$

(138)

On the other hand, current I of dynamo 12 is a function of current I_b flowing in its shunt field:

$$I = f(I_b)$$

or

$$I_b = \phi(I)$$

(139)

and therefore Equation 138 may be written

$$\sum_{\delta=\gamma}^{\nu+2} K_{ca}^\delta I_\delta = -K_{ca}^\alpha I - K\phi(I) \equiv F(I)$$

(140)

Current I of dynamo 12 is thus made a function of the pilot currents.

Suppose, for instance, that the two terminals $T1$ and $T2$ of the main dynamo are connected to a consumer having constant resistance; hence,

$$I_b = AI$$

where A is a constant. Equation 140 then gives

$$I = \frac{-1}{K_{ca}^\alpha + KA} \sum_{\delta=\gamma}^{\nu+2} K_{ca}^\delta I_\delta$$

Current I is thus made a linear combination of the pilot currents.

Suppose, further, that the two terminals $T1$ and $T2$ are connected to a motor that develops an electromotive force v. In this case

$$I_b = AI + Bv$$

(141)

where A and B are constants. Then let the pilot current of index $\nu + 2$ be a shunt current derived from the motor that develops the electromotive force v, and adjust the resistance $R_{\nu+2}$ of the variator winding to satisfy the relation

$$R_{\nu+2} = - \frac{K_{ca}^{\nu+2}}{BK}$$

Then from Equation 140 and from the last relation is obtained

$$I = \frac{-1}{K_{ca}^{\alpha} + KA} \sum_{\delta = \gamma}^{\nu+1} K_{ca}^{\delta} I_{\delta}$$

This means that current I has been made a linear combination of the first $\nu + 1$ pilot currents. These two examples show the possibilities of the arrangement represented schematically by Fig. 209.

3. DIESEL ELECTRIC LOCOMOTIVES FOR THE ILLINOIS CENTRAL

When the author considered the problem of the Diesel electric locomotive, he planned to use a metadyne as the main generator; but, when he was asked to proceed with the first unit, the main generator, a dynamo, was already completed. Thus, he suggested the scheme of the amplifier metadyne controlling the current of the main dynamo generator as indicated in the previous section in order to transfer to the main dynamo some of the particular characteristics inherent in the metadyne. Since then, this procedure has been applied in a large number of cases.

Figure 210 gives the simplified scheme of the Diesel electric locomotive. The main dynamo generator, 12, driven by shaft 19 of the Diesel engine, is excited by the field winding 9 connected to the secondary brushes of the amplifier metadyne, 1. Current I, supplied by the main dynamo to traction motors 17 and 18 (only two of them are represented, for the sake of simplicity), flows through secondary variator winding 14 of the amplifier metadyne.

Amplifier metadyne 1 comprises two other secondary variator windings: a winding 2, carrying a pilot current I_{γ} derived from an auxiliary constant-voltage source and controlled by rheostat 20; and a winding 15, carrying a regulator current I_{ρ} which acts as the third pilot current. Regulator current I_{ρ} is supplied by a shunt-excited regulator dynamo, 16, connected to a battery 6. A rheostat 21 is inserted into the circuit of the field excitation, allowing adjustment of the critical speed.

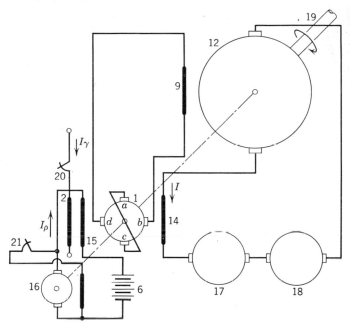

Fig. 210.   Electric drive for a Diesel locomotive equipped with metadyne control.

Write the fundamental equations:

$$-\frac{1}{n}R_a I_a - \frac{1}{n}E_{ca} = KI_b \mid K_{ca}^{\alpha}I \mid K_{ca}^{\gamma}I_{\gamma} \mid K_{ca}^{\rho}I_{\rho}$$

$$\frac{1}{n}E_{bd} = KI_a$$

(142)

The first member of the first equation is very small compared to each term of the second member. Thus

$$0 = KI_b + K_{ca}^{\alpha}I + K_{ca}^{\gamma}I_{\gamma} + K_{ca}^{\rho}I_{\rho} \tag{143}$$

may be written with only negligible error.

Current I_b may be given the form 141, where A and B are positive constants if the dynamo is not saturated, or may be some function of v if saturation of the iron is considered. Hence

$$0 = KAI + KBv + K_{ca}^{\alpha}I + K_{ca}^{\gamma}I_{\gamma} + K_{ca}^{\rho}I_{\rho} \tag{144}$$

If I_b is positive and dynamo 12 is supplying voltage in the proper direction, K_{ca}^{α} will be positive and K_{ca}^{γ} negative. Suppose I_{ρ} positive when $n < n_0$; the coefficient K_{ca}^{ρ} will be positive, so that when $n < n_0$

the regulator current tends to reduce I for a given value of v, and when $n > n_0$ it tends to increase I as Equation 144 shows. The regulator thus tends to keep the speed constant, and it succeeds in accomplishing this with such accuracy that the mechanical regulator remains idle. Thus current I_ρ causes the following relation to be satisfied:

$$IE = C = (RI + v)I \tag{145}$$

where E is the electromotive force induced by the dynamo, R the total resistance of the circuit carrying current I, v the electromotive force in-

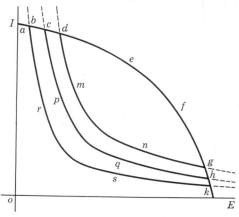

Fig. 211. Current-voltage characteristics of the locomotive generator with metadyne excitation.

duced by the motors, and C a constant equal to the power transmitted by the shaft of the engine for a given constant opening of the throttle in the fuel line, and for the speed n_0.

The independent variable is voltage v developed by the traction motors. For a given value of v and a given value of the parameter I_γ, Equations 145 and 144 determine the value of the regulator current I_ρ.

Now consider in the diagram of Fig. 211 the hyperbola $dmng$ corresponding to a given value of C, say the maximum value, obtained when the throttle of the engine is completely open. Let points d and g correspond to $I_\rho = 0$. For these points the following equation is satisfied:

$$0 = (KA + K_{ca}^\alpha)I + KBv + K_{ca}^\gamma I_\gamma \tag{146}$$

For the point d, the second term of this equation is relatively small. Thus

$$I = -\frac{K_{ca}^\gamma I_\gamma}{KA + K_{ca}^\alpha} + \epsilon_1 \equiv I_m + \epsilon_1 \tag{147}$$

where ϵ_1 is a negligible current with respect to I.

Fig. 212. Metadyne and generator unit for a Diesel locomotive. (*Courtesy of the General Electric Co., Erie, Pa.*)

For point g, the first term of the same equation is relatively small, so that

$$v = \frac{K_{ca}^{\gamma} I_{\gamma}}{KB} + \epsilon_2 \equiv v_m + \epsilon_2 \tag{148}$$

where ϵ_2 is a negligible voltage with respect to v_m.

For points located on the hyperbola and more distant from the origin, the regulator current becomes negative and $n > n_0$. For all points of the segment *dmng* comprised between the two points *d* and *g*, the regulator current remains positive and $n < n_0$.

The author chose values of the constants K appearing in the equations developed above and selected a value of parameter I_γ such as to cause current I_m, given by Equation 147, to be the maximum safe cur-

Fig. 213.   Rear view of the unit shown in Fig. 212.   (*Courtesy of the General Electric Co., Erie, Pa.*)

rent that the traction motors may handle, and to cause voltage v_m, given by Equation 148, to be the maximum safe voltage that the traction motors may develop.   The reversal of the direction of current I_ρ for points located farther from the origin *o* than points *g* and *d* is then utilized for the automatic disconnection of the regulator winding and the gradual closing of the throttle.   The representative point then slides along segments *dcba* and *ghk*.

Segments *dcba* and *ghk* are part of a curve *abcdefghk* that can be constructed with a good approximation by plotting it point by point on the assumptions that $I_\rho = 0$ and that the ohmic drop RI is negligible. From a given value of E as a starting point, one may obtain, by taking into account the magnetic characteristic of dynamo 12, the value of I_b, which defines E_{bd}, and hence I_a. Then I is derived from the first Equation 142, where I_ρ is set equal to zero. This curve, useful for design purposes, is referred to as the "perimetric characteristic."

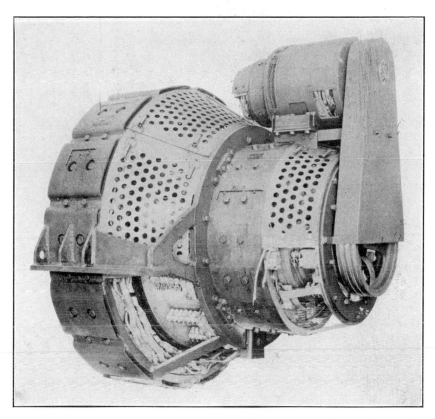

Fig. 214.   Another railway generator unit.   (*Courtesy of the General Electric Co., Erie., Pa.*)

If the opening of the throttle is reduced, the hyperbola of the diagram of Fig. 211 moves towards the origin, and the intersections of the hyperbola with the "perimetric characteristic" define the maximum current and the maximum voltage. If current I_γ is increased, the "perimetric characteristic" moves farther from the origin, and the values of the maximum current and maximum voltage increase.

The operator has at his disposal two rheostats: rheostat 20, with which he determines the maximum values of the current and voltage supplied to the traction motors; and rheostat 21, with which he deter-

Fig. 215. Note that the controller of this locomotive has no detents. (*Courtesy of the General Electric Co., Erie, Pa.*)

mines the critical speed n_0. The departure of the speed n from the critical value is about 1% to 2% when the representative point slides over the whole segment *dmng* of the hyperbola corresponding to the maximum opening of the throttle.

If for some reason the torque of the engine decreases, for instance if a cylinder fails to act, the power supplied to the traction motor decreases accordingly and the hyperbola of Fig. 211 approaches the origin o of the coordinates. Thus, it is impossible to overload the engine. Since the handle of rheostat 21 is usually coupled with the mechanism controlling the opening of the throttle, the value of the critical speed n_0 for each opening of the throttle is chosen to correspond to the highest efficiency of the engine.

Figure 212 shows the main dynamo generator with the regulator dynamo and the amplifier metadyne fixed on top of the dynamo. Figure 213 gives another view. Figure 214 shows another, similar genera-

Fig. 216. An Illinois Central locomotive equipped with metadyne control. (*Courtesy of the General Electric Co., Erie, Pa.*)

tor. Figure 215 shows the single handle that controls simultaneously the opening of the throttle and the critical speed; since there are no detents on the handle, completely continuous control is possible. Figure 216 shows a locomotive equipped with the above-described equipment for the Illinois Central. Figure 217 is an oscillogram made during tests of the equipment. In order to get the best utilization of the main dynamo generator, the same hyperbola of Fig. 211 is passed over three times by the representative point: the first time with the six motors in series; a second time with the motors in series-parallel, three motors in series and two rows in parallel; and a third time with the motors in series-parallel, two motors in series and three rows in parallel.

During the transition from one connection to the other, the switchgear cuts off some circuits and reestablishes others, short-circuiting some of the motors. Because of these abrupt variations of the main circuit, the excitation of the main generator is usually cut off in order to eliminate peaks of current. Thus, the tractive effort is abruptly brought to zero and consecutively reestablished at its full value.

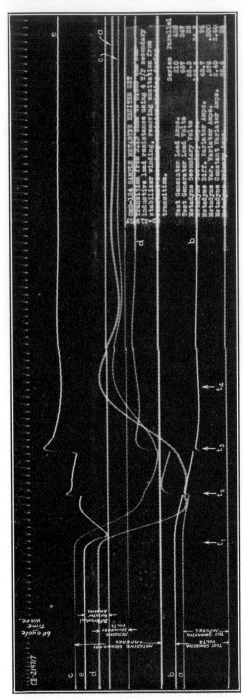

Fig. 217. Oscillogram of the behavior of the metadyne-controlled locomotive equipment.   (Courtesy of the General Electric Co., Erie, Pa.)

With the metadyne equipment, the tests have shown that the dynamic behavior is so satisfactory during transition that there is no reason for interrupting the excitation of the dynamo. The oscillogram of Fig. 217 shows a record of this test. The curve a-a records current I; the curve b-b records voltage E; the curve c-c records current I_b; the curve d-d records voltage E_{bd}, and, finally, the curve e-e records current I_ρ.

The transition begins at time t_1 and ends at time t_4, lasting only $\tfrac{22}{60}$ of a second. At time t_2 one pair of motors is abruptly short-circuited, and at time t_3 another pair of motors is abruptly short-circuited. Thus the tractive effort is subject only to a partial reduction. In spite of the abrupt partial short-circuiting, the representative point slides along the hyperbola representing I very closely to the static characteristic and shows only small peaks at the instants t_2 and t_3. Voltage E shows two jumps indicating the extremely rapid adjustment of the voltage. Regulator current I_ρ shows moderate peaks. On the contrary, current I_b and, even more, voltage E_{bd}, show large oscillations, which prove the energetic action of the amplifier metadyne in striving to control current I and voltage E in order to force them to remain close to the corresponding static values.

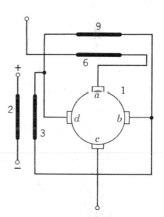

Fig. 218. An illustrative example based on the connections for an Alpha motor metadyne.

4. AN AMPLIFIER METADYNE CONTROLLING THE STATOR WINDINGS OF A LARGE METADYNE

There is a great variety of stator windings for a metadyne, and generally many of them are used. The algebraic sum of their ampere-turns in a given direction is generally smaller than the arithmetic sum. If it were possible to combine some or all of these windings into one winding creating the resultant ampere-turns, i.e., the algebraic sum, an important gain in losses, in copper weight and size would be obtained. Such a gain is particularly valuable for a metadyne because the armature acts as the magnetizing member, and the stator windings generally act as demagnetizing members. Therefore, the resultant ampere-turns due to the stator windings are small compared with the ampere-turns of the field of a dynamo, say one-third.

The amplifier metadyne may be used for such a reduction of the stator coils. Consider the Alpha motor metadyne of Fig. 218 as an example.

The stator has four different windings: a secondary hypercompensator, 3, a secondary independent variator, 2, a primary hypocompensator, 6, and a primary variator, 9, shunt-connected across the secondary brushes. Let I_β, I_γ, I_a, and I_δ be the respective currents flowing in these windings; further, let R_1 and R_2 be the total resistances of the circuits of windings 3 and 9, respectively.

The fundamental equations may be written

$$\frac{1}{n} E_{ca} = K I_b + K_{ca}^\beta \frac{E_{bd}}{R_1} + K_{ca}^\gamma I_\gamma$$

$$\frac{1}{n} E_{bd} = K I_a + K_{bd}^\alpha I_a + K_{bd}^\delta \frac{E_{bd}}{R_2}$$

(149)

There is, further,

$$I_b = E_{bd} \frac{R_1 + R_2}{R_1 R_2}$$

(150)

From the second fundamental equation is obtained

$$E_{bd} = \frac{n(K + K_{bd}^\alpha) I_a}{1 - K_{bd}^\delta(n/R_2)}$$

(151)

Substitution into the first fundamental equation yields

$$\frac{1}{n} E_{ca} = \frac{n(K + K_{bd}^\alpha) I_a}{1 - K_{bd}^\delta(n/R_2)} \left[K \frac{R_1 + R_2}{R_1 R_2} + \frac{K_{ca}^\beta}{R_1} \right] + K_{ca}^\gamma I_\gamma$$

(152)

Suppose that the Alpha motor metadyne is inserted into a loop of a distribution system supplying constant current. Then I_a is constant and $(1/n)E_{ca}$ is proportional to the developed torque.

Notice further that K_{bd}^α is of opposite sign to K and of smaller absolute value. From Equation 152 it may therefore be deduced that the starting torque is proportional to the independent current I_γ and has the same sign as this current. Therefore, when n increases, the torque decreases slowly because the term within the parentheses is negative; when the speed n increases and approaches the value n_0 defined by the relation

$$n_0 = \frac{R_2}{K_{bd}^\delta}$$

(153)

the torque decreases rapidly toward zero; further, it becomes negative as its absolute value increases toward infinity. Such a characteristic, showing a small reduction of torque at low speed and a very sharp bend at a speed slightly smaller than n_0 is very valuable. The value of the starting torque is controlled by the current I_γ, and the value of the speed n_0 is controlled by the resistance R_2.

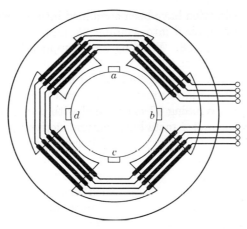

Fig. 219. Stator-coil arrangement for the Alpha metadyne of Fig. 218.

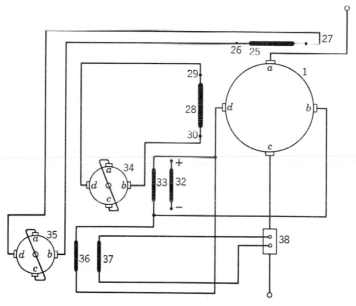

Fig. 220. Scheme for reducing the number of windings on the Alpha metadyne.

This Alpha motor metadyne has four coils on each polar segment, a coil for each winding as Fig. 219 shows. Obviously the ampere-turns they create oppose one another.

Consider the scheme of Fig. 220; it corresponds to the Alpha motor metadyne of Fig. 218, but the stator windings that have their magnetic axis in the same direction have been combined into one winding. Windings 6 and 9 are combined into winding 25, and windings 2 and 3 are combined into winding 28. Winding 25 is supplied by amplifier metadyne '35, which has its secondary variator windings, 36 and 37, excited by the pilot currents. Winding 36 is shunt-connected across secondary brushes b and d of the motor metadyne, 1, and it corresponds to winding 9 of Fig. 218. Winding 37 is supplied with a current proportional to current I_a of the motor metadyne (current derived from a shunt 38),

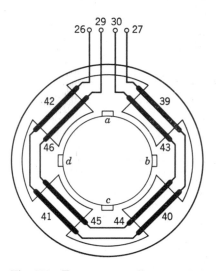

Fig. 221. Fewer stator coils are needed for the Alpha metadyne when auxiliary amplifier metadynes are employed.

and it corresponds to winding 6 of Fig. 218. Similarly, winding 28 is supplied by amplifier metadyne 34, which has two secondary variator windings, 32 and 33, carrying pilot currents and corresponding to windings 2 and 3, respectively, of Fig. 218.

The external appearance of the machine is given schematically by Fig. 221. Coils 39, 40, 41, and 42 constitute winding 25, with 26 and 27 as terminals. Coils 43, 44, 45, and 46 constitute winding 28, with 29 and 30 as its terminals. Thus, instead of four coils on each polar segment, there are now only two coils and hence less copper.

Consider again for each polar segment the arithmetic sum of the ampere-turns of the two coils and compare it with their algebraic sum; make this comparison for all points of the global characteristic of the metadyne along the segment actually used. It is generally found that the algebraic sum is smaller than the arithmetic sum for most parts of this segment of the characteristic. Thus it seems logical to repeat the procedure and to combine the two coils of each polar segment into a single coil supplied by an amplifier metadyne.

The external appearance is then shown by Fig. 223, and the corresponding scheme is given by Fig. 222. Again, there are only two amplifier metadynes because of the symmetry of the machine. In fact, the ampere-turns interlinked with polar segments 180 electrical degrees apart have equal absolute value and opposite direction with respect to the center of the machine, for any point of the global characteristic; therefore, they may be fed by the same amplifier metadyne, provided that the right connections are made.

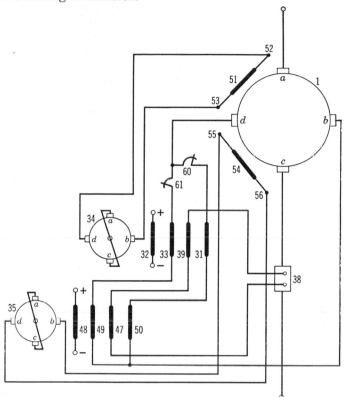

Fig. 222. A scheme for further reducing the number of stator windings of the main metadyne.

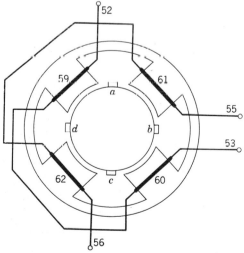

Fig. 223. The stator-coil arrangement of the Alpha metadyne shown in Fig 222.

Thus, coils 59 and 60, constituting one winding with points 52 and 53 as terminals, are fed by amplifier metadyne 34. This winding is indicated schematically in Fig. 222 by 51. In a similar way, coils 61 and 62 form a single winding with points 55 and 56 as terminals and with amplifier metadyne 35 as the source of current. In Fig. 222, this winding is indicated by 54.

Each amplifier metadyne must supply a current creating the same resultant ampere-turns as the original four stator windings upon a given polar segment; therefore, each amplifier metadyne is generally provided with as many secondary variator windings excited by pilot currents as there were original coils combined into a single one. Thus, in Fig. 222 each amplifier metadyne is provided with four secondary variator windings excited by pilot currents. One pilot current, flowing through variator windings 32 and 48, is derived from an independent constant-voltage source and is intended to play the role of the current flowing through the original winding 2 of Fig. 218. A second pilot current, flowing in windings 39 and 47, is derived from a shunt 38 and plays the role of the current I_a flowing in winding 6 of Fig. 218. A third pilot current, passing through windings 33 and 49, is derived from the secondary brushes b and d of the motor metadyne and substitutes for the current flowing in winding 3 of Fig. 218. Finally, a fourth pilot current, flowing through windings 31 and 50, is derived from the secondary brushes b and d of the motor metadyne and acts as the current that was flowing in winding 9 of Fig. 218.

One may think that the latter two pilot currents might be combined into one single current derived from brushes b and d of the motor metadyne; this may not always be possible, because each generally requires control by rheostats 60 and 61 independently of one another. It should be recalled that the amplifier metadynes mentioned here are represented in the figures with their secondary variator windings excited by the pilot currents, for the sake of simplicity, but actually they are provided with any combination of the other stator windings described in Chapter 17, windings designed to improve the fidelity and the effectiveness of the amplification.

The procedure applied to the example given above may easily be extended to others. The use of amplifier metadynes to control the stator windings of a main metadyne is generally justified when the main metadyne is relatively large; in this case, the amplifier metadynes reduce the copper weight and the copper losses, and they allow easy control of the large machine with control of comparatively very small currents, the pilot currents of the amplifier metadynes.

5. A DIESEL ELECTRIC LOCOMOTIVE WITH A MAIN GENERATOR METADYNE

The scheme is given by Fig. 224. The engine drives the main generator metadyne, 1, a shunt-excited regulator dynamo, 9, and a base dynamo, 37.

Three amplifier metadynes, 5, 34, and 35, are driven by an auxiliary motor, 38, supplied by base dynamo 37. The base dynamo, provided

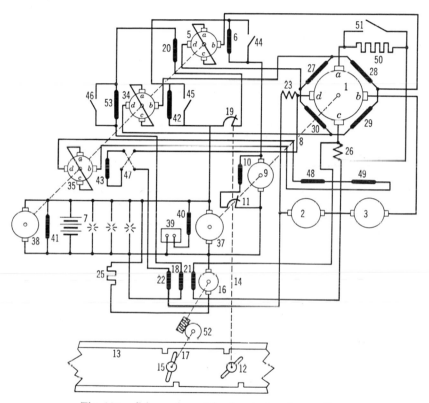

Fig. 224. Scheme for a Diesel-metadyne locomotive.

with a voltage regulator, 39, and the battery, 7, form the source of an auxiliary network at a low, constant voltage.

The main generator metadyne, 1, supplies power to the traction motors, 2 and 3, through its secondary brushes, b and d. Its primary brushes, a and c, are either short-circuited when switch 51 is closed or connected to a resistor, 50, when the switch is open.

The four stator coils, 27, 28, 29, and 30, of the main generator meta-dyne are connected into a closed rectangular circuit, which is supplied by amplifier metadynes 5 and 34 at its diagonally opposite terminals as is a Wheatstone bridge. The current supplied by amplifier metadyne 5 creates ampere-turns along the secondary commutating axis, whereas the current supplied by amplifier metadyne 34 creates ampere-turns along the primary commutating axis.

Among the stator windings of the amplifier metadynes only two secondary variator windings carrying the pilot currents are indicated in the figure, for the sake of simplicity. One pilot current, say I_α, de-rived from the auxiliary constant-voltage network, excites the wind-ings 20, 53, and 18; it is controlled by rheostat 19. The regulator current, I_ρ, is the second pilot current, and it flows in windings 6 and 42.

The admission of the fuel at 13 into the engine is regulated by two throttles in cascade. The first throttle, 12, is controlled directly by hand by the engineer, and the second throttle, 15, is controlled by aux-iliary dynamo 16, called the "governor dynamo," through a mechanical transmission 52, preferably a worm gear.

Governor dynamo 16 has its armature shunt-connected across the wires of the auxiliary constant-voltage network with a ballast resistance 25 in series. The governor dynamo comprises three field windings: the first field winding, 18, already mentioned, carries the pilot current I_α; a second field winding, 21, shunt-connected across coils 26 of the primary commutating poles of main generator 1, is excited by a current propor-tional to the primary current, I_a, of the main generator; a third field winding, 22, connected in series with secondary variator winding 43 of amplifier metadyne 35, is shunt-connected across coils 23 of the second-ary commutating poles of the main generator metadyne and is excited by a current proportional to the secondary current, I_b, of the main generator metadyne. Amplifier metadyne 35 supplies current to field windings 48 and 49 of traction motors 2 and 3.

Suppose that the locomotive is motoring. Switches 51 and 45 are closed, and switches 44 and 46 are open. The handle that sets throttle 12 simultaneously operates rheostat 11 and rheostat 19. These three pieces of apparatus are mechanically coupled by transmission 14. When the engineer wants to start the train, he simply places the handle actuat-ing transmission 14 in a given position, thus defining simultaneously the opening of throttle 12, the value of pilot current I_α, and the value of the critical speed n_0.

The fundamental equations of the main metadyne during motoring may be written

$$\frac{1}{n}E_{ca} = KI_b + K_{ca}^{\alpha}I_{\alpha} + K_{ca}^{\rho}I_{\rho} = -\frac{1}{n}R_aI_a$$

$$\frac{1}{n}E_{bd} = KI_a + K_{bd}^{\alpha}I_{\alpha}$$

(154)

$$2\pi T = K_{ca}^{\alpha}I_{\alpha}I_a + K_{ca}^{\rho}I_{\rho}I_a - K_{bd}^{\alpha}I_{\alpha}I_b$$

$$I_{\rho} = (n - n_0)K_{\rho}$$

where $-T$ is the torque supplied by the shaft of the engine. Recall here that T is positive when the metadyne develops an accelerating torque.

These equations may be simplified for $n = n_0$, so that the fourth equation is eliminated. Further, note that the term $(1/n)R_aI_a$ is negligible when compared with any of the three terms of the other member of the first equation. Therefore,

$$KI_b + K_{ca}^{\alpha}I_{\alpha} + K_{ca}^{\rho}I_{\rho} = 0$$

$$\frac{1}{n_0}E_{bd} = KI_a + K_{bd}^{\alpha}I_{\alpha}$$

(155)

$$2\pi T = K_{ca}^{\alpha}I_{\alpha}I_a + K_{ca}^{\rho}I_{\rho}I_a - K_{bd}^{\alpha}I_{\alpha}I_b$$

On the other hand, consider governor dynamo 16. Usually it rotates at a rather low speed or it remains at rest; the ballast resistor absorbs the greatest part of the voltage of the auxiliary network, whatever the speed of the armature of the governor dynamo may be, within practical limits. Therefore, it may be stated that this armature is energized with a practically constant current and that its torque is proportional to the resultant ampere-turns of its field windings.

The ampere-turns of the field windings of the governor dynamo will be defined as positive when they tend to open throttle 15. Current I_{α} flows in coil 18 and creates some positive ampere-turns, say $G_{\alpha}I_{\alpha}$; coil 21 creates ampere-turns, say G_aI_a, proportional to the primary current, negative when I_a is positive; coil 22 creates ampere-turns, say G_bI_b, also negative when I_b is positive.

The torque of the governor dynamo is thus proportional to the algebraic sum $G_{\alpha}I_{\alpha} + G_aI_a + G_bI_b$, and throttle 15 moves towards its open position or its closed position when this sum is positive or negative, respectively. The larger the absolute value of this sum is, the quicker the throttle moves. The throttle is at rest when

$$G_{\alpha}I_{\alpha} + G_aI_a + G_bI_b = 0$$

(156)

At starting, current I_a is small and negative, as the second equation of system 2 shows and as the diagram of Fig. 225 indicates. Therefore, since the equation is satisfied only when the current I_b reaches a large value, the opening of throttle 15 will increase until it reaches its fully open position; governor motor 16 stalls, and current I_b reaches the maximum value $(I_b)_{max}$ satisfying Equation 156; the locomotive accelerates, and the representative point moves along the segment ab until it reaches the hyperbola bmc corresponding to that power of the engine defined by the opening of throttle 12 and by the critical speed n_0 corresponding to this opening.

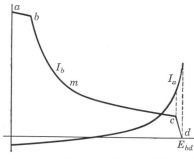

The locomotive then accelerates further, while the representative point moves along the hyperbola bmc. In fact, the last Equation 155 may be written

$$2\pi T = \frac{1}{n}(R_a I_a^2 - E_{bd} I_b)$$

Fig. 225.   Current characteristics of the locomotive metadyne.

If the very small first term of the second member is neglected, and if it is recalled further that T remains at a constant negative value corresponding to the torque of the engine for the steady-state opening of throttle 12, and, finally, if it is observed that n is kept practically constant because of the quick action of the regulator dynamo together with the amplified action of the amplifier metadynes, then it is evident that

$$E_{bd} I_b = \text{constant}$$

The first member of Equation 156 is positive for any position of the representative point along the segment bmc of the hyperbola, as may easily be proved from well-known properties of the hyperbola. The governor motor is kept stalled at the limit position for which throttle 15 is kept fully open.

When the representative point reaches the extreme point c of the segment of the hyperbola, Equation 156 is satisfied. If the locomotive is still accelerating, a higher voltage is required by the traction motors; the first member of Equation 156 becomes negative because of the rapid increase of the primary current I_a due to saturation of the iron (see Fig. 225), and governor dynamo 16 gradually closes throttle 15 while the representative point slides along the segment cd.

Now consider the braking operation. It is well known that braking through the traction motors is better than by mechanical means. The scheme considered here permits satisfactory electrical braking operation. For braking, switches 51 and 45 are kept open; switches 44 and 46 are kept closed, and throttle 12 is closed.

The fundamental equations are now

$$\frac{1}{n} E_{ca} = K I_b + K_{ca}^\alpha I_\alpha \tag{157}$$

$$\frac{1}{n} E_{bd} = K I_a + K_{bd}^\rho I_\rho$$

The regulator equation may be written

$$2\pi T_0 = K_{ca}^\alpha I_\alpha I_a - K_{bd}^\rho I_\rho I_b \tag{158}$$

where T_0 is the torque due to mechanical friction of the engine and of the main metadyne.

To these equations, the following ones should be added:

$$E_{ca} = -R_0 I_a$$

$$E_{bd} = s K_m I_b + R_2 I_b \tag{159}$$

where R_0 is the total resistance of the primary circuit; s is the speed of the traction motors; K_m is a constant when the iron of the traction motors is not saturated, and a function of I_b when the iron becomes saturated; and R_2 is the resistance of the secondary circuit. From the five equations above, the five variables E_{ca}, E_{bd}, I_a, I_b, I_ρ may easily be determined as a function of the speed s of the traction motors.

One may get an approximate idea of the variation of these variables from the following procedure:

From Equations 157,

$$I_b = \frac{E_{ca}}{nK} - \frac{K_{ca}^\alpha}{K} I_\alpha \equiv I_{b\mu} + I_{bw}$$

$$I_a = \frac{E_{bd}}{nK} - \frac{K_{bd}^\rho}{K} I_\rho \equiv I_{a\mu} + I_{aw} \tag{160}$$

The magnetizing component is generally a fraction of the component due to the variator winding. Therefore, current I_b is mainly determined by stator current I_α, and current I_a is mainly determined by regulator current I_ρ.

Thus, by choosing the value of current I_b with rheostat 19, the operator of the locomotive defines the resisting torque of the traction motors and, consequently, the rate of the decelerating torque of the train. The regulator dynamo, on the other hand, continuously sets the value of current I_a so as to dissipate the regenerated power in resistor 50 and to keep the engine-metadyne set running around the critical speed.

The regulator equation 158 may also be written

$$2\pi n T_0 = E_{ca}I_a - E_{bd}I_b \tag{161}$$

If the first member, which is generally small with respect to each of the two terms of the second member, is neglected and, if Equations 159 are considered, in which the term $R_2 I_b$ is neglected, there results

$$\frac{I_a}{I_b} = \sqrt{\frac{sK_m}{R_0}} \tag{162}$$

which is an approximate equation, useful to the designer who must determine the resistance of resistor 50.

It is important to note that when the operator of the locomotive keeps the handle of rheostat 19 at a given position, the deceleration, as well as the acceleration, of the train occurs at a practically constant rate, and that braking is obtained even at very low speeds of the locomotive. When the train is approaching standstill, the operator must nevertheless allow some fuel to enter the engine to keep it running. If necessary, the engine may act as a compressor during long periods of braking, for instance, when the train descends mountains or high hills.

Amplifier metadyne 35 is arranged to become saturated when current I_b of the main metadyne approaches its maximum value $(I_b)_{max}$, and therefore to limit the maximum value of the shunt-field current of the traction motors while the current I_b flowing in the armature of the motors increases towards its maximum value. The inverting switch, 47, permits the reversal of the field excitation of the traction motors. Main metadyne 1 operates as an S generator metadyne when the train accelerates, and it operates simultaneously as a Cross transformer metadyne and a motor metadyne when the train is braking.

6. A METADYNE PLANT FOR STEEL MILLS

The metadyne system has many applications in large steel mills. Figure 226 shows the scheme of a plant operating satisfactorily in Milan, Italy. A synchronous motor, 1, drives a large S generator metadyne, 2, the secondary brushes, b and d, of which are connected to the brushes of a large dynamo, 3, coupled with the cylinders of a blooming mill. A flywheel, 14, is directly coupled to one end of the main shaft of the dynamo, and a small series regulator dynamo, 4, is coupled to the other end by means of a mechanical transmission not indicated on the diagram. The current created by the series regulator dynamo, 4, flows through a secondary variator winding, 9, of an amplifier metadyne, 7, and a resistor, 12, which controls the value of the critical speed.

Amplifier metadyne 7 is provided with another secondary variator winding, 10, supplied by a constant-voltage auxiliary source delivering a current, say I_α, controlled by the rheostat, 13. The amplifier metadyne supplies current to the secondary variator winding, 8, of the main S generator metadyne 2.

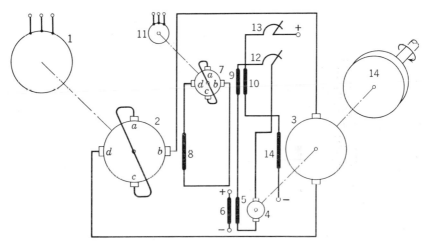

Fig. 226. Steel-mill drive employing metadyne equipment.

The requirements of the customer are the following:

(a) Synchronous motor 1 must operate at its nominal power as long as possible, but it must not be overloaded. This condition is imposed because the price of energy is relatively low when nominal power is supplied. The price is not reduced proportionally when the power decreases; on the contrary, it is greatly increased when peaks of power appear, and even penalties are imposed if the peak exceeds a given limit.

(b) Since the blooming mill is intended for steel bars of many different sizes, the no-load speed of the driving motor must be able to oscillate between two limits that are separated as much as possible.

(c) With hard ingots, the mill may decelerate at a large rate or even stall the motor. Although a mechanical device is provided to limit the transmission of a torque greater than a given limit, it is required that no harm shall occur to the electric machines of the plant and that no peak of power or peak of current can possibly result.

These requirements have been fully met by providing the plant with the characteristic torque T versus speed s shown by Fig. 227 and by Fig. 228.

The operator adjusts rheostat 12 to define the no-load speed and rheostat 13 to determine the starting torque. Since the handles of the two rheostats are mechanically interlocked, for each position of the handle of rheostat 12 the handle of rheostat 13 is allowed to move from its zero position up to a maximum position; the lower the torque setting, the higher is the corresponding critical speed.

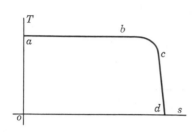

Fig. 227. Torque-speed characteristic of the steel-mill equipment.

For a given position of the handles of the two rheostats, current I_α is given a definite value; the secondary current, I_b, of the S generator metadyne and the field excitation of

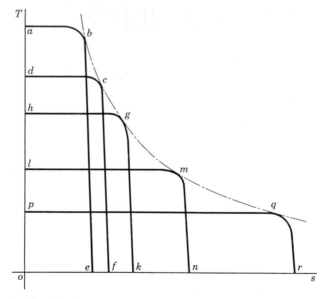

Fig. 228. The family of torque-speed curves has a constant maximum-power value.

mill motor 13 are then defined. Secondary current I_b remains precisely constant throughout the range of secondary voltage E_{bd} corresponding to practical operation. The straight-line segment ab of Fig. 227 is thus obtained, indicating a constant torque.

At point b the critical speed is approached and a very sharp bend of the characteristic is obtained, owing to the quick reduction of secondary current I_b towards zero. The no-load point, d, is thus attained through a segment cd nearly vertical.

The mechanical interlock between the handles of the two rheostats is set to bring the bend of the maximum torque characteristic, corre-

Fig. 229. Synchronous motor coupled to the S generator metadyne of the steel-mill set. (*Courtesy of the San Giorgio Co., Genoa.*)

sponding to a definite no-load speed, along a hyperbola $bcgmd$ as shown by Fig. 228. The synchronous motor is therefore loaded each time to its nominal load, and no overload is possible.

If a hard ingot requires a torque larger than the maximum torque allowed by a given characteristic, the mill decelerates and the flywheel supplies a large supplementary torque, which is larger the greater the rate of deceleration is. Consider the diagram of Fig. 228 and add this supplementary torque, calculated for the maximum safe deceleration rate, to the maximum torque due to the electric motor for the corresponding characteristic. Thus peaks are obtained which all reach the same value of resultant torque on the shaft, equal to about 70% of the torque for which the mechanical safety device of the transmission breaks.

Resistors 12 and 13 are relatively small; the control is very simple and the response is quick. Figure 229 gives a view of the synchronous motor and S generator metadyne set; Fig. 230 gives a view of the main mill motor.

In the description given above, only those windings are mentioned for each application which are characteristic to the special application

Fig. 230.   The main motor of the steel-mill drive.   (*Courtesy of the San Giorgio Co., Genoa.*)

considered.   The same comment applies to the equations developed.   It is tacitly understood that other windings have been used, which were indicated in the general description of the corresponding metadyne.   It is tacitly understood also that the conditions of both static and dynamic stability have been fulfilled in every case.

19 · Hyperstatic Metadynes—The "Eight" Transformer Metadyne

1. FUNDAMENTALS OF THE "EIGHT" TRANSFORMER METADYNE

When the fundamental static equations, developed in the first part of this volume, permit the determination of the brush currents of a reactive metadyne on the assumption that the values of the voltage required by or impressed on the loads are given, the reactive metadyne under consideration is said to be "statically determined." All the particular reactive metadynes described in the previous chapters of Part II are statically determined. From here on reactive metadynes are often described which are not statically determined; these are called "hyper-

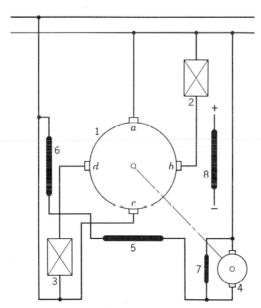

Fig. 231. Basic scheme of the Eight transformer metadyne.

static metadynes." One of the most important hyperstatic metadynes is the "Eight" transformer metadyne.

Figure 231 shows the scheme of such a metadyne. It has four equidistant brushes per cycle, a, b, c, d; two nonconsecutive brushes, a and c, designated as primary, are connected to a constant-voltage line; secondary brush b is connected to one terminal of consumer 2, the other terminal of which is connected to brush a, and secondary brush d is connected to one terminal of another consumer, 3, the other terminal of which is connected to brush c. A regulator dynamo, 4, is shown, shunt-excited and supplied from the constant-voltage line. The regulator current, I_ρ, flows through two stator windings, 5 and 6, having their magnetic axes along the primary and secondary commutating axes, respectively. A third stator winding, 8, is shown; it is a secondary variator winding, assumed to be excited by an independent current I_α.

Now write the fundamental equations. The brush currents here are no longer necessarily canonical currents as in all cases considered in the previous chapters of Part II. They simply satisfy the equation

$$I_a + I_b + I_c + I_d = 0 \qquad (163)$$

Therefore, the fundamental equations must be written

$$\frac{1}{n} E_{ca} = K_{ca}^a I_a + K_{ca}^b I_b + K_{ca}^c I_c + K_{ca}^d I_d + K_{ca}^\rho I_\rho + K_{ca}^\alpha I_\alpha$$

$$(164)$$

$$\frac{1}{n} E_{bd} = K_{bd}^a I_a + K_{bd}^b I_b + K_{bd}^c I_c + K_{bd}^d I_d + K_{bd}^\rho I_\rho$$

In order to write the regulator equations, the expression for the total power supplied to the metadyne through its four brushes must be written, and as the currents are no longer canonical, Theorem X mentioned in Section 4 of Chapter 3 must be applied. With brush c as the common point for the connection of the shunt winding of the wattmeters as indicated in the theorem, the expression for the total power, P, supplied to the metadyne may be written

$$P = E_{ca} I_a + E_{cb} I_b + E_{cd} I_d \qquad (165)$$

On the other hand, there is

$$E_{cb} = \tfrac{1}{2}(E_{ca} - E_{bd})$$

$$E_{cd} = \tfrac{1}{2}(E_{ca} + E_{bd})$$

After substitution in the previous equation, there results

$$2\pi T = \frac{1}{n} E_{ca} \left(I_a + \frac{1}{2} I_b + \frac{1}{2} I_d \right) + \frac{1}{n} E_{bd} \left(\frac{1}{2} I_d - \frac{1}{2} I_b \right)$$

If E_{ca} and E_{bd} are expressed by the second member of Equation 164 and if Theorem IX is recalled, the final result becomes

$$2\pi T = (K_{ca}^{\rho}I_\rho + K_{ca}^{\alpha}I_\alpha)(I_a + \tfrac{1}{2}I_b + \tfrac{1}{2}I_d) + K_{bd}^{\rho}I_\rho(I_d - I_b)\tfrac{1}{2} \quad (166)$$

where T is the torque due to the losses in the metadyne and the regulator.
Finally, there is

$$I_\rho = K_\rho(n - n_0) \quad (167)$$

Five equations are thus available, Equations 163, 164, 166, and 167, but even when both the voltages E_{ca} and E_{bd} are given, the remaining variables I_a, I_b, I_c, I_d, I_ρ, n are six in number and therefore cannot be determined.

One may think that the expression for the current, I_L, supplied by the constant-voltage line, may yield a further equation for the desired determination. Write these equations, with the assumptions that I_L represents the current supplied by the wire connected to brush a and consumer 2 and that I_L' represents the current supplied by the other wire connected to brush c and to consumer 3. There is

$$I_L = I_a + I_b$$
$$I_L' = I_c + I_d \quad (168)$$

Since $I_L + I_L' \equiv 0$, these equations reduce to Equation 163 again, and no new relation between the brush currents results. The introduction of two systems of canonical currents, one of which is a "void system," as defined in Section 3 of Chapter 2, permits a simplification in writing the equations and a better understanding of the difficulty.

Consider the following system of canonical currents: the system I_{ac} and I_{bd}, and the system I_{ab} and I_{cd}; current I_{ab} passes through consumer 2, and current I_{cd} passes through consumer 3. This second system comprises two equal currents,

$$I_{ab} = I_{cd} \quad (169)$$

Between the canonical currents and the brush currents, the following relations hold:

$$I_a = I_{ac} + I_{ab}$$
$$I_b = I_{bd} - I_{ab} \qquad I_{ac} = \tfrac{1}{2}(I_a - I_c)$$
$$I_c = -I_{ac} + I_{cd} \qquad I_{bd} = \tfrac{1}{2}(I_b - I_d) \quad (170)$$
$$I_d = -I_{bd} - I_{cd} \qquad I_{ab} = I_{cd} = \tfrac{1}{4}(I_a - I_b + I_c - I_d)$$

The system of canonical currents I_{ab} and I_{cd} satisfying relation 169 is evidently a "void system," as the diagram of Fig. 232 proves by simple inspection. The fundamental equations may therefore be written

$$\frac{1}{n} E_{ca} = KI_{bd} + K_{ca}^{\rho} I_{\rho} + K_{ca}^{\alpha} I_{\alpha}$$

$$(171)$$

$$\frac{1}{n} E_{bd} = KI_{ac} + K_{bd}^{\rho} I_{\rho}$$

Equation 166 is now simplified as follows:

$$2\pi T = (K_{ca}^{\rho} I_{\rho} + K_{ca}^{\alpha} I_{\alpha}) I_{ca} - K_{bd}^{\rho} I_{\rho} I_{bd} \qquad (172)$$

since the void system of canonical currents gives no torque. For further simplification, assume that $T = 0$ and $n = n_0$, and drop Equation 167.

Equations 171 and 172 define the variables I_{ac}, I_{bd}, and I_{ρ}. Thus the artifice of the two systems of canonical currents, chosen above, has resolved the solution into two components, the first component solution belonging to a statically defined metadyne, and the second component constituted simply by the "void canonical system" defined above, the current intensity of which remains indefinite.

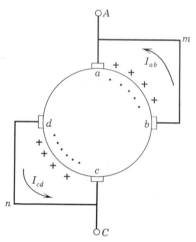

Fig. 232. The void system of currents.

2. CONSIDERATION OF THE STATICALLY DEFINED SYSTEM

Consider separately the statically defined component solution. Note that Equations 171 and 172, defining this solution, correspond to the Cross transformer metadyne; therefore the main results obtained in Section 2 of Chapter 12, devoted to the Cross transformer metadyne, will be repeated here. In particular, recall the following:

The characteristic, obtained for $I_{\alpha} = $ constant, of I_b versus E_{bd} is a hyperbola having its two asymptotes parallel to the axes. The center of this hyperbola may be moved wherever desired, and the power of this hyperbola may be given any value. The scheme of Fig. 231 has been drawn with only one secondary variator winding, the winding 8, for the sake of simplicity, but it may be completed with a primary variator winding excited by an independent current, and with variator windings shunt-connected across the brushes.

Under the same conditions, but without the regulator winding 6, the characteristic I_b versus E_{bd} is a straight line that may be located at any position on the coordinate plane except the vertical position, $E_{bd} = $ constant.

The voltage across the consumer of the Eight transformer metadyne is not E_{bd} but E_{ba} and E_{cd}. There is

$$E_{ba} = E_{cd} = \tfrac{1}{2}(E_{ca} + E_{bd}) \tag{173}$$

and therefore the characteristic mentioned above, when referred to the voltage E_{ba} or E_{cd} of the consumer, will simply be shifted parallel to the axis of voltage.

Equations 173 involve the important limitation that the two consumers, 2 and 3, must at any instant require the same voltage and the same current. Therefore, they generally must be similar to one another and operate under exactly the same conditions.

The Eight transformer metadyne has one fundamental difference from all the transformer metadynes considered in the previous chapters of Part II, except the Caduceus transformer metadyne: the Eight and the Caduceus transformer metadynes control a certain power different from the power transformed by the metadyne itself, whereas the other transformer metadynes described control only the power that they transform.

For the Eight, the power controlled by the metadyne is the power supplied to the consumers, $E_{ba}I_b + E_{cd}I_b = 2E_{ba}I_b$; the power transformed by the metadyne is $E_{bd}I_b$. The ratio, τ, between these two values is

$$\tau = \frac{2E_{ba}}{E_{bd}} = \frac{E_{ca}}{E_{bd}} + 1 \tag{174}$$

and therefore τ depends on the load.

Figure 233 gives some vector diagrams corresponding to different values of load. Diagram A corresponds to $E_{ba} = 0$, when the power absorbed by the consumers is zero; for this load $E_{ca} = -E_{bd}$, and $\tau = 0$.

Diagram B corresponds to $E_{ba} = \tfrac{1}{2}E_{ca}$, $E_{bd} = 0$, and $\tau = \infty$; if I_b and E_{ca} are positive, the two consumers absorb the power $2E_{ba}I_b = E_{ca}I_b$; yet the metadyne transforms no power, since $E_{bd} = 0$. For diagram C, $E_{ba} = E_{ca} = E_{bd}$, and therefore $\tau = 2$; the two consumers absorb the power $2E_{ca}I_b$, but the metadyne transforms only the power $E_{bd}I_b = E_{ca}I_b$.

For diagram D, $E_{ba} = E_{cd} > E_{ca}$, and $\tau < 2$; for further, higher values of the voltage absorbed by the consumers, the value of τ decreases and tends toward 1. If I_b is assumed always to be positive, diagrams E and F correspond to the case in which the consumers supply power. τ is then positive, $0 < \tau < 1$, and tends toward 1 when E_{ba} increases. For any diagram comprised between diagrams A and B, τ has a negative value; it takes any value between 0 and $-\infty$.

Thus τ may have any value. The designer will arrange the plan so that during practical operation τ remains at an absolute value that is as high as possible.

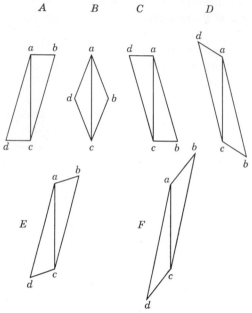

Fig. 233.   Vector diagrams of the Eight transformer metadyne.

Consider Equation 172; it may be written as follows when losses are neglected and the torque T is made zero:

$$E_{ca}I_a - E_{bd}I_b = 0 \qquad (172a)$$

Calculating the current I_a from this equation yields

$$I_a = -I_b, \quad I_L = 0 \qquad \text{for diagram } A$$
$$I_a = 0, \quad\quad I_L = I_b \qquad \text{for diagram } B$$
$$I_a = +I_b, \quad I_L = 2I_b \quad \text{for diagram } C$$
$$I_a > I_b, \quad\quad I_L > 2I_b \quad \text{for diagram } D$$
$$I_a < -I_b, \quad I_L < 0 \qquad \text{for diagrams } E \text{ and } F$$

The inequalities hold for $I_b > 0$; they are inverted if $I_b < 0$.

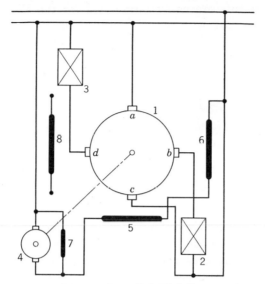

Fig. 234. Scheme of the "left Eight" connections.

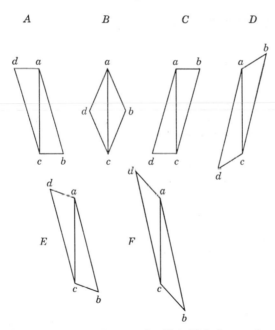

Fig. 235. Vector diagrams for "left Eight" operation.

Similar comments are easily formulated for the Eight transformer metadyne of Fig. 234, with the aid of the vector diagrams of Fig. 235. Nevertheless, there is a fundamental difference between the two schemes. Suppose that I_b is positive, the winding being right-handed and the rotation clockwise. The scheme of Fig. 231 permits the consumers to absorb power over a large range and permits the consumers to supply power within a restricted range only; on the contrary, the scheme of Fig. 234 permits operation of the consumers for absorbing power within a restricted range only, and permits operation of the consumers for supplying power over a large range. If I_b is negative, the above statement is reversed.

On the other hand, it is easier to operate with I_b positive, since the copper weight and copper losses are smaller. Therefore, it may be stated that scheme 231 is preferable when the consumers absorb electric power and that scheme 234 is preferable when the consumers supply electric power. The two schemes are distinguished by these names: "right Eight" for the transformer metadyne of Fig. 231, and "left Eight" for Fig. 234.

3. ELIMINATION OF THE VOID SYSTEM—THE TOULOUSE TRAIN

A locomotive or a motor car is generally provided with an even number of traction motors. These motors may be separated into two equal groups to be inserted into the two loops of the Eight transformer metadyne; they run at exactly the same speed at any moment, and therefore they always require the same voltage and the same current.

Whereas a switching locomotive may run at a very low speed for a long time, a regular locomotive or motor car runs a long time at a medium or a high speed and only a very short time at a very low speed. Therefore, the Eight transformer metadyne is suited for a regular locomotive and for a regular motor car, in which it will operate with a high value of τ for most of the operating time. Then the size of the metadyne may be expected to be comparatively small.

To make the Eight transformer metadyne successful it is necessary to eliminate the void system, which has an indefinite current intensity, the source of much trouble. The author devised four procedures for eliminating or for reducing this void system intensity to a negligible value; two of these procedures are described in this volume on statics. The other two procedures are based on the results of dynamic analysis.

The first procedure consists essentially in the use of two separate armature windings associated with separate commutators. In this case, there is necessarily

$$I_b + I_d = 0$$

$$I_a + I_c = 0$$

Of these two equations, only one is independent from the fundamental equations developed in the previous section, but this one makes the machine statically definite; thus the void system of indefinite intensity is eliminated. In this form, the Eight transformer metadyne has found many applications.

The field of traction provided the first application. A small local line, running from Toulouse, France, had motor coaches supplied by a battery that was subdivided into six equal groups operating in parallel and supplying 260 volts. The author suggested replacing one group of batteries by an Eight transformer metadyne, having calculated that the saving of energy would permit the performance of the same service with five groups of batteries instead of six; and this was the result.

The saving of energy over a rheostatic system occurs because there are no rheostatic losses during starting, and because braking takes place with a recovery of energy. From this energy saving must be deducted the losses of the metadyne set throughout the entire operation. As the distance between stations is relatively large, necessitating few starting periods, the balance of energy saving is reduced; and it does not reach the required 17%.

Yet the service was provided regularly. This result was due to the fact that a battery discharged through the metadyne equipment yields a higher total energy; in other words, it yields more ampere-hours than when discharged on a rheostatic equipment, because peaks of current which weaken the battery are eliminated, and because frequent though brief chargings during operation renew the battery and are favorable for obtaining a longer and more effective discharge. Other things being equal, these favorable factors increase the ampere-hours supplied by a regularly charged battery by, say, 5% to 10%, as in the case of the Toulouse train.

The battery must be replaced after a given number of complete discharges. With the metadyne equipment this number is increased; in other words, the life of the battery is prolonged. Operation is easier and the amount of switchgear less.

Figure 236 gives the main features of the complete diagrams. Eight transformer metadyne 1 has its primary winding and its primary brushes a and c connected to battery 15 through contactor 11; it has its secondary winding and its secondary brushes b and d connected to the two groups of the propulsion motors 16, 17, 18, and 19.

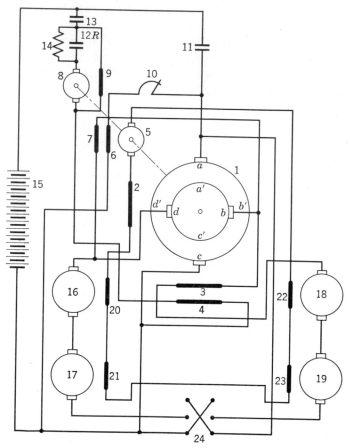

Fig. 236.   Scheme of the metadyne equipment for the Toulouse train.

On the shaft of the metadyne proper are coupled a shunt-excited regulator dynamo, 8, and a modulator dynamo, 5. Regulator dynamo 8 is connected to the battery, and regulator current I_ρ flows through the regulator winding, 4, which has its magnetic axis along the primary commutating axis.

It was decided to have current I_b always in the same direction, the positive one. Therefore, the right-hand Eight was chosen for motoring and the left-hand Eight for braking and regenerating. The transition from the one connection to the other is obtained with the inverter, 24.

Vector diagrams A, B, C, and D of Fig. 237 refer to the motoring operation. They correspond, respectively, to the starting point, to running at half speed, to running at full speed, and to running at high

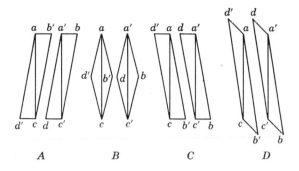

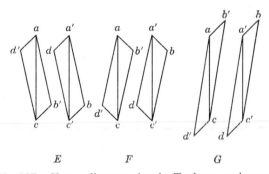

Fig. 237. Vector diagrams for the Toulouse equipment.

speed with a voltage impressed on the motors larger than the battery voltage. Points a, b, c, and d of the diagrams give the potential of the homonymous brushes; points a', b', c', d' correspond to a fictitious brush located as clearly indicated by the scheme of Fig. 236. Vector diagrams $ab'cd'$ correspond to the primary commutator, and vector diagrams $a'bc'd$ correspond to the secondary commutator. The potentials of a and a', b and b', c and c', d and d' are equal because the four traction motors operate at the same speed and have their field windings 20, 21, 22, and 23 excited by the same current, current I_α that flows in the secondary variator winding, 2, and is supplied by the modulator dynamo, 5.

Vector diagrams E, F, and G refer to the braking operation. They correspond, respectively, to a low speed, to nearly full speed, and to a high-speed operation, the high speed allowing the motors to develop a voltage higher than the battery voltage during charging.

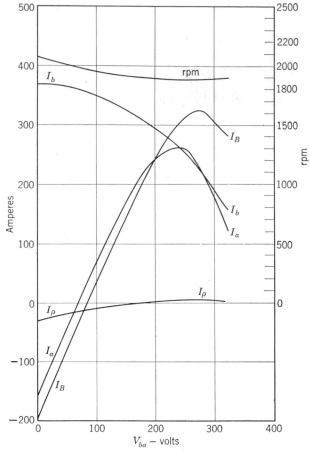

Fig. 238. Some test results for the Toulouse equipment. (*Courtesy of Als-Thom, Paris.*)

The metadyne is provided with a secondary stabilizing winding, 3. The modulator dynamo, 5, is provided with two field windings: shunt winding 7, shunt-connected across the secondary brushes, b and d; and winding 6 supplied from the battery and carrying a current controlled by resistor 10. Current I_α thus obtained, which flows in the secondary variator winding, has a drooping characteristic that provides a satisfactory torque-speed characteristic for the traction motors.

Figure 238 records some of the results: secondary current I_b is represented as a function of the voltage applied to the motors, V_{ba}, the speed of rotation, n, and the regulator current, I_ρ. It is easy to check the relation

$$I_B = I_b + I_a + \frac{P_a}{V_{ca}} + I_\rho$$

where P_a is the power absorbed by the losses and I_B the current supplied by the battery.

The set is started by the regulator dynamo by means of resistor 14,

Fig. 239.   The train of Toulouse.   (*Courtesy of Als-Thom, Paris.*)

automatically short-circuited by contactor 12R when the normal speed is reached. Contactor 11 is then closed.

During reversal of inverter 24 to make the change from motoring to braking or vice versa, contactor 11 is opened, the interrupted current then being practically zero. The engineer manipulates a single handle controlling resistor 10 and contactor 11. Many details of the scheme have been omitted as nonessential for its characterization; a like simplification holds for almost all the schemes of plants recorded here.

Figure 239 gives a view of the train; the five groups of the batteries and the metadyne, which occupies the place of the sixth group, are clearly shown. Figure 240 shows the metadyne set in the test bed in Paris. It is suspended to permit checking the dynamical balance of the masses of the rotor. Clearly visible are the regulator dynamo and the modulator dynamo. The metadyne was installed on the Toulouse motor coach when the campaign started for Diesel electric trains, which economically are far preferable to a battery train, whatever the electric equipment may be.

Fig. 240.   The Toulouse metadyne unit.   (*Courtesy of Als-Thom, Paris.*)

4. FURTHER APPLICATIONS OF THE EIGHT TRANSFORMER METADYNE WITH TWO ARMATURE WINDINGS

If two armature windings are used, the potential of the brushes bearing upon one commutator is independent of the potentials of the brushes

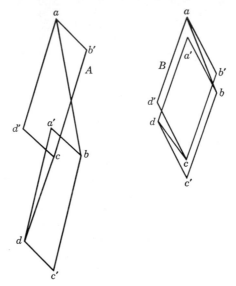

Fig. 241.   Vector diagrams for a two-commutator Eight transformer metadyne for independent operation of the consumers.

bearing upon the other commutator.   Therefore, the limitation requiring consumers in each loop of the Eight which induce exactly the same voltage at any time is no longer necessary.   No matter what kind of consumers may be inserted into the loops, these consumers will operate independently of one another.

Fig. 242. An Eight transformer metadyne with its auxiliaries. (*Courtesy of the San Giorgio Co., Genoa.*)

Consider the two vector diagrams of Fig. 241. The rectangle $ab'cd'$ refers to the primary winding, and the rectangle $a'bc'd$ refers to the secondary winding; between their middle points may be any difference of potential. Thus, for diagram B, the voltage required by the upper loop is indicated by vector ba, a larger value than the voltage indicated by vector *cd* corresponding to the lower loop. In both loops, the consumers absorb power if $I_b > 0$. For diagram *A*, the upper loop absorbs voltage *ba* and its consumer absorbs power; on the other hand, the lower loop supplies voltage *cd*, and its consumer is generating power. Thus, the Eight transformer metadyne with two armature windings is appropriate for application when the consumers operate independently of one another.

Figure 242 gives a view of an Eight transformer metadyne with a vertical axis of rotation; Fig. 243 shows its rotor, which comprises the armature of the metadyne proper, the armature of the regulator dynamo, and the armature of an S generator metadyne for the auxiliary loop of the plant to supply the switchgear and the secondary variator windings of the motor metadynes inserted into the main loop.

5. REDUCTION OF THE VOID SYSTEM—LONDON SUBWAY

The second procedure devised by the author for suppressing the void system consists essentially in the use of strong stabilizing windings on the motors inserted into the loops. This procedure does not eliminate the void system, but it reduces its indefinite current intensity to a value generally negligible.

This second procedure has been applied to the equipment for the motor coaches of the London subway. Figure 244 shows the main features of the chosen scheme. Eight transformer metadyne 1 has a single armature winding and is provided with four stator windings: two windings, 2 and 3, which have their magnetic axis along the primary commutating axis; and two windings, 4 and 5, which have their magnetic axis along the secondary commutating axis. Windings 3 and 4 are stabilizing windings, winding 2 is a regulator winding, and winding 5 is a secondary

Fig. 243. The rotor of the equipment of Fig. 242. (*Courtesy of the San Giorgio Co., Genoa.*)

variator winding excited by current I_α under the control of the operator.

On the shaft of the metadyne are mounted the shunt-excited regulator dynamo, 6, and the modulator dynamo, 7, which is excited by two field windings: winding 9, shunt-connected across the motors of the left-hand

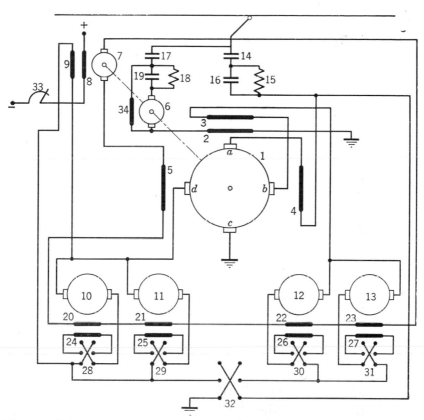

Fig. 244. Scheme of the Eight transformer equipment for the London subway cars.

loop; and winding 8, excited by a current derived from an auxiliary constant-voltage source and controlled by rheostat 33.

The direction of secondary current I_b is maintained positive throughout the entire operating cycle, braking, as well as motoring. Therefore, when the operation changes from motoring to braking, or vice versa, the Eight is inverted from "right" to "left," or the reverse, by means of the inverter, 32.

There are four traction motors, 10, 11, 12, 13, controlled by the metadyne, two motors connected in parallel with one another in each loop. The field excitation of the traction motors is due to two windings:

a series stabilizing winding 24, 25, 26, and 27; and an independently excited winding, 20, 21, 22, and 23, excited by modulator dynamo 7.

The metadyne set can be started either by the metadyne proper, through resistor 15, or by the regulator dynamo, through resistor 18. This permits driving the set by the regulator dynamo and permits cutting off the metadyne proper in the event of a long stop at a station.

Precautions have been taken (not indicated on the scheme) automatically to bring current I_L practically to zero every time contactor 14 is opened; thus this contactor interrupts practically no current. Since inverter 32 is reversed only when 14 is open, no current is inter-

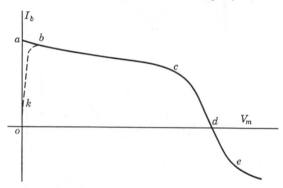

Fig. 245.   Operating characteristics of the London subway equipment.

rupted by this inverter; nevertheless, this apparatus must be constructed with care because it operates very often, every time the engineer switches from motoring to braking and vice versa. Inverters 28, 29, 30, 31 of the series excitation of the motors do not interrupt current for the same reason; further, they are very rarely operated. In fact, the train always runs in the same direction except when it reaches the terminal station; the series windings remain connected in the same sense while motoring and braking, and inverters 28, 29, 30, and 31 are not reversed when the change is made from motoring to braking, or the reverse. The handle operated by the engineer controls rheostat 33 and, at the proper time, inverter 32 and contactor 14.

Figure 245 gives the diagram of a characteristic of I_b versus the voltage V_m applied to the motors. Its segment abc follows the slope due to the reduction of the coefficient of friction when the speed increases. The segment cd corresponds to stable operation at high speed, and the segment de corresponds to automatic braking if the maximum safe speed is exceeded.

The segment okb, indicated by a dotted line, corresponds to the smooth but quick increase of the torque at starting due to a special arrangement, not indicated in the scheme, for permitting the train to start without discomfort to the passengers. The metadyne trains have been particularly appreciated for their smooth running and freedom from jerkiness. Three characteristics are at the disposal of the engineer, similar to the one indicated by Fig. 245, but with lower current intensity.

It is important to note that, as a result of the great difference of the load over a period of 24 hours, the voltage of the line varies between wide limits. The normal voltage is 600 volts; it sometimes drops to

Fig. 246. The London subway metadyne and its auxiliary dynamos. (*Courtesy of the Metropolitan-Vickers Co., Ltd., Sheffield.*)

400 volts during the rush hours, and it rises to 700 volts during the first hours after midnight, particularly when the metadyne train is regenerating.

In spite of such a variation, the main characteristic of Fig. 245 remains practically unaltered; this means that the accelerating or braking torque, the maximum voltage impressed on the traction motors, and the maximum safe speed of the train remain the same. In fact, the speed of the metadyne set depends only on the critical speed of regulator dynamo 6, and the ampere-turns created by secondary variator winding 5 are independent of the overhead-line voltage, because field winding 9 of the modulator is supplied by the voltage of the traction motors, and field winding 8 is excited by a small auxiliary set supplying constant voltage for the illumination of the train.

Many test runs have been performed to measure the energy saving compared with a train provided with rheostatic equipment. A total energy saving of 24% has been found, almost exactly what had been predicted. The average distance between two consecutive stations is half a mile, the maximum speed is about 40 miles an hour, and the average time for covering the distance between two stations and for changing passengers in one station is 80 seconds.

The maximum rate of acceleration has been kept around 90 centimeters per second per second. This value is below the half value permitted by the coefficient of friction, because the London subway coaches

Fig. 247. The commutator of the subway metadyne after an especially severe test. (*Courtesy of the Metropolitan-Vickers Co., Ltd., Sheffield.*)

have only two motor axles out of four axles. Yet the equipment would very easily make possible a higher acceleration, not only because of the facility with which it can develop a higher tractive effort but also because the passengers can stand high accelerations much easier when the train is driven by metadyne equipment.

The cost of the energy saving indicated above could provide for easy amortization, but economies from other sources are just as important; for instance, the saving on brake blocks, and the saving on wheel and rail repairs.

With a given overhead line and a given system of substations, the metadyne equipment permits an increase in traffic. The overhead line must supply the train with 24% less current; the particular peaks of current which usually appear with the simultaneous starting of many trains are eliminated; finally, part of the current absorbed by an accelerating train may be supplied by a train operating under the same section of overhead line and regenerating at this very moment. With this regeneration, a current is supplied which passes through all the substations.

Fig. 248. Some typical coaches constructed with the metadyne equipment. (*Courtesy of the Metropolitan-Vickers Co., Ltd., Sheffield.*)

Similar arguments apply to the substations. The economy derived from the better utilization of the substations is especially valuable in large, crowded centers.

The most important economy that the metadyne system could offer arises from the possibility of an increase in the rate of acceleration and the rate of deceleration without reaching the limits at which the passengers are disturbed. This increase would permit a greater volume of traffic with the same overhead line and substation system, with the same rolling stock and personnel, and, above all, with a much-appreciated reduction of the loss of time for the passengers. This point has not yet attracted the attention it deserves.

Figure 246 shows the metadyne set with the regulator dynamo at one end of the shaft and the modulator dynamo at the other end. Particular care has been given to making their operation as silent as possible.

Figure 247 shows the commutator after a test that lasted one month, with the metadyne running 20 hours a day with its cover sealed. Commutation was satisfactory, and it left the commutator clean even after such a long period of continuous operation. Usually the commutators of all traction motors are inspected and cleaned every week.

Figure 248 shows some motor coaches. About 200 such motor coaches have run for more than 14 years now; during the turbulent period of World War II, they continued to render service even though their maintenance probably did not receive especially careful attention.

Figure 249 shows an oscillogram recording the operation from one station to another. The voltage on the motors increases with speed and reaches a maximum value; it is practically zero during coasting; then it changes sign during the braking period and tends toward zero when the train decelerates.

The current supplied to the motor (equal to $\frac{1}{2}I_b$) increases smoothly but quickly at starting, so that there is no jerk. The engineer stops momentarily at the first characteristic, passes quickly to the second and finally to the third characteristic corresponding to the highest value of current I_b. Then I_b decreases slowly as the speed increases, but with much less change than with series motors and rheostatic equipment. During coasting, current I_b is reduced to the magnetizing component. During the braking period, I_b is large and practically constant during the whole period.

Line current I_L is practically zero at starting and increases gradually with the speed of the train; when it has reached its flat maximum, it remains practically constant during the rest of the accelerating period; this is a valuable characteristic because it permits a quick acceleration without overloading the overhead line and the substations. During coasting, the line current is reduced to the value corresponding to the losses. During the braking period, the line current changes sign and decreases toward zero with the speed.

Consider the question of the weight of the metadyne equipment. It has already been shown that the Cross transformer metadyne operates in a way similar to an autotransformer in an alternating-current network. The Eight transformer metadyne, operating under the conditions met in a subway, weighs a little more than half of the corresponding Cross transformer metadyne; its size and weight are thus much reduced as compared with the size and the total weight of the traction motors it controls.

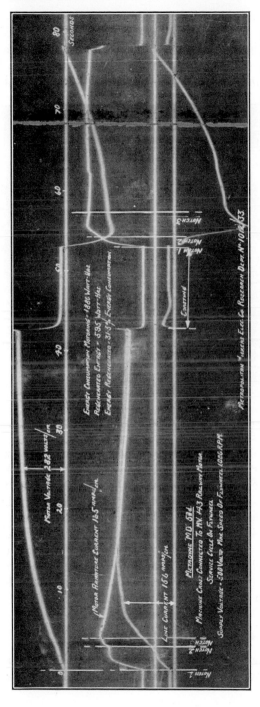

Fig. 249. Observed characteristics of the London subway metadyne. (*Courtesy of the Metropolitan-Vickers Co., Ltd., Sheffield.*)

Figure 250 shows the whole equipment on the test bed. In the fore-ground are the four traction motors directly coupled to a flywheel having an inertia that permits storage of the same mechanical energy as that of the two motor coaches driven by the equipment, through two driving axles upon each coach. In the background is the metadyne

Fig. 250. Test arrangement for the metadyne and motors of the London subway coaches. (*Courtesy of the Metropolitan-Vickers Co., Ltd., Sheffield.*)

proper with the regulator and modulator dynamo. The weight of the metadyne set is equal to 35% of the total weight of the controlled motors. The metadyne equipment of the London subway was designed shortly after the original invention; very little experience had been had with the machine, at the time. No improvement has been made in this equipment. This is a proof of the accuracy with which the English manufacturing company has constructed this metadyne, competing in the traction field, where generations of designers have given great care to every detail. Such daring applications cannot succeed without the firm sponsorship of an important personality—here, W. S. Graff-Baker.

6. LARGE BATTERY LOCOMOTIVES

Between 2 and 4 A.M., public operation on the London subways is generally suspended, and supervision and maintenance are undertaken.

During this time, the overhead line is obviously not alive, and large battery locomotives provide the transportation of personnel and material.

Fig. 251. Battery locomotive for the London subway. (*Courtesy of the Metropolitan-Vickers Co., Ltd., Sheffield.*)

Such battery locomotives must stop frequently, move a long, heavy freight train, and be able to run sometimes at high speed, sometimes at very low speed. Metadyne equipment is thus appropriate. The most

Fig. 252. The transformer metadyne for the battery locomotive. (*Courtesy of the Metropolitan-Vickers Co., Ltd., Sheffield.*)

expensive part of these locomotives is the battery; for performing a given service, the metadyne equipment requires a battery that is smaller by about 20 per cent or more.

The London subway battery locomotives provided with metadyne equipment proved satisfactory. The scheme adopted is similar to the scheme of Fig. 244 applied on the twin motor coaches. Figure 251 shows such a locomotive, and Fig. 252 shows the metadyne set comprising the metadyne proper, the regulator dynamo, and the modulator dynamo.

The Eight transformer metadyne with one commutator, used on the London subway battery locomotive, is relatively much smaller in size than the Eight transformer metadyne with two armature windings, used on the Toulouse train, if the great difference in the power between the two vehicles is taken into consideration. The most important losses are the copper losses in the armature. Consider the two cases, with the same armature diameter and length of laminations in each. Let R be the resistance of the single armature winding measured between two diametrically opposite brushes. The copper losses are, then,

$$R(I_a^2 + I_b^2)$$

Now consider two independent windings in the same slots; they must induce the same voltage, and therefore the windings must have the same number of peripheral conductors. This would increase the resistance between two diametrically opposite brushes from 1 to 2 in the event that the total area of the copper section in a slot could be maintained equal. But with two independent windings, the insulation takes up a large part of the cross section. Then the armature resistance becomes $2kR$, where k is a coefficient larger than 1, increasing when the induced voltage increases and when the diameter of the armature decreases; for the Toulouse train, k is about 1.25. The copper losses thus become

$$2Rk(I_a^2 + I_b^2)$$

or about 2.5 times larger.

The Toulouse train equipment was the first equipment designed with an Eight transformer metadyne; the London subway is the second. If the Toulouse train had had a single-winding metadyne, the energy saving would increase to about 26%. Since the design of the London subway equipment, radical improvements have been devised by the author, but they have not been applied as yet.

7. THE MOTOR COACHES FOR THE ITALIAN STATE RAILWAYS

Along the Riviera between Toulon, in France, and La Spezia, in Italy, extends a most beautiful region, densely populated, and having as its only means for transportation a single highway and one double-track railway line. The Italian State Railways intends to organize a rapid transit service over this 300-mile railway along the Riviera.

The average distance between stations is 1.3 miles, and the maximum speed may be 60 miles per hour. The train consists of motor coaches with the full weight of the motors on the axles.   The rate of acceleration and deceleration is very high.

The author has designed complete equipment for these motor coaches. Figure 253 gives the main features of the scheme.   An Eight trans-

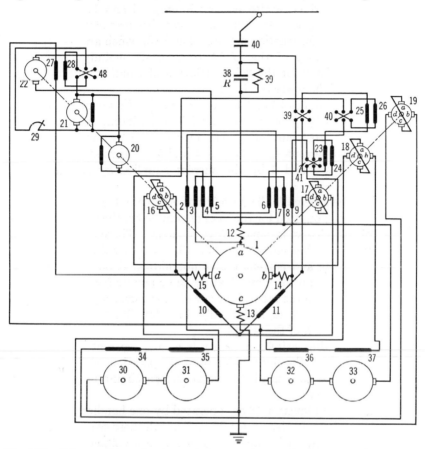

Fig. 253.   Scheme of transformer metadyne equipment for motor coaches for the Italian State Railways.

former metadyne, 1, controls four traction motors, 30, 31, 32, 33.   Secondary current I_b is positive for motoring and negative for braking and regenerating; therefore, the connections of the motors to the brushes of the metadyne remain unchanged, and the much-used inverter 32 of Fig. 244, pertaining to the London subway, is eliminated.   The metadyne set starts by itself as a series dynamo, by means of resistor 39, which is automatically short-circuited by contactor 38R when the voltage drop across resistor 39 becomes very low.

The metadyne proper drives two sets of auxiliary machines; one set comprises a shunt-excited regulator dynamo, 20, a base dynamo, 21, a modulator dynamo, 22, and an amplifier metadyne, 16; another set comprises three amplifier metadynes, 17, 18, and 19. Two amplifier metadynes, 16 and 17, excite stator windings 10 and 11 of the Eight transformer metadyne. Amplifier metadyne 18 provides for the field excitation current for traction motors 32 and 33, which are inserted into the upper right loop of the Eight transformer metadyne; amplifier metadyne 19 is used for the field excitation of traction motors 30 and 31 inserted into the lower left loop.

Amplifier metadynes 16 and 17 are provided with secondary variator windings excited by pilot currents as follows: winding 2 by a current proportional to brush current I_d; windings 3 and 8 by a current proportional to brush current I_a; windings 4 and 7 by regulator current I_ρ; finally, windings 5 and 6 by the current supplied by the modulator dynamo 22.

Although the schematic diagram is not complete, for some secondary details have been omitted for the sake of simplicity, the reduction in the amount of switchgear is nonetheless obvious. There is the starting switchgear comprising circuit breaker 40, contactor 38R, resistor 39, and some voltage and current relays not indicated on the schematic. There is also rheostat 29, controlled by the engineer for changing from one characteristic to the other, inverter 48, for changing from motoring to braking and vice versa, and, finally, inverters 39, 40, and 41 for reversing the direction of the train.

Only the starting switchgear controls a large current circulated by the high voltage of the line; under normal operation, the line current is always reduced to a negligible value before circuit breaker 40 and contactor 38R operate.

Rheostat 29 and inverter 48 are operated by one handle; inverters 39, 40, and 41 are operated by a second handle. All these switches control a very low current, just a few amperes at a very low voltage, say 24 volts.

This reduction and simplification of the switchgear is due to the special scheme, on one hand, and, on the other hand, to the presence of small auxiliary rotating machines, dynamos, and amplifier metadynes. There are seven such machines. These machines are relatively small, say of 3 to 6 kilowatts each, and operate at a very low voltage. They are of low weight, and they occupy little space. They need little supervision, and their operation is not influenced by the jerks and oscillations of the train.

Normal switchgear, even carefully constructed according to the best rules for traction equipment, needs frequent supervision and is responsible for the greatest number of accidents during operation. Experience has led the author to favor small rotating machines operating at low voltage as compared with switchgear expected to perform a linear or angular movement just at the moment for operation and to remain still for the long time between two consecutive operations.

Notice that base dynamo 21, rotating at a practically constant speed whatever the overhead-line voltage and the load on the traction motors

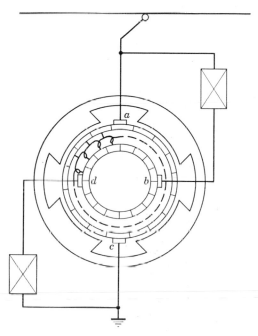

Fig. 254. This is a single-winding, two-commutator machine.

may be, is also used to supply current for illuminating the motor coach and for charging a battery as an emergency source. It also supplies current for driving the air compressor for the mechanical braking system. The mechanical braking system is always kept operating independently of the electric braking through the metadyne. The coach is safer if both braking systems are ready to operate; further, the mechanical braking system is necessary for the long stops in the stations.

The base dynamo eliminates the normal motor-generator set required for the pneumatic brakes. This motor-generator set has a weight equal to the weight of the seven small auxiliary machines of the metadyne set, because the motor must operate from the overhead-line voltage.

The normal illuminating set, eliminated by the base dynamo, also has a weight that is not negligible.

The characteristics of armature current in the traction motors versus the voltage supplied to them and of tractive effort versus train speed are similar to the corresponding characteristics of the London subway. The same arguments concerning economy of the operation also apply

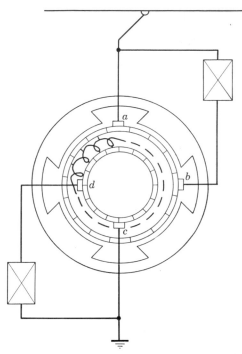

Fig. 255.   The two-commutator machine with an alternative brush arrangement.

here, except that the corresponding figures are higher.   For instance, under the conditions indicated at the beginning of this section, the energy saving reaches about 39%.

The additional weight of the transformer metadyne is considerably compensated by the reduction in weight of the traction motors, which are designed specifically for the metadyne equipment considered here. The cables along the coach, necessary for the control of the operation of the coach, are smaller than the cables of the customary rheostatic equipment.

The overhead-line voltage is nominally 3000 volts, but it can oscillate between 2400 volts and 3600 volts.   This high value of voltage constitutes one of the severest conditions to be met by the designer.

The traction motors are independent of the oscillations of the over-head-line voltage as has already been demonstrated in the previous section. They are protected against any voltage surge by the action of the metadyne. The metadyne alone is subjected to the overhead-line voltage.

Great care went into meeting this condition. The author adopted the arrangement of connecting to the single armature winding two dis-tinct commutators, as the scheme of Fig. 254 shows, one commutator

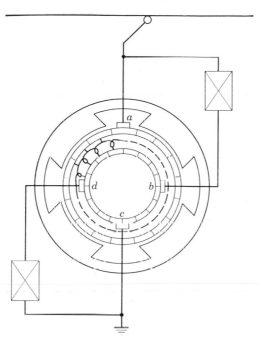

Fig. 256. A third variant of the two commutator idea.

on each side of the armature. One commutator bears only the primary brushes, and the other commutator bears only the secondary brushes. This construction does not weaken the insulation of the armature winding as does the use of an armature with two separate windings, each winding connected to a separate commutator; and this special construc-tion provides more effective protection against flashover.

Actually, the same arguments may be repeated here that were devel-oped in Section 5 of Chapter 12 concerning the behavior of the Cross transformer metadyne for the shunting locomotive of the Italian State Railways, with respect to flashover. In this case, the protection is even better because of the two following facts:

(a) The chain of small arcs between two consecutive segments of the primary commutator, beginning, say, at brush a, must now be maintained along the interpolar segment around to b', which corresponds to brush b on the secondary commutator; but along this segment there is practically no voltage between two consecutive segments.

(b) The same chain of small arcs must reach brush c, which is located at 180 geometrical degrees from brush a.

Figure 255 shows a variant arrangement of the double-commutator device; one commutator bears brushes a and b, and the other commutator bears brushes c and d.

The most dangerous flashover is the one connecting the primary brushes a and c, but to join them the flashover must go from one commutator to the other. A flashover between brushes a and b or between brushes c and d would simply short-circuit the two loops of the Eight and die out, because such a condition is a normal operating condition.

Figure 256 shows another variant; one commutator bears only brush a, and the other commutator bears the three remaining brushes, b, c, and d. A flashover starting from the high-voltage brush, a, cannot reach any other brush.

There is another interesting traction application of the transformer metadyne in Italy. The author has constructed many small mine locomotives to operate from either a battery or an overhead line. Here the transformer metadyne is provided with a regulator winding without any regulator dynamo. This regulator winding is a shunt stator winding connected across the secondary brushes, as shown in Section 2 of Chapter 6.

20 · Some Metadynes of a Degree Different from 4; $m \neq 4$

1. THE Y METADYNE

The Y metadyne is characterized by three brushes per cycle, two brushes being diametrically opposite. Figure 257 shows a general arrangement of the brushes a, b, c; coils 1 and 2 each are interlinked with a single polar segment; coil 3 is interlinked with two polar segments. Coil 3 is used if the ampere-turns of coil 3 are favorable to the commu-

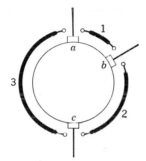

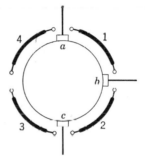

Fig. 257. The general Y metadyne.

Fig. 258. A common brush arrangement for a third-degree metadyne.

tation of the current I_b, or at least if they practically do not disturb it. Figure 258 shows a particular arrangement of the brushes, brush b being located at 90 electrical degrees from brushes a and c, which are diametrically opposite. This is a common arrangement. The polar segments and the stator coils, 1, 2, 3, and 4, are then identical geometrically. Many types of Y metadyne may be derived from a metadyne of degree $m = 4$ having equidistant brushes, if brush d is shifted until it is coincident with brush c.

Consider the scheme of Fig. 259 concerning a Yawl transformer metadyne. Brushes a and c are connected to a constant-voltage source; consumer 2 is connected between brushes b and c. The shaft of metadyne 1 is coupled to a shunt-excited regulator dynamo 3, which supplies regulator current I_ρ to regulator winding 4. A variator winding, 5, excited by current I_α, is shown extending over the polar segment comprised between brushes a and b. It should be recalled here that the

341

diametrically opposite polar segments are always assumed to have coils of the same windings, each coil creating the same value of ampere-turns but directed towards the center of the machine for one polar segment and directed in the opposite direction, away from the center of the machine, for the other polar segment.

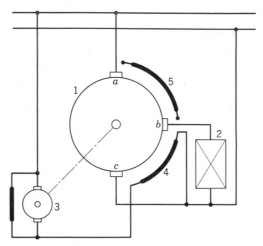

Fig. 259.   An elementary Yawl transformer metadyne.

The three brush currents, I_a, I_b, and I_c, may be replaced by the two canonical currents I_{ac} and I_{bc}, defined by the equations

$$I_{ac} = I_a$$

$$I_{bc} = I_b$$

$$I_{ac} + I_{bc} = -I_c$$

The fundamental equations may then be written as follows, if the slight departures of the speed from the value of the critical speed of the regulator dynamo are neglected:

$$\frac{1}{n} E_{ca} = K_{ca}^{bc} I_{bc} + K_{ca}^{\alpha} I_{\alpha} + K_{ca}^{\rho} I_{\rho}$$

$$\frac{1}{n} E_{cb} = K_{cb}^{ac} I_{ac} + K_{cb}^{\rho} I_{\rho} \tag{175}$$

$$2\pi T = K_{ca}^{\alpha} I_{\alpha} I_{ac} + K_{ca}^{\rho} I_{\rho} I_{ac} + K_{cb}^{\rho} I_{\rho} I_{bc}$$

If these equations are compared with the fundamental equations of the Cross transformer metadyne, it becomes evident that, for I_{α} constant, the characteristic of the current versus the voltage supplied to consumer 2 is a hyperbola having its asymptotes parallel to the axis. The comments are similar to those developed for the Cross transformer metadyne.

The scheme of Fig. 260 concerns a Yawl transformer metadyne similar to the one previously examined except for the regulator windings 4 and 6, now covering an angle of 180 electrical degrees with the magnetic axis

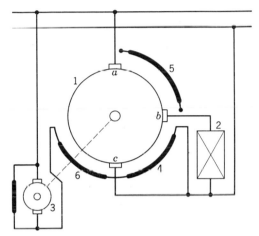

Fig. 260. Compare the form of the regulator winding of this scheme with that of Fig. 259.

along the commutating axis of brushes a and c. On the assumption that $n = n_0$, the fundamental equations are now

$$\frac{1}{n} E_{ca} = K_{ca}^{bc} I_{bc} + K_{ca}^{\alpha} I_{\alpha}$$

$$\frac{1}{n} E_{cb} = K_{cb}^{uv} I_{ac} + K_{cb}^{\rho} I_{\rho} \qquad (176)$$

$$2\pi T = K_{ca}^{\alpha} I_{\alpha} I_{ac} + K_{cb}^{\rho} I_{\rho} I_{bc}$$

from which a straight line is obtained as the characteristic of I_{bc} as a function of E_{cb}, and particularly $I_{bc} = $ constant if E_{ca} and I_{α} are constant. If a second variator winding, located exactly like winding 5 and shunt-connected across brushes b and c, is added, the straight line representing I_{bc} as a function of E_{cb} will take on any desired inclination.

Figure 261 gives the scheme of a Y generator metadyne. To write the fundamental equations, choose the following system of canonical currents: I_{ac} and I_{ab}. These currents yield

$$\frac{1}{n} E_{ba} = \frac{-1}{n}\left[R_a I_{ab} + \frac{1}{2} R_{ac} I_{ac} \right] = K_{ba}^{ac} I_{ac} + K_{ba}^{\alpha} I_{\alpha} + K_{ba}^{\beta} \frac{E_{ca}}{R_1}$$

$$\frac{1}{n} E_{ca} = K_{ca}^{ab} I_{ab} + K_{ca}^{\beta} \frac{E_{ca}}{R_1} \qquad\qquad (177)$$

$$2\pi T = \frac{1}{n}[E_{ca} I_{ac} + E_{ba} I_{ab}] \approx \frac{1}{n} E_{ca} I_{ac}$$

where R_a is the resistance of the closed circuit through which the current I_{ab} flows; where R_{ac} is the resistance of the armature between brushes a and c; where I_{α} is the current flowing in the variator winding 4; and where R_1 is the resistance of the shunt variator winding 3. The sign $\approx$ means nearly equal. Since the voltage E_{ba} is very small compared to E_{ca}, the former has been neglected in the third equation. The system of Equations 177 may be compared with the fundamental equations of the S generator metadyne having three variator windings: a secondary variator winding, excited by the parametrical current I_{α}; and two shunt-excited variator windings, connected across the secondary brushes (a primary and a secondary one).

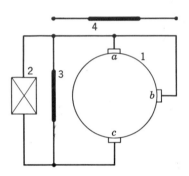

Fig. 261. A simple form of the Y generator metadyne.

The scheme of Fig. 262 permits easier control of the main characteristic of I_{ac} versus E_{ca}. In fact, the corresponding first two fundamental equations are simplified as follows:

$$\frac{1}{n} E_{ba} = K_{ba}^{ac} I_{ac} + K_{ba}^{\alpha} I_{\alpha}$$

$$\qquad\qquad (178)$$

$$\frac{1}{n} E_{ca} = K_{ca}^{ab} I_{ab} + K_{ca}^{\beta} \frac{E_{ca}}{R_1}$$

if E_{ba} is neglected as compared to E_{ca}.

Let R_a be the resistance of the complete circuit carrying the current I_{ab}, and let R_0 be the resistance of the armature, measured between two diametrically opposite points of the commutator. To Equations 178 may be added the following one:

$$E_{ba} = -R_a I_{ab} - \tfrac{1}{2} R_0 I_{ac} \tag{179}$$

Eliminating the variables I_{ab} and E_{ba} from this equation and from Equations 178 yields

$$I_{ac} = E_{ca} \frac{-R_a}{nK_{ab}^{ac} + (R_0/2)} \left[\frac{1}{nK_{ca}^{ab}} - \frac{K_{ca}^{\beta}}{R_1 K_{ca}^{ab}} \right] - \frac{K_{ba}^{\alpha} I_{\alpha}}{K_{ab}^{ac} - (R_0/2n)} \tag{180}$$

$$\equiv I_{ac\mu} + I_{acw}$$

A linear characteristic is thus obtained, which decreases when the voltage E_{ca} supplied to the load increases. For the S generator metadyne, this characteristic is deformed by iron saturation into the satisfactory shape shown in Fig. 124, but the Y generator metadyne scheme does not permit equally good utilization of the material.

Now consider a motor; Fig. 263 gives the scheme of an Ypsilon motor metadyne to be inserted into a loop of a series distribution system and

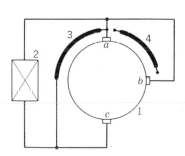

Fig. 262. This modification of the Y generator metadyne recalls the properties of the S generator metadyne.

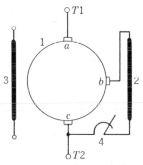

Fig. 263. The Ypsilon motor metadyne is a third-degree imitation of the Alpha motor metadyne.

endowed with a mechanical characteristic similar to the Alpha motor metadyne. Brushes a and c are connected to the terminals $T1$ and $T2$ of the machine; on the stator there are two windings: a hypercompensator, 2, excited by brush current I_b; and a variator winding, 3. Let I be the constant current supplied by the series distribution system, and let I_{α} be the current flowing in variator winding 3.

Choose the canonical currents I_{ac} and I_{bc}, and write the fundamental and auxiliary equations:

$$\frac{1}{n} E_{ca} = K_{cd}^{bc} I_{bc} + K_{ca}^{\beta} I_{bc} + K_{ca}^{\alpha} I_{\alpha}$$

$$\frac{1}{n} E_{cb} = K_{cb}^{ac} I_{ac} + K_{cb}^{\beta} I_{bc} + K_{cb}^{\alpha} I_{\alpha}$$

$$(181)$$

$$2\pi T = \frac{1}{n} E_{ca} I_{ac}$$

$$E_{cb} = -R_b I_{bc} - \tfrac{1}{2} R_0 I_{ac}$$

where R_b is the resistance of the closed circuit carrying I_{bc}, and R_0 the armature resistance measured between two diametrically opposite brushes. In the equation for the torque, the small losses due to the hypercompensator have been neglected for the sake of simplicity.

If I_{ac} and I_{α} are considered to be constants, and if E_{ca}, E_{cb}, and I_b are eliminated from these equations, the expression obtained gives the torque, T, as a function of the speed, n. This function is simplified if the scheme of Fig. 264 is considered. Then,

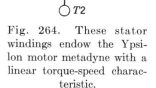

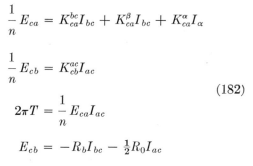

Fig. 264. These stator windings endow the Ypsilon motor metadyne with a linear torque-speed characteristic.

$$\frac{1}{n} E_{ca} = K_{ca}^{bc} I_{bc} + K_{ca}^{\beta} I_{bc} + K_{ca}^{\alpha} I_{\alpha}$$

$$\frac{1}{n} E_{cb} = K_{cb}^{ac} I_{ac}$$

$$(182)$$

$$2\pi T = \frac{1}{n} E_{ca} I_{ac}$$

$$E_{cb} = -R_b I_{bc} - \tfrac{1}{2} R_0 I_{ac}$$

from which there is

$$2\pi T = -I_{ac}^2 (K_{ca}^{bc} + K_{ca}^{\beta}) \frac{2nK_{cb}^{ac} + R_0}{2R_b} + K_{ca}^{\alpha} I_{\alpha} I_{ac} \qquad (183)$$

If it is recalled that $K_{ca}^{bc} + K_{ca}^{\beta}$ and K_{cb}^{ac} have negative values, the linear, drooping characteristic of torque versus speed, with iron saturation, turns into the very useful characteristic indicated by Fig. 140.

The value of the no-load speed, n_0, is obtained when the second member of Equation 183 is set equal to zero. The utilization of the

material here again is less adequate than with the Alpha motor metadyne. Similarly, other kinds of metadynes with three brushes may be
developed by imitation of the schemes of the metadynes of degree
$m = 4$.

With the previously considered schemes there must be four polar
segments. The scheme of Fig. 265 with three equidistant brushes needs
only three polar segments, provided that the armature winding pitch is
taken equal to about 120 electrical degrees. The corresponding slight
gain in the better utilization of the material, due to the fact that there
are only three free interpolar segments, is overbalanced by the great
dispersion of flux created by the stator coil covering 120 electrical degrees. All the metadynes considered in Part
II are symmetrical with respect to their
center. This symmetry allows the arrangement of two diametrically opposite stator
coils creating the same ampere-turns along
the same direction of a diameter of the machine. This arrangement creates a flux along
a clearly defined direction with but little stray
flux. Since the metadyne of Fig. 265 has no
symmetry with respect to its center, the arrangement of a pair of coils diametrically opposite each other is impossible. Because the
flux is due to a single stator coil and is

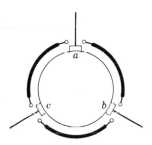

Fig. 265. Third-degree
metadyne with 120-degree
winding pitch.

therefore easily deflected from the desired direction, there is a large
stray flux.

All the metadynes of degree $m = 3$ have one serious disadvantage:
Each of the brushes must commutate the algebraic sum of the currents
of the other two brushes; thus the action of the commutating flux is
generally unsatisfactory.

In summary, the metadyne of degree $m = 3$ may be endowed with
most of the characteristics pertaining to the metadynes of degree $m = 4$,
but they generally have a poorer utilization of the material, and they
show no favorable conditions for good commutation. That is why
metadynes of degree $m = 3$ are constructed only for a small nominal
power, a few kilowatts. Small Y generator pseudometadynes for charging a small battery were well-known before the advent of the metadyne;
this form is still constructed on a large scale. Figure 266 is a photograph of a small set comprising an induction motor and a metadyne
generator for supplying the arc lamp of a cinema projector.

Fig. 266.   Cinema arc supply employing a metadyne generator.   (*Courtesy of the Lovati Co., Milan.*)

2. THE "SPIDER" TRANSFORMER METADYNE

The degree of this type is $m = 6$.   All the brushes are diametrically opposite, two by two.   Their arrangement, shown by Fig. 267, has two axes of symmetry: the diameter passing through primary brushes a and d, and the diameter electrically normal to it.   Primary brushes a and d are connected to a constant-voltage source; brushes f and b are connected to the first consumer, 2; the other two brushes, c and e, are connected to the second consumer, 3.

Because of the relation $E_{bf} = E_{ce}$, the two consumers must at any moment induce the same voltage.   Generally, they are identical and operate under identical conditions.

The shunt-excited regulator dynamo 7 is shown coupled to the shaft of metadyne 1 and connected to the constant voltage of the primary source.   Only three stator windings are indicated—the most characteristic—the variator winding 5, and the regulator windings 4 and 6.

The Spider metadyne is a hyperstatic metadyne.   Its system of brush currents may be resolved into two systems of canonical currents, the first system composed of currents I_{ad}, I_{bf}, and I_{ce} satisfying the relation

$$I_{bf} = I_{ce} \tag{184}$$

These constitute a system of brush currents of a statically defined meta-

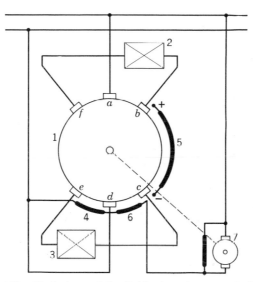

Fig. 207.   Basic form of the Spider transformer metadyne.

dyne.   The second system is composed of the currents $I_{bf}^{(1)}$ and $I_{ce}^{(1)}$ with the relation

$$I_{bf}^{(1)} = -I_{ce}^{(1)} \tag{185}$$

These constitute a void system of canonical currents, the intensity of which is undetermined.

Write the fundamental equations:

$$\frac{1}{n} E_{da} = 2K_{da}^{ce}I_{ce} + K_{da}^{\alpha}I_{\alpha}$$

$$\frac{1}{n} E_{cb} = 2K_{cb}^{ce}I_{ce} + K_{da}^{\alpha}I_{\alpha} \tag{186}$$

$$\frac{1}{n} E_{ce} = K_{ce}^{ad}I_{ad} + K_{ce}^{\rho}I_{\rho}$$

where I_{α} is the current flowing in the variator winding 5.   There are only three equations because there are only three independent brush voltages also.   The currents $I_{bf}^{(1)}$ and $I_{ce}^{(1)}$ do not appear because they constitute a void system.

Neglect the slight departure of the speed from the critical speed, and write the regulator equation:

$$2\pi T = K_{da}^\alpha I_\alpha I_{ad} - 2K_{ce}^\rho I_\rho I_{ce} \qquad (187)$$

where T is the torque due to the losses and to the regulator dynamo. The unknown variables are I_{ad}, I_{ce}, E_{cb}, and I_ρ when E_{ce} is taken as the independent variable and I_α as a parameter. For $E_{da} = $ constant, the

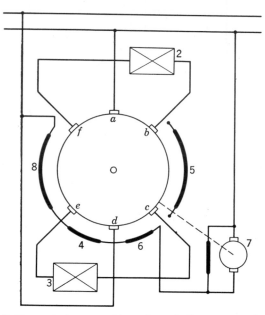

Fig. 268.   This Spider metadyne provides a hyperbolic current-voltage distribution to the consumers.

current I_{ce} is constant also and it is easily resolved into a magnetizing component and a component opposing the ampere-turns of the variator winding:

$$I_{ce\mu} = \frac{E_{da}}{2nK_{da}^{ce}}$$

$$I_{cew} = -I_\alpha \frac{K_{da}^\alpha}{2K_{da}^{ce}} \qquad (188)$$

The primary current I_{ad} may then be derived from the regulator equation, if the small value of T is neglected, and the equation is written in the form

$$0 = E_{da} I_{ad} - 2E_{ce} I_{ce} \qquad (189)$$

Then the third Equation 186 immediately yields I_ρ.

If a hyperbola is desired for the characteristic of I_{ce} as a function of E_{ce}, the scheme of Fig. 268 must be adopted, regulator windings 6, 4, and 8 being extended to cover segments cd, de, ef (and those diametrically opposite to them), the sense and number of turns of coil 8 being generally different from those of coils 4 and 6. Figure 269 gives three vector diagrams relative to the operation of the Spider metadyne. Diagram A corresponds to a supply of zero voltage to the consumers, diagrams B and C are obtained when the consumers operate as motors and as generators, respectively, currents I_{bf} and I_{ce} being assumed positive. The void system of canonical currents $I_{bf}^{(1)}$ and $I_{ce}^{(1)}$ is reduced

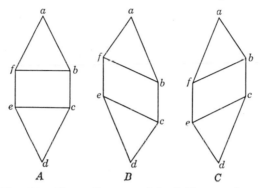

Fig. 269. Vector diagrams of the Spider metadyne.

to a negligible intensity by the same procedures indicated for the Eight transformer metadyne.

The Spider transformer metadyne is suitable for applications where the voltage of the source is high with respect to the maximum voltage required by the consumers, and where there is an even number of consumers that require the same voltage and the same current at any moment. The Spider transformer metadyne is also suited for applications where there are two distinct sources of low voltage and one consumer requiring a maximum value of voltage relatively high with respect to the voltage of the sources. The two low-voltage sources are then connected to brushes b and f and to brushes c and e, respectively, whereas the high-voltage consumer is connected to brushes a and d. Similar comments may easily be made on the operation of the Spider transformer metadyne inserted into a constant-current series distribution system.

3. THE "HEXAGON" TRANSFORMER METADYNE

The degree is $m = 6$ and the arrangement of the brushes is the same as for the Spider transformer metadyne, but the external connections are different, as the scheme of Fig. 270 shows. Note that, whereas the magnetic axes of coils 4 and 6 in Fig. 267 and Fig. 268 are both centripetal or both centrifugal, in Fig. 270 the magnetic axes of coils 4 and 6 are oriented so that one is centripetal and the other centrifugal. The Hexagon transformer metadyne is a nonreactive metadyne, and it operates very similarly to a shunt dynamo. The two consumers, 2 and

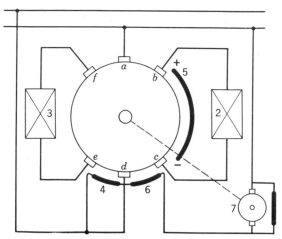

Fig. 270.   The Hexagon transformer metadyne.

3, connected, respectively, to brushes b and c and to brushes e and f must require the same voltage at any moment. If the network is just a consumer, we have an H generator metadyne, the stator windings of which may be arranged as for the K generator metadyne considered in Section 5, Chapter 17.

4. THE "CRONOS" TRANSFORMER METADYNE

The degree is $m = 6$, and the brushes are arranged as in the Spider transformer metadyne and as in the Hexagon transformer metadyne, but the external connections are different, as the scheme of Fig. 271 indicates. Brushes a and d are connected to a constant-voltage line; brushes c and b are connected to consumer 2, and brushes e and f are connected to consumer 3; further, brushes b and f and brushes c and e are short-circuited.

The Cronos transformer metadyne is a potential transformer, which is supplied by a line at constant voltage and which supplies to the loads direct current at constant voltage, the value of which may be easily controlled at will, as with the K generator metadyne or as with

the Hexagon transformer metadyne. Whereas the latter two metadynes are nonreactive, however, the Cronos transformer metadyne is a
reactive type, and it is endowed with all the properties pertaining to
that type.

In the scheme of Fig. 271, a shunt-excited regulator dynamo is shown
coupled to the same shaft as metadyne 1 and connected to the constant

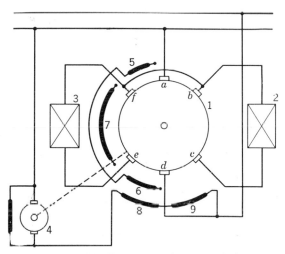

Fig. 271. The Cronos transformer metadyne.

voltage of the line. Regulator winding 8 and 9 is shown with its magnetic axis along the commutating axis of brushes d and a. Two variator
windings are indicated, variator winding 7 and variator winding 5
and 6. This machine is a hyperstatic metadyne. The system of brush
currents is equivalent to two systems of canonical currents, the system
I_{ad}, I_{bc}, I_{bf}, I_{fe}, and I_{ce} with the relations

$$I_{bc} = I_{fe}$$
$$I_{bf} = I_{ce}$$

(190)

and the system $I_{bf}^{(1)}$, $I_{ce}^{(1)}$ with the relation

$$I_{bf}^{(1)} = -I_{ce}^{(1)}$$

(191)

Because of the short-circuit between brushes b and f and between
brushes c and e, any difference between the currents flowing in consumers 2 and 3 does not interfere with the distribution of currents I_{bc}
and I_{fe} in the armature of the metadyne. These two currents are equal
if the machine is accurately constructed. Similar arguments hold for

currents I_{bf} and I_{cc}. The scheme of Fig. 272, in which a single consumer appears, is equivalent to the scheme of Fig. 271 as far as the values of the brush currents are concerned.

The system $I_{bf}^{(1)}$, $I_{ce}^{(1)}$ is a void canonical system. Since these currents pass through the bars short-circuiting brushes b and f, and brushes c and e, respectively, the intensity of the currents of this system can be reduced only by means of devices that result from dynamic analysis. On the other hand, this void system cannot degenerate into a system of alternating currents of low frequency, the most harmful kind of void

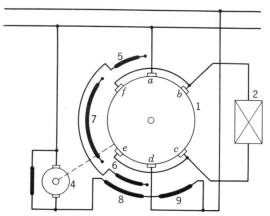

Fig. 272.   The Cronos transformer with one consumer.

system of canonical currents, because the short-circuiting bars store practically no electromagnetic energy, the oscillation of which from one branch to another is the main cause of the harmful alternating current.

The system of canonical currents I_{ad}, I_{bc}, I_{fe}, I_{bf}, and I_{ce} correspond to a statically determinate metadyne. The fundamental and auxiliary equations (assuming $n = n_0$) may be written

$$\frac{1}{n} E_{da} = 2K_{da}^{ce}I_{ce} + K_{da}^{\alpha}I_{\alpha} + K_{da}^{\beta}I_{\beta}$$

$$\frac{1}{n} E_{ce} = K_{ce}^{ad}I_{ad} + K_{ce}^{bc}I_{bc} + K_{ce}^{\rho}I_{\rho}$$

$$\frac{1}{n} E_{cb} = 2K_{cb}^{ce}I_{ce} + K_{cb}^{\alpha}I_{\alpha} \qquad\qquad (192)$$

$$2\pi T = \frac{1}{n}[E_{da}I_{ad} + 2E_{cb}I_{bc} + E_{da}I_{\rho} - 2E_{ce}I_{ce}]$$

$$E_{ce} = R_{ce}I_{ce}$$

where R_{ce} is the resistance of the closed circuit carrying I_{ce}, where I_α and I_β are the currents passing through variator winding 7 and variator winding 5 and 6, respectively, the last two coils creating the same number of ampere-turns, both in the same direction. Similarly, coils 8 and 9 of the regulator winding create the same number of ampere-turns, which are in the same direction with respect to the center of the machine.

Choose as independent variables the following ones: line voltage E_{da}; voltage E_{cb} and the algebraic sum, $2I_{bc}$, of the currents corresponding to the two consumers, 2 and 3; parameter I_α. Equations 192 then determine all the other variables, E_{ce}, I_{ad}, I_ρ, I_β, and I_{ce}.

Neglect some terms that are small compared with the other terms in the same equation, and simplify the system of Equations 192 as follows:

$$\frac{1}{n} E_{da} = 2K_{da}^{ce} I_{ce} + K_{da}^{\alpha} I_\alpha + K_{da}^{\beta} I_\beta$$

$$0 = K_{ce}^{ad} I_{ad} + K_{ce}^{bc} I_{bc} + K_{ce}^{\rho} I_\rho$$

$$(193)$$

$$\frac{1}{n} E_{cb} = 2K_{cb}^{ce} I_{ce} + K_{cb}^{\alpha} I_\alpha$$

$$0 = E_{da} I_{ad} + 2E_{cb} I_{bc}$$

The simplified solutions follow:

$$I_{ce} = \frac{E_{cb}}{2nK_{cb}^{ce}} - I_\alpha \frac{K_{cb}^{\alpha}}{K_{cb}^{ce}} \equiv I_{ce\mu} + I_{cew} \qquad (194)$$

$$I_\beta = \left[\frac{E_{da}}{nK_{da}^{\beta}} - \frac{2E_{cb}K_{da}^{ce}}{nK_{cb}^{ce}K_{da}^{\beta}} \right] + I_\alpha \left[\frac{2K_{da}^{ce}K_{cb}^{\alpha}}{K_{da}^{\beta}K_{cb}^{ce}} - \frac{K_{da}^{\alpha}}{K_{da}^{\beta}} \right]$$

$$= I_{\beta\mu} + I_{\beta w} \qquad (195)$$

$$I_{ad} = -2I_{bc} \frac{E_{cb}}{E_{da}}$$

$$(196)$$

$$I_\rho = I_{bc} \left[\frac{2K_{ce}^{ad}E_{cb}}{K_{ce}^{\rho}E_{da}} - \frac{K_{ce}^{bc}}{K_{ce}^{\rho}} \right]$$

Equation 194 leads to a convenient choice of current I_α for a given value of E_{cb}, so that I_{ce} becomes negligible; the optimum value for the current I_α is thus proportional to the voltage E_{cb}. Equation 195 suggests a convenient design for coils 5 and 6. Equation 196 permits a good

choice for coils 8 and 9.   Figure 273 gives some vector diagrams corresponding to various values of voltage E_{cb}.

The Cronos transformer metadyne is an excellent voltage transformer.
It easily handles quick voltage variations from the line and from the

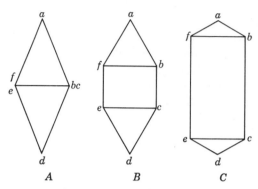

Fig. 273.   Vector diagrams for the Cronos transformer metadyne.

consumers.   It has very low armature losses.   It keeps its speed steady
automatically and exhibits the properties of good commutation.   Its
armature is partially compensated.

21 · The Rosacean Transformer Metadynes

1. DEFINITION

Consider a metadyne having m brushes per cycle, and let numerals in their natural sequence indicate the brushes in their angular sequence along the same angular direction. Choose a brush of numeral c and connect it through an external circuit to the brush of numeral $c + k$. Similarly, connect the brush of numeral $c + h$ to the brush of numeral $c + h + k$ through another external circuit. Further, connect the brush of numeral $c + 2h$ to the brush of numeral $c + 2h + k$, and so on, the letters c, k, and h being given any desired integer value. The metadyne thus obtained is a simple Rosacean metadyne. Superimposing upon these connections new ones determined in a similar way, by giving to the letters c, h, and k another set of integer values, creates a double Rosacean metadyne. In a similar way, a triple and, more generally, a multiple Rosacean metadyne is obtained. It is obvious that the numeral q, where $q > m$, corresponds to the brush of numeral $q - pm$, where p is an integer and where $m + 1 \geqslant q - pm \geqslant 0$.

The location of the m brushes may have a diameter as an axis of symmetry, or even two perpendicular diameters as axes of symmetry, upon

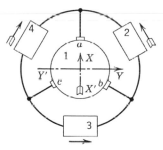

Fig. 274. A third-degree simple Rosacean metadyne with a continuous corolla.

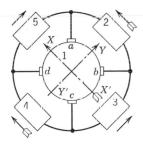

Fig. 275. A similar fourth-degree Rosacean metadyne.

taking into account the electrical angles, i.e., the geometrical angle multiplied by the number of cycles. The external circuits mentioned above, connecting two brushes of the metadyne, may be any of these: a low-resistance conductor; a resistor; an arrangement of resistors, reactors, and capacitors; a dynamo; a metadyne; or even a complete power system.   They are generally represented by a rectangle.

Figures 274 through 285 represent the scheme of Rosacean metadynes. The brush arrangements of Figs. 274 and 279 have one diameter of sym-

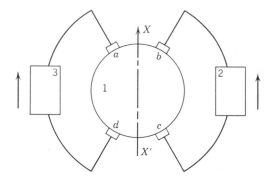

Fig. 276.   A fourth-degree Rosacean metadyne with a discontinuous corolla.

metry; the arrangements of the other ten figures have two diameters, perpendicular to one another, as axes of symmetry.

For Fig. 274, $m = 3$, and for the following six figures $m = 4$; for Figs. 281 through 285, $m = 6$.   Figures 274, 275, 276, 279, 281, and 282 rep-

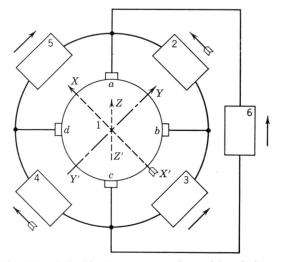

Fig. 277.   A double Rosacean metadyne of fourth degree.

resent the scheme of simple Rosacean metadynes; Figs. 277, 278, 280, 283, and 284 represent the scheme of double Rosacean metadynes; finally, Fig. 285 gives the scheme of a triple Rosacean metadyne.

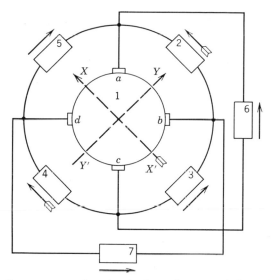

Fig. 278. This Rosacean metadyne has both continuous and discontinuous corollas.

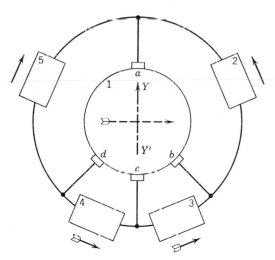

Fig. 279. A fourth-degree Rosacean metadyne with a continuous corolla but only one axis of symmetry.

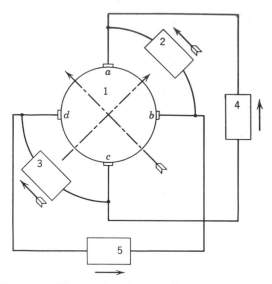

Fig. 280.   This metadyne has two discontinuous corollas.

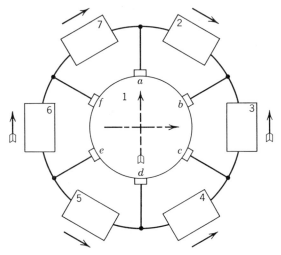

Fig. 281.   A symmetrical sixth-degree Rosacean metadyne with a continuous corolla.

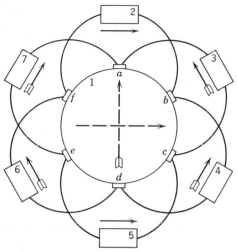

Fig. 282. Although this scheme has two continuous corollas, it can satisfy the definition of a simple Rosacean metadyne.

The definition may be applied to obtain Fig. 274 by taking $k - 1$ and $h = 1$; similarly, for Figs. 275, 279, and 281. To obtain the scheme of Fig. 276, take $k = 1$ and $h = 2$. For Fig. 282, take $k = 2$ and $h = 2$.

For Fig. 277, first take $k = 1$ and $h = 1$, and then take $k = 2$ and $h = 2$. For Fig. 278, take $k = 1$ and $h = 1$ first, and then $k = 2$ and $h = 1$. For Fig. 280, the first time take $k = 1$ and $h = 2$ and the second time $k = 2$ and $h = 1$. For Fig. 283, first use $c = 1$, $k = 3$, and $h = 3$, and next $c = 3$, $k = 2$, and $h = 3$. For Fig. 284, use $k = 2$, $h = 1$ the first time, and the second time $k = 3$ and $h = 3$. For Fig. 285, first take $c = 1$, $k = 3$, $h = 3$, next take $c = 2$, $k = 1$, $h = 3$, and the third time $c = 3$, $k = 2$, $h = 3$.

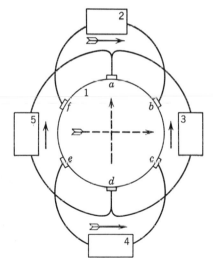

Fig. 283. The symmetrical disposition of branches 3 and 5 constitutes a continuous corolla.

Certain schemes may be obtained from the definition in several different ways. For instance, the Rosacean metadyne of Fig. 282 may also be considered a double one obtained by taking first $c = 1$, $k = 2$,

$h = 2$ and the second time $c = 2$, $k = 2$, $h = 2$. Similarly, the Rosacean metadyne of Fig. 284 may be considered a triple one. In order to avoid confusion, the lowest possible order will always be given; therefore, Figs. 282 and 284 correspond to a simple and to a double Rosacean metadyne.

The two branches 3 and 5 of Fig. 283, 8 and 9 of Fig. 284, and 4 and 5 of Fig. 285, having the same brushes as terminals, really form only one

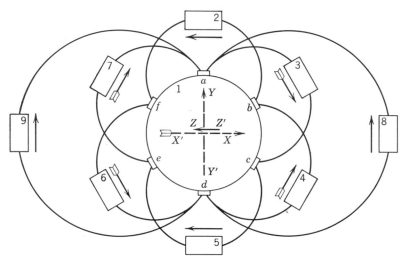

Fig. 284. Branches 8 and 9 may be considered as the single branch of a discontinuous corolla.

branch. Their representation as double branches was done only for the sake of symmetry.

All the external apparatus and connections obtained for a given application of the definition constitute a "corolla." One should distinguish "continuous corollas," which may form a closed loop for a current never entering the metadyne armature, and "discontinuous corollas," not fulfilling this condition. Thus the Rosacean metadynes of Figs. 274, 275, 279, and 281 have a continuous corolla. The Rosacean metadyne of Fig. 276 has a discontinuous corolla. The Rosacean metadynes of Figs. 277 and 278 have two corollas, one continuous and one discontinuous. Figures 280 and 283 show two discontinuous corollas. Figure 284 shows two continuous corollas and a discontinuous one. Finally, Fig. 285 shows three discontinuous corollas, one comprising the apparatus 2 and 3, another comprising the apparatus 4 and 5, and a third one comprising the apparatus 6 and 7; the first and third corollas constitute a single compound continuous corolla.

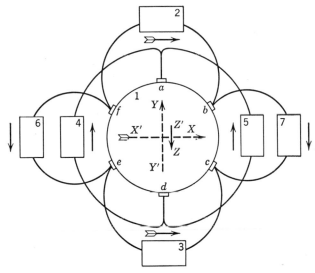

Fig. 285. Example of a triple Rosacean metadyne.

2. FUNDAMENTAL EQUATIONS

The Rosacean metadynes may operate as transformers, as generators, or as motors, but only their operation as transformers will be considered here. The operation as a generator or as a motor may easily be derived from the operation as a transformer by following the procedure indicated many times in this book.

The fundamental metadyne equations may be written

$$\frac{1}{n} E_{mc} = \sum_{e=a}^{m-1} K_{mc}^e I_e + \sum_{\gamma=\alpha}^{\nu} K_{mc}^\gamma I_\gamma \qquad c = a, b, \cdots, m-1 \quad (197)$$

The regulator equation, with the usual simplifications, can be written in two forms:

$$\sum_{c=a}^{m-1} E_{mc} I_c = 0 \qquad \text{or} \qquad \sum_{c=a}^{m-1} \sum_{\gamma=\alpha}^{\nu} K_{mc}^\gamma I_\gamma I_c = 0 \qquad (198)$$

Then there are the equations of the external circuit. Let Y_{gk} be the current flowing in the branch of the corolla connected to brushes g and k and going through that branch from brush g to brush k, when it is positive. There is an equation stating the relation between current Y_{gk} and brush voltage E_{gk}, which may be represented by

$$F_{gk}(E_{gk}, Y_{gk}) = 0 \qquad (199)$$

There are as many of these equations as there are branches, say p.

Finally, there are the relations between brush currents I_c and corolla currents Y_{gk}, which may be written

$$I_g = \sum_{c=a}^{m} Y_{cg} - \sum_{k=a}^{m} Y_{gk} \qquad (200)$$

If the Rosacean metadyne has only one corolla, each of the sums appearing in the second member of Equations 200 is reduced to a single term; if the Rosacean metadyne has many corollas, there may be sums having as many terms as there are corollas. Although there are m Equations 200, it is obvious that the sum of all the first members of these m equations, and of all the second members, is separately zero. Therefore, only $m - 1$ Equations 200 are independent of one another.

Thus there are $(m - 1) + 1 + p + (m - 1)$ equations. The variables are $m - 1$ brush voltages, $m - 1$ brush currents, the regulator current I_ρ, and the p corolla branch currents Y_{gk}: in all, $2m - 1 + p$, or as many variables as there are equations. Thus, except for singular points in the operation, all voltages and currents are generally determined.

Consider group 200; $m - 1$ equations are independent. The number of variables Y_{gk} is p, where p can be smaller than, equal to, or larger than $m - 1$.

The values of Y_{gk} determine one and only one set of values for I_g; on the other hand, the values of the brush currents generally do not determine a set of values of the corolla currents Y_{gk}. Consider, for example, a single continuous corolla: if the values Y_{gk} satisfy Equations 200, the values $Y_{gk} + Y_0$, where Y_0 is a constant, will also satisfy the same equations. Thus, the form of Equations 200 leads us to hope that the ratio τ between the controlled power and the transformed power may attain high values with some particular Rosacean metadynes.

3. CAPITAL AND SUBSERVIENT GROUPS

A transformer metadyne is frequently used when there is a periodic or a quasi-periodic operation to be performed. In such cases, electric power is often conveyed from the source to the consumer during one part of the period, and, conversely, from the consumer to the source during another part of the period. The metadyne transformer is then used to control this transfer of power and to transform the voltages and the currents from the values they have as delivered by the source to the values they must have when applied to the consumer.

These considerations lead to a subdivision of the machines and the apparatus of the metadyne plant into two groups. The first, comprising the consumers, will be called the Capital group, and the second, comprising the machines and the apparatus which must supply power to the consumers or absorb power from them, will be called the Subservient group.

To permit the Rosacean transformer metadyne to control the transfer of power, the author arranges the connections of the circuits of the Capital group to the metadyne brushes so that the armature ampere-turns due to the currents of the circuits of the Capital group may be represented by a vector having a direction, preferably fixed in space, to be referred to as the Capital direction. Similarly, he arranges the connections of the circuits of the Subservient group to the metadyne brushes so that the corresponding vector of the armature ampere-turns may have a direction, preferably fixed in space, to be referred to as the Subservient direction. Further, the particular displacement between the Capital direction and the Subservient direction is caused to be always different from zero and preferably 90 electrical degrees. The metadyne thus obtained is a reactive metadyne.

In order to obtain a Capital direction fixed in space, the author uses one of the following arrangements:

Arrangement a

The chord joining the two brushes connected to a circuit of the Capital group forms zero electrical degrees with the Capital direction.

Arrangement b

The chord of a pair of brushes connected to a circuit of the Capital group forms with the Capital direction an electrical angle different from zero, but there is a corresponding chord located symmetrically with respect to the Capital direction, with proper accounting of electrical angles; furthermore, the currents of the two corresponding circuits of the Capital group are of the same intensity and have directions symmetrical to the Capital direction.

Arrangement c

The chord of a pair of brushes connected to a circuit of the Capital group forms with the Capital direction an electrical angle different from zero, but there is a corresponding chord located symmetrically with respect to a diameter normal to the Capital direction, with due consideration of the electrical angles; further, the currents of the two corresponding circuits of the Capital group are of the same intensity but have directions that are not symmetrical with respect to the specified normal diameter.

It is easy to see that the rules given above yield the desired result when the winding pitch is diametrical, as is usually assumed in this book. It is also easy to pass to the more general case of a winding having a nondiametrical pitch.

Look at Fig. 275, and let 2 and 4 form the Capital group and let 3 and 5 form the Subservient group; further, let the direction of the current be indicated by the arrows near the rectangles. Then the Capital direction is the direction XX', and the Subservient direction is the direction YY'. These directions remain fixed in space, whatever the value of the currents may be in the various branches of the continuous corolla.

In Fig. 274, assume that the currents have the directions of the arrows indicated near the rectangles, and assign the rectangles 2 and 4 to the Capital group and the rectangle 3 to the Subservient group; then the Subservient direction is fixed along the line YY' and the Capital direction is fixed along the line XX', provided that the currents of 2 and 4 have the same intensity. If these currents do not have the same intensity, the Capital direction will be inclined with respect to the direction XX'.

Now consider Fig. 276; the armature ampere-turns are always along the direction XX', whatever the current may be in the rectangles 2 and 3. This metadyne is a nonreactive metadyne.

Consider Fig. 277, in which 2 and 4 will be the Capital group, and 3, 5, and 6 will form the Subservient group. The Capital direction will be fixed along the direction XX', whereas the Subservient direction will oscillate between two extreme positions YY' and ZZ', depending on the ratio of the intensity of the current in the rectangle 6 to that in the rectangles 3 and 5.

In Fig. 278, let 2 and 4 be the Capital group; 3, 5, 6, and 7 will be the Subservient group. The Capital direction is along XX', and the Subservient direction will be along YY' if the currents in 6 and 7 have the same intensity; it will oscillate around the direction YY', if these two currents do not have the same intensity.

Similar comments may be made on the schemes of Figs. 279 and 285, in which the rectangles of the Capital group have been indicated by a feathered arrow and the rectangles of the Subservient group have been indicated by a simple arrow.

In Fig. 284 three vectors are shown. Vector XX' along the Capital direction represents the ampere-turns of the Capital group, 3, 4, 6, and 7, on the assumption that all the corresponding currents have the same intensity; vector YY' along a direction electrically normal to the Capital direction corresponds to members 8 and 9 of the Subservient group;

finally, vector ZZ' along the Capital direction corresponds to members 2 and 5 of the Subservient group. Thus the electrical angle between the Capital and the Subservient direction here is generally different from 90 degrees, but Subservient member 2 may draw the greater part of the current from Capital members 4 and 6 outside the metadyne; a similar diversion of current is obtained with members 7, 3, and 5.

Similarly, three vectors are indicated in Fig. 285. Vector ZZ' corresponds to members 6 and 7.

The rectangles corresponding to the Capital group and those corresponding to the Subservient group may be interchanged. The arrangements indicated here are obviously not the only ones possible with the figures under consideration. The author arranges the stator windings in such a way as to have the vector representing the ampere-turns of the variator windings in a direction forming an electrical angle different from zero, preferably 90°, from the direction of the vector representing the ampere-turns of the regulator winding.

The system of the stator variator windings and regulator windings is superimposed as a whole in various ways upon the system formed by the armature connected to its corolla, each way being adapted to the particular application considered, the magnetic axes of this system being suitably located or shifted with respect to the magnetic axes of the system constituted by the armature connected to its corolla. In many cases, the variator ampere-turns are directed to act upon the armature ampere-turns along the Capital direction, and the regulator ampere-turns are directed to act upon the armature ampere-turns along the Subservient direction. Some examples are given in the following sections.

1. THE CLOVER TRANSFORMER METADYNE

The simplified scheme is given by Fig. 275. There are four equidistant brushes per cycle and one continuous corolla obtained from the definition of the Rosacean metadyne by taking $k = 1$ and $h = 1$.

In Fig. 286 the scheme of the Clover transformer metadyne has been repeated with the location of the stator windings. Members 2 and 4, of the Capital group, are represented as dynamos, but they may be any other suitable electric machine or apparatus. The rectangles 3 and 5 indicate members of the Subservient group. The stator windings are represented by 6 and 7; the extension of the arc and the direction of the radius through its midpoint indicate the extent of the winding and its magnetic axis, respectively.

Brush currents I_a, I_b, I_c, I_d may be replaced by two systems of canonical currents, system I_{ac}, I_{bd} and void system $I_{ab}^{(1)} = I_{cd}^{(1)}$, $I_{bc}^{(1)} = I_{da}^{(1)}$. They satisfy the equations

$$I_a = I_{ac} + I_{ab}^{(1)} - I_{bc}^{(1)}$$

$$I_b = I_{bd} - I_{ab}^{(1)} + I_{bc}^{(1)}$$

$$I_c = -I_{ac} + I_{ab}^{(1)} - I_{bc}^{(1)}$$

$$I_d = -I_{bd} - I_{ab}^{(1)} + I_{bc}^{(1)}$$

(201)

There are only three independent equations whereas there are four unknown variables among the currents of the two chosen canonical

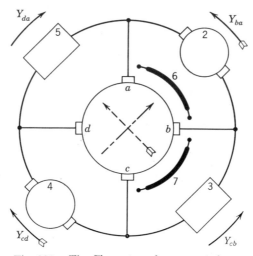

Fig. 286.   The Clover transformer metadyne.

currents. Thus, although the canonical currents define the brush currents, the latter do not define all the former. From Equations 201,

$$I_{ac} = \frac{I_a - I_c}{2}$$

$$I_{bd} = \frac{I_b - I_d}{2}$$

(202)

$$I_{ab}^{(1)} - I_{bc}^{(1)} = I_a + I_c$$

The Clover metadyne is thus a hyperstatic one.

Applying the first Kirchhoff law at the brushes gives

$$-I_{ac} - I_{ab}^{(1)} + I_{bc}^{(1)} + Y_{ba} + Y_{da} = 0$$

$$-I_{bd} + I_{ab}^{(1)} - I_{bc}^{(1)} + Y_{cb} - Y_{ba} = 0$$

$$+I_{ac} - I_{ab}^{(1)} + I_{bc}^{(1)} - Y_{cb} - Y_{cd} = 0$$

$$+I_{bd} + I_{ab}^{(1)} - I_{bc}^{(1)} + Y_{cd} - Y_{da} = 0$$

$$(203)$$

Among these equations only three are independent, as the sum of the first members is zero. Thus corolla currents Y cannot be determined from the systems of the canonical currents. On the other hand, brush currents I_a, I_b, I_c, I_d are determined by corolla currents Y. This is easily understood from Fig. 286. Observe that, from one system of brush and corolla currents, infinitely many other systems may be obtained by adding a circular current flowing through the continuous corolla without entering the armature of the Rosacean metadyne. This circular current will leave the armature currents unmodified while it modifies all the corolla currents.

Now write the fundamental metadyne equations. Because of the symmetry of the brushes with respect to the center, the independent equations are reduced to two, which may be written

$$\frac{1}{n} E_{ba} = \frac{1}{2} KI_{ac} + \frac{1}{2} KI_{bd} + \sum_{\gamma=\alpha}^{\nu} K_{ba}^{\gamma} I_{\gamma}$$

$$\frac{1}{n} E_{cb} = -\frac{1}{2} KI_{ac} + \frac{1}{2} KI_{bd} + \sum_{\gamma=\alpha}^{\nu} K_{cb}^{\gamma} I_{\gamma}$$

$$(204)$$

where K is the simplification of the well-known symbol $K_{ca}^{bd} = K_{bd}^{ac}$. Assume, as usual, that the armature winding has a diametrical pitch.

Suppose that the currents of the void canonical system are eliminated or reduced to a negligible value. Some procedures for obtaining this result have been indicated in Chapter 19. Then Equations 201 and 203 are simplified and Equations 204 may be written

$$\frac{1}{n} E_{ba} = \frac{1}{2} K(Y_{cb} + Y_{da}) + \sum_{\gamma=\alpha}^{\nu} K_{ba}^{\gamma} I_{\gamma}$$

$$\frac{1}{n} E_{cb} = -\frac{1}{2} K(Y_{ba} + Y_{cd}) + \sum_{\gamma=\alpha}^{\nu} K_{ba}^{\gamma} I_{\gamma}$$

$$(205)$$

The two members of each group, the Capital and the Subservient, operate at the same voltage, and it may be assumed that they are identical and that they operate under identical conditions. Therefore,

$$Y_{cb} = Y_{da}$$
$$Y_{ba} = Y_{cd} \tag{206}$$

in which case Equations 205 are simplified as

$$\frac{1}{n} E_{ba} = KY_{cb} + \sum_{\gamma=\alpha}^{\nu} K_{ba}^{\gamma} I_{\gamma}$$

$$\frac{1}{n} E_{cb} = -KY_{ba} + \sum_{\gamma=\alpha}^{\nu} K_{cb}^{\gamma} I_{\gamma} \tag{207}$$

and Equations 200 are reduced to

$$I_{ac} = Y_{ba} + Y_{cb}$$
$$I_{bd} = Y_{cb} - Y_{ba} \tag{208}$$

The regulator equation may then be written simply as follows, if the losses and the regulator current are neglected:

$$E_{ba}Y_{ba} + E_{cb}Y_{cb} = 0 \tag{209}$$

Now some simple applications of the Clover metadyne will be considered. First, assume that the Capital group is constituted by the separately excited motors of a locomotive and that the Subservient group is constituted by two resistors having an equal resistance R.

Further simplify the sums appearing in the second members of Equations 207 each to a simple term: the term $K_{ba}^{\rho}I_{\rho}$ (the winding 6 on Fig. 286), corresponding to a regulator winding for the first equation; and the term $K_{cb}^{\alpha}I_{\alpha}$ (the winding 7 on Fig. 286), corresponding to a variator winding for the second equation. Solve the equations for the corolla currents:

$$Y_{cb} = \frac{1}{nK} E_{ba} - \frac{K_{ba}^{\rho}}{K} I_{\rho}$$

$$Y_{ba} = \frac{K_{cb}^{\alpha}}{K} I_{\alpha} - \frac{1}{nK} E_{cb} \tag{210}$$

Further, there is

$$Y_{cb}R = E_{cb} \tag{211}$$

The second Equation 210 shows that the corolla current Y_{ba} passing through the traction motors is controlled by the variator current I_{α}. The term $(1/nK)E_{cb}$ is a magnetizing current, relatively small compared with Y_{ba}. The first Equation 210 shows how the regulator current I_{ρ}

controls the corolla current Y_{cb} so as to force the resistor, which has a fixed resistance, to absorb the proper power.

Now suppose that the traction motors of a locomotive constitute the Capital group, whereas the Subservient group is constituted by dynamos operating at constant voltage. Then E_{cb} is constant. Equations 210 are valid. The corolla current Y_{ba} is then controlled by the variator current I_α, and the regulator current I_ρ regulates the current Y_{cb}, thus obliging the dynamos of the Subservient group to supply or to absorb the right power.

Figure 287 gives some vector diagrams. Diagram I corresponds to the behavior when the Subservient group is constituted by resistors; the resistors carry a current larger than currents Y_{ba} and Y_{cb}. Diagram I also corresponds to the dynamos operating as Subservient machines; the traction motors are braking and the power is received by the dynamos, the voltage of the braking traction motors being higher than the voltage of the dynamos.

If Y_{ba} and Y_{cb} are always assumed positive, diagram II corresponds to the dynamos operating as Subservient machines and delivering power to the traction motors, which are working at a voltage higher than the voltage supplied by the dynamos. Similarly, diagram III corresponds to the starting period of the locomotive, the current Y_{ba} being much larger than Y_{cb}.

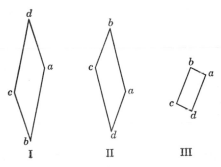

Fig. 287. Vector diagrams for the Clover metadyne.

Finally, consider the Clover metadyne mechanically coupled to an electric motor or to an electric generator or to a prime mover, for instance, to a Diesel engine. The same equations apply except for the regulator Equation 209, which must be modified as follows:

$$\pi Tn + E_{ba}Y_{ba} + E_{cb}Y_{cb} = 0 \tag{212}$$

where T represents the torque supplied by the motor measured in newton-meters, and where n represents the rotational speed measured in revolutions per second.

The very simple comments given above show the possibilities of the machine considered here, but they are by no means an exhaustive study of this case; static stability and dynamic stability must be assured. These same considerations must be kept in mind while reading the following sections.

5. THE STEM AND CLOVER TRANSFORMER METADYNE

Figure 288 gives the scheme, the points P and Q being the terminals of a power system, and the stator windings being arranged as for the Clover transformer metadyne considered in the previous section. Figure 288 is derived from Fig. 277. The arrows indicate the positive directions of the corresponding currents.

Retain the two systems of canonical currents considered in the previous section and follow the same analytical procedure, revising the

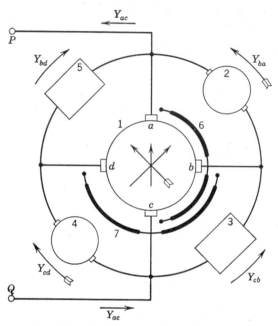

Fig. 288.   The Stem and Clover metadyne.

equations when it is necessary. Thus, Equations 201 and 202 are valid. Equations 203 must be extended as follows:

$$-I_{ac} - I_{ab}^{(1)} + I_{bc}^{(1)} + Y_{ba} + Y_{da} - Y_{ac} = 0$$
$$-I_{bd} + I_{ab}^{(1)} - I_{bc}^{(1)} + Y_{cb} - Y_{ba} = 0$$
$$+I_{ac} - I_{ab}^{(1)} + I_{bc}^{(1)} - Y_{cb} - Y_{cd} + Y_{ac} = 0$$
$$+I_{bd} + I_{ab} - I_{bc} + Y_{cd} - Y_{da} = 0$$

$$(213)$$

Equations 204 are valid.

Assume that the currents of the void canonical systems are eliminated or reduced to a negligible value. Further, assume that members 2 and

4 and members 3 and 5 are identical and operate under the same conditions. Then Equations 206 hold, and Equations 213 are simplified as follows:

$$I_{ac} = Y_{ba} + Y_{cb} - Y_{ac}$$

$$I_{bd} = Y_{cb} - Y_{ba}$$

$$(214)$$

Fundamental metadyne Equations 204 may also be written

$$\frac{1}{n} E_{ca} = K I_{bd} + \sum_{\gamma=\alpha}^{\nu} K_{ca}^{\gamma} I_{\gamma} = K(Y_{cb} - Y_{ba}) + \sum_{\gamma=\alpha}^{\nu} K_{ca}^{\gamma} I_{\gamma}$$

$$\frac{1}{n} E_{bd} = K I_{ac} + \sum_{\gamma=\alpha}^{\nu} K_{bd}^{\gamma} I_{\gamma} = K(Y_{ba} + Y_{cb} - Y_{ac}) + \sum_{\gamma=\alpha}^{\nu} K_{bd}^{\gamma} I_{\gamma}$$

$$(215)$$

and the regulator equation may be written

$$2 E_{ba} Y_{ba} + 2 E_{cb} Y_{cb} - E_{ca} Y_{ac} = 0 \qquad (216)$$

Assume that the system having its terminals at P and Q is a constant-voltage network and that the sum $\sum K_{ca}^{\gamma} I_{\gamma}$ is simplified to a single term, $K_{ca}^{\alpha} I_{\alpha}$, corresponding to a variator winding, whereas the sum $\sum K_{bd}^{\gamma} I_{\gamma}$ is reduced to a single term, $K_{bd}^{\rho} I_{\rho}$, corresponding to a regulator winding, 7. Finally, assume that members 3 and 5 of the Subservient group are metadynes supplying constant current. Then Y_{ab} is a constant, and variator current I_{α} controls current Y_{ba} of members 2 and 4 of the Capital group according to the equation

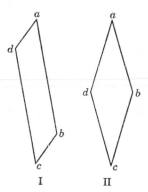

$$Y_{ba} = \frac{K_{ca}^{\alpha}}{K} I_{\alpha} + Y_{cb} - \frac{1}{nK} E_{ca} \quad (217)$$

and the regulator current regulates the supply from the constant-voltage system according to the equation

$$-Y_{ac} = \frac{1}{nK} E_{bd} - Y_{ba} - Y_{cb} - \frac{K_{bd}^{\rho}}{K} I_{\rho} \quad (218)$$

Fig. 289. Vector representation of the operation of the Stem and Clover transformer.

Figure 289 gives two vector diagrams corresponding to this case. Consider both diagrams and assume that Y_{ba} is positive and Y_{cb} negative; the members 2 and 4 are regenerating power while the members 3 and 5 are absorbing power. If Y_{ba} is negative and Y_{cb} is positive, the reverse occurs. If $Y_{ba} = -Y_{cb}$ while vector diagram II represents the operation, $Y_{ac} = 0$, $I_{bd} = -2Y_{ba}$, $I_{ac} = 0$, and the Rosacean metadyne transforms no power at all.

Now suppose that the power system with its terminals at P and Q is a series one supplying constant current. The current Y_{ac} is then constant. Then let winding 7 be a variator winding and let winding 6 be a regulator winding. Equations 215 may then be written

$$\frac{1}{n} E_{ca} = K(Y_{cb} - Y_{ba}) + K_{ca}^{\rho} I_{\rho}$$

$$\frac{1}{n} E_{bd} = K(Y_{ba} + Y_{cb} - Y_{ac}) + K_{bd}^{\alpha} I_{\alpha}$$

(219)

If one realizes that current $(1/Kn)E_{bd}$ is a magnetizing current and therefore small compared with Y_{cb} or Y_{ac}, and if one assumes that members 3 and 5 are metadynes supplying a constant current, Equations 219 show that variator current I_{α} controls current Y_{ba} flowing through the members of the Capital group and that the regulator current regulates the voltage, E_{ca}, absorbed, i.e., regulates the power supplied or absorbed by the series network.

6. THE CROSS AND CLOVER TRANSFORMER METADYNE

Figure 290, derived from Fig. 278, represents this machine schematically. The two systems of canonical currents indicated in Section 4 will be retained, but the canonical currents and the corolla currents satisfy new equations. With the assumptions that the currents of the void canonical system are zero and that members 2 and 4 and members 3 and 5 operate under exactly the same conditions at any moment, these new equations are simplified as follows:

$$I_{ac} = Y_{ba} + Y_{cb} - Y_{ac}$$

$$I_{bd} = Y_{cb} - Y_{ba} - Y_{bd}$$

(220)

Under the same conditions, the fundamental metadyne equations may be written

$$\frac{1}{n} E_{ca} = K(Y_{cb} - Y_{ba} - Y_{bd}) + \sum_{\gamma=\alpha}^{\nu} K_{ca}^{\gamma} I_{\gamma}$$

$$\frac{1}{n} E_{bd} = K(Y_{ba} + Y_{cb} - Y_{ac}) + \sum_{\gamma=\alpha}^{\nu} K_{bd}^{\gamma} I_{\gamma}$$

(221)

In Fig. 290, the vector x represents the Capital armature ampere-turns, and the vectors s, v, and z represent the Subservient armature ampere-turns created by currents due to members 3 and 5, the power system having its terminals at P and Q, and member 7, respectively.

Assume that P and Q are the terminals of a constant-voltage system and that members 3, 5, and 7 of the Subservient group are metadynes supplying constant current. Then E_{ca}, Y_{cb}, and Y_{bd} are constants. Reduce the sums appearing in the second members of Equations 221

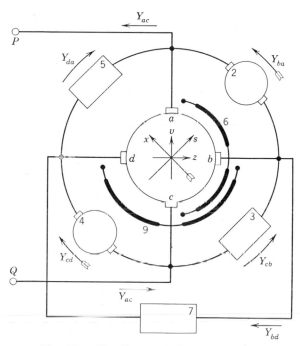

Fig. 290.   The Cross and Clover metadyne.

each to a single term: the term $K_{ca}^{\alpha}I_\alpha$, corresponding to a variator winding, 6, for the first equation; and the term $K_{bd}^{\rho}I_\rho$, corresponding to a regulator winding, 9, for the second equation. The variator current I_α controls the value of current Y_{ba} flowing through members 2 and 4 of the Capital group, and the regulator current adjusts current Y_{ac} supplied to the constant-voltage system.

The regulator current I_ρ may be calculated from the regulator equation, which may be written

$$K_{ca}^{\alpha}I_\alpha(Y_{ba} + Y_{cb} - Y_{ac}) - K_{bd}^{\rho}I_\rho(Y_{cb} - Y_{ba} - Y_{bd}) = 0 \quad (222)$$

if the Rosacean metadyne is running uncoupled with any other machine. On the other hand, if it is coupled mechanically to a generator or to a motor rotating at n revolutions per second and supplying a torque T, the regulator equation may be written

$$2\pi T + K_{ca}^{\alpha} I_{\alpha}(Y_{ba} + Y_{cb} - Y_{ac}) - K_{bd}^{\rho} I_{\rho}(Y_{cb} - Y_{ba} - Y_{bd}) = 0$$

$$(223)$$

Figure 291 gives some vector diagrams I, II, and III, which represent the starting of a locomotive, its running at a medium speed, and its running at a high speed. The arrows near each vector represent the direction of the corolla current corresponding to the same vector. Thus

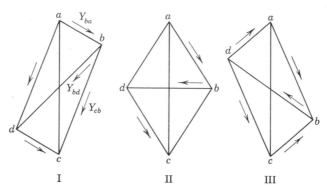

Fig. 291. Vector diagrams of a railway application of the Cross and Clover transformer.

the arrow near the vector ab represents corolla current Y_{ba} flowing in member 2 of the Capital group; therefore, Y_{ba} is negative.

At low motoring speed the current supplied by the constant-voltage system is transformed and the corresponding power is absorbed by the traction motors and metadynes 3, 5, and 7 of the Subservient group, if constant current Y_{bd} was given a positive value by Subservient metadyne 7, and if currents Y_{cb} and Y_{da} were given negative values by Subservient metadynes 3 and 5. At medium speed the constant-voltage system supplies power only to the traction motors, if Subservient metadynes 3 and 5 supply current $Y_{cb} = Y_{da} = 0$. At high speed the traction motors are supplied by the constant-voltage system and by the three metadynes 3, 5, and 7 simultaneously, if the constant current, Y_{bd}, supplied by Subservient metadyne 7 is positive, and if currents Y_{cb} and Y_{da} supplied by Subservient metadynes 3 and 5 are positive.

Now assume that P and Q are the terminals of a constant-current series system and that members 3, 5, and 7 are metadynes supplying constant current; then Y_{ac}, Y_{cb}, and Y_{bd} are constants. Reduce the sums appearing in the second members of Equations 221 to the term

$K_{ca}^\rho I_\rho$, corresponding to a regulator winding, 6, for the first equation, and to the term $K_{bd}^\alpha I_\alpha$, corresponding to a variator winding, 9, for the second equation. The variator current controls the intensity of the current, Y_{ba}, passing through the members of the Capital group and the regulator current adjusts the voltage, E_{ca}, absorbed from the series system.

7. THE CROSS AND EIGHT TRANSFORMER METADYNE

Figure 292 gives the essential scheme, derived from Fig. 280. Switches 10 and 11 are open, and switches 12 and 13 are closed.

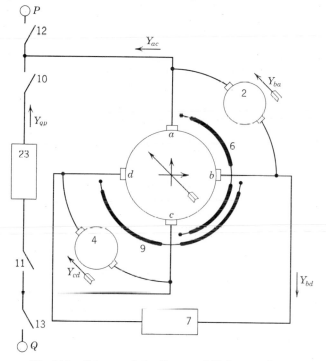

Fig. 292. Scheme of the Cross and Eight metadyne.

With the same procedure of analysis as in the previous cases and with similar simplifying assumptions, the equations become

$$I_{ac} = -Y_{ac} + Y_{ba}$$

$$I_{bd} = -Y_{bd} - Y_{ba}$$

(224)

$$\frac{1}{n} E_{ca} = -K(Y_{bd} + Y_{ba}) + \sum_{\gamma=\alpha}^{\nu} K_{ca}^{\gamma} I_{\gamma}$$

$$\frac{1}{n} E_{bd} = K(Y_{ba} - Y_{ac}) + \sum_{\gamma=\alpha}^{\nu} K_{bd}^{\gamma} I_{\gamma}$$

(225)

Assume that the terminals P and Q belong to a constant-voltage system, that member 7 of the Subservient group is a constant-current metadyne, and that the sums of the second members of the first and second Equation 225 are reduced to single terms, $K_{ca}^{\alpha} I_{\alpha}$ and $K_{bd}^{\rho} I_{\rho}$, corresponding to a variator winding, 6, and to a regulator winding, 9, respectively. In this case, E_{ca} and Y_{bd} are constants, and variator current I_{α} controls current Y_{ba} flowing through the members of the Capital group, and regulator current I_{ρ} adjusts the current supplied by the constant-voltage system.

Instead of a constant-voltage shunt system, one may assume that there is a constant-current series system; interchanging the location of the variator and the regulator winding again permits satisfactory operation.

Consider another member, 23, of the Subservient group. Assume that it is a constant-current metadyne, let switches 10 and 11 be closed, and call Y_{qp} the corresponding current.

This addition does not modify Equations 224 and 225, and it leaves unaltered the results derived therefrom. The current delivered or supplied by the network having its terminals at P and Q is now $-Y_{ac} - Y_{qp}$. If, for instance, the network is a series one and Y_{qp} is made equal to the constant current Y_{ac} supplied by this system, the system will neither supply power to nor absorb power from the metadyne plant considered here.

Let stator windings 6 and 9 be shunt windings connected across brushes a and c and across brushes b and d, respectively, excited by stator currents I_{α} and I_{β}. Set their resistance in such a way that their corresponding terms are equal to the first member of the corresponding equation:

$$K_{ca}^{\alpha} I_{\alpha} = \frac{1}{n} E_{ca}$$

$$K_{bd}^{\beta} I_{\beta} = \frac{1}{n} E_{bd}$$

(226)

In other words, let these shunt windings be astatic, or have them set at their "singular state." If there are no other stator windings, then there will be

$$Y_{ba} = -Y_{bd}$$

$$Y_{ca} = Y_{ba} \tag{227}$$

Assume first that switches 10 and 11 are open and switches 12 and 13 closed; in this case, to control the current flowing through members 2 and 4 of the Capital group, it suffices to control the corolla current

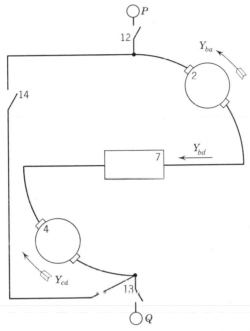

Fig. 293.   Elimination of the Rosacean metadyne from Fig. 292.

Y_{bd}. The Rosacean metadyne has no torque since $I_{ac} = I_{bd} = 0$, and it will rotate at a constant speed, n, provided that the friction losses are compensated.

It then becomes obvious that the Rosacean metadyne may be eliminated, and the simple scheme of Fig. 293 may be used, switch 14 being assumed open and switches 12 and 13 being assumed closed.   Figure 294 gives some vector diagrams corresponding to this case. If members 2 and 4 are the traction motors of a locomotive, the diagrams correspond to the accelerating stage; diagrams I, II, and III are obtained at a low speed, a medium speed, and a high speed, respectively.   Assume that Subservient metadyne 7 supplies a constant current Y_{bd} having a positive value. Then at low speed, member 7 absorbs energy until the voltage across each element of the Capital group becomes equal to half the overhead-line voltage; just at this moment element 7 absorbs no power; from this moment on, the same element will supply power increasing in amount with increasing locomotive speed. For the braking stage it is necessary either to change the direction of the current Y_{bd} or to alter the connections from the "right-hand Eight" to the "left-hand Eight."

Another way to obtain a simple braking operation with the scheme of Fig. 293 consists in opening switches 12 and 13, thus disconnecting the system from the overhead line, in closing switch 14, and in causing Subservient metadyne 7 to supply a constant negative current Y_{bd}.

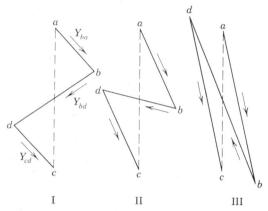

Fig. 294.   Vector diagrams for the arrangement of Fig. 293.

Figure 295 gives some of the resulting vector diagrams; diagram I corresponds to high-speed braking and diagram II to low-speed. It is obvious that element 7 must have double its previous capacity, and, what is much more difficult, it must induce a voltage twice as high.

Suppose, now, that element 23 is added, switches 10, 11, 12, and 13 of Fig. 292 being closed. The vector diagrams of Fig. 296 represent the operation, diagram I corresponding to the accelerating stage and diagram II corresponding to the braking stage, the braking effect being obtained by reversal of current Y_{ba}.

If the Rosacean metadyne is eliminated, the diagram is simplified as shown by Fig. 297 with switches 12 and 13 open. The vector diagrams of Fig. 298 then represent the operation; diagram I is for the accelerating stage and diagram II for the braking stage; the latter operation is obtained without reversing currents Y_{bd} and Y_{qp}.

The last considerations developed above may lead to the wrong conclusion, that the Rosacean metadyne may be eliminated. If the Rosacean metadyne is eliminated, many difficulties arise concerning the stability of operation. For instance, currents Y_{bd} and Y_{qp} must be exactly

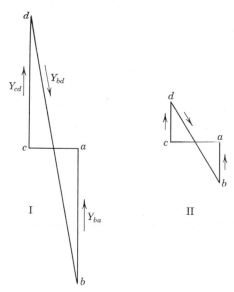

Fig. 295. Vector diagrams for braking operation with a modified form of Fig. 293.

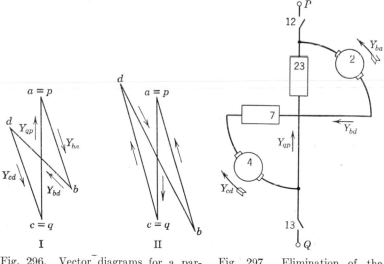

Fig. 296. Vector diagrams for a particular form of the scheme of Fig. 292.

Fig. 297. Elimination of the Rosacean metadyne from the circuit having the vectors of Fig. 296.

the same, a condition difficult to satisfy; another trouble is the indefiniteness of the voltages of metadynes 7 and 23; finally, the dynamic stability appears precarious.

The addition of the Rosacean metadyne eliminates these troubles. For instance, the Rosacean metadyne easily compensates for the differences between currents Y_{bd} and Y_{qp}; it controls the voltages across the terminals of metadynes 23 and 7; and, finally, it eliminates dynamic instability. The addition of the constant-voltage network may even im-

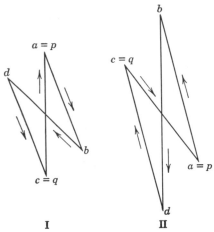

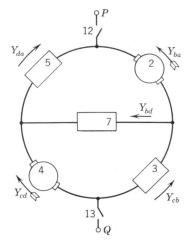

Fig. 298.   Vector diagrams for Fig. 297.

Fig. 299.   Elimination of the Rosacean metadyne from the Cross and Clover scheme.

prove the stability. It is important to note that the connection to the constant-voltage network does not necessarily imply that during the braking stage the network must absorb any current. Metadynes 23 and 7 may even absorb more power than the members of the Capital group can supply, thus requiring the constant-voltage network to supply some power even during the braking stage.

What has been said above concerning the elimination and the utility of the Rosacean metadyne for stability of operation may be repeated for all the schemes considered in the previous sections. Take, for instance, the Cross and Clover metadyne, with brushes a and c connected to the terminals of a network. Set the stator windings at their "singular state," for which all armature currents are zero. Then, if the Rosacean metadyne is eliminated, the simple scheme of Fig. 299 is obtained, which is like the Wheatstone bridge. Instead of the network, another member of the Subservient group, member 23, may be connected; or member 23 and the network may even be connected simultaneously, as Fig. 300 shows.

Although in certain applications the simplified scheme may be used, i.e., the corolla alone after the Rosacean metadyne has been eliminated, the complete scheme comprising the Rosacean metadyne and the corolla allows for more stable operation and easier control. The very fact that it seems possible to eliminate the Rosacean metadyne, or, more exactly, the fact that the armature currents of the Rosacean metadyne can be reduced to a relatively negligible value while the members of the corolla are still completely controlled, is a proof of the high values that may be attained for the ratio of the controlled power to the power transformed by the Rosacean metadyne itself. The Rosacean metadyne operates, then, as a center of stabilizing power and as a center of control for the distribution of power. The latter function is pointed out in this chapter; the former function can be examined through appropriate dynamic analysis.

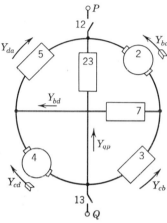

Fig. 300. Another Cross and Clover scheme, from which the Rosacean metadyne has been eliminated.

8. A ROSACEAN METADYNE OF ORDER $m = 6$

The particular case represented by the scheme of Fig. 301 is briefly considered here. Figure 301 is derived from Fig. 284, but members 2 and 5 of the corolla are chosen as members of the Capital group whereas members 3, 4, 6, and 7 are chosen as members of the Subservient group. The system is strongly hyperstatic.

Assume that the members are symmetrically disposed with respect to the center and that they all carry currents of the same intensity. Further, assume that all void canonical systems of currents have been eliminated and that there is left simply the following statically determined canonical system of currents:

$$I_{ad}$$
$$I_{bf} = I_{ce}$$
$$I_{ac} = I_{fd}$$
$$I_{bd} = I_{ae}$$

(228)

In Fig. 301, four vectors are indicated through the center of the metadyne: Vector x represents the armature ampere-turns due to canonical currents $I_{bf} = I_{ce}$; vector s represents the ampere-turns of canonical

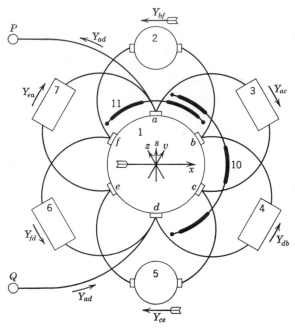

Fig. 301. A sixth-degree Rosacean metadyne.

current I_{ad}; vector v represents the ampere-turns of canonical currents $I_{bd} = I_{ae}$; finally, vector z represents the ampere-turns of canonical currents $I_{ac} = I_{fd}$.

The relations between the canonical currents and the corolla currents are simplified as follows:

$$I_{ad} + I_{ac} + I_{bd} = -Y_{ad} + Y_{db} - Y_{ac}$$

$$I_{bd} + I_{bf} = Y_{db} - Y_{bf} \tag{229}$$

$$-I_{ac} + I_{bf} = Y_{ac} - Y_{bf}$$

Hence there are three equations with eight variables: I_{ad}, I_{bf}, I_{ac}, I_{bd}, Y_{ad}, Y_{bf}, Y_{ac}, and Y_{db}.

The following arbitrary relation may be added:

$$I_{ad} = -Y_{ad} \tag{230}$$

Then Equations 229 are simplified as follows:

$$I_{ac} + I_{bd} = -Y_{ac} + Y_{db}$$

$$I_{bd} + I_{bf} = Y_{bd} - Y_{bf}$$

$$I_{ac} - I_{bf} = -Y_{ac} + Y_{bf}$$

The determinant of the coefficients of both the first members and the second members is zero. Nevertheless, the solution

$$I_{ac} = -Y_{ac}$$

$$I_{bd} = Y_{db} \tag{231}$$

$$I_{bf} = -Y_{bf}$$

is obvious.

The fundamental metadyne equations are reduced to three independent equations that may be written

$$\frac{1}{n} E_{da} = 2K_{da}^{bf} I_{bf} + 2K_{da}^{ac} I_{ac} + 2K_{da}^{bd} I_{bd} + \sum_{\gamma=\alpha}^{\nu} K_{da}^{\gamma} I_{\gamma}$$

$$\frac{1}{n} E_{bf} = K_{bf}^{ad} I_{ad} + 2K_{bf}^{ac} I_{ac} + 2K_{bf}^{bd} I_{bd} + \sum_{\gamma=\alpha}^{\nu} K_{bf}^{\gamma} I_{\gamma} \tag{232}$$

$$\frac{1}{n} E_{cb} = 2K_{cb}^{bf} I_{bf} + 2K_{cb}^{ac} I_{ac} + 2K_{cb}^{bd} I_{bd} + \sum_{\gamma=\alpha}^{\nu} K_{cb}^{\gamma} I_{\gamma}$$

Assume that the network with its terminals at P and Q is a constant-voltage network; that members 3, 4, 6, and 7 of the Subservient group are constant-current metadynes, the intensity of their current being arbitrarily controlled; finally, that the stator windings are reduced to only two, a variator winding, 10, and a regulator winding, 11.

Taking into account relations 231 and considering some obvious relations between coefficients K, one may simplify the first two Equations 232 as follows:

$$\frac{1}{n} E_{da} = -2K_{da}^{bf} Y_{bf} + 2K_{da}^{bd}(Y_{db} + Y_{ac}) + K_{da}^{\alpha} I_{\alpha}$$

$$\tag{233}$$

$$\frac{1}{n} E_{bf} = -K_{bf}^{ad} Y_{ad} + 2K_{bf}^{bd}(Y_{db} - Y_{ac}) + K_{bf}^{\rho} I_{\rho}$$

Let the intensity of currents Y_{db} and Y_{ac} be controlled arbitrarily. Variator current I_{α} will then control the intensity of current Y_{bf} flowing in the members of the Capital group; and the regulator current I_{ρ}

will set the current Y_{ad}, supplied by the constant-voltage network, at the proper value.

In particular, currents Y_{bf}, Y_{ac}, and Y_{db} may be made of equal intensity. In this case armature currents I_{ac}, I_{bd}, and I_{bf} compensate one another in the armature; no power is supplied by the Rosacean metadyne to members 2, 3, 4, 5, 6, and 7; and no power can be absorbed by it from the constant-voltage network. Therefore, I_{ad} and Y_{ad} are zero, and no current passes through the armature of the Rosacean metadyne; the transfer of power occurs between the members 2 and 5 of the Capital group and members 3, 4, 6, and 7 of the Subservient group. The Rosacean metadyne will then control the transfer of power without transforming any itself.

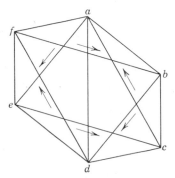

Fig. 302. A vector diagram for the metadyne of Fig. 301.

One may think that the Rosacean metadyne may then be eliminated completely. Instead, one must realize that the Rosacean metadyne is necessary: (1) to absorb the slight differences of currents, since it is practically impossible to have exactly $Y_{bf} = Y_{fd} = Y_{db} = Y_{ce} = Y_{ea} = Y_{ac}$; (2) to keep the right voltage relation between the members of the Capital and of the Subservient group; and (3) to supply the electromotive forces stabilizing the whole operation.

As another particular case, assume that the intensity of currents Y_{db} and Y_{ac} has been set to be zero. Then the Rosacean metadyne will transform power and control the transfer of power between the constant-voltage network and the members of the Capital group.

In a similar way, one may consider a series network having its terminals at P and Q, supplying a constant current Y_{ad}. The function of stator windings 10 and 11 may then be interchanged, and again stable, satisfactory operation is obtained. This operation can be discussed in a way similar to that of the operation with a constant-voltage network. Figure 302 gives a vector diagram corresponding to a condition in which the Capital group absorbs power.

9. THE CROSS TRANSFORMER METADYNE SUPPLIED WITH A SPEED-MODERATOR DEVICE

Apply the definition of the Rosacean metadyne to a metadyne having $m = 4$ equidistant brushes per cycle so that $k = 2$ and $h = 2$; a Cross transformer metadyne is obtained. This result offers the opportunity to point out that the considerations of the Rosacean metadynes made here are the generalizations of the developments of the first chapters of Part II of this volume.

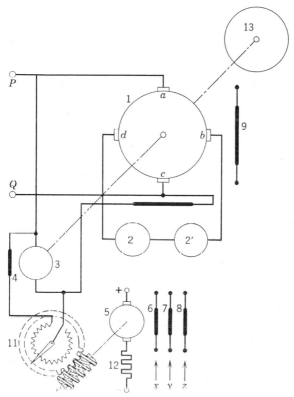

Fig. 303. This Cross transformer, considered as a Rosacean metadyne, is equipped with a speed variator.

In this section, closing Chapter 21, a simple case is examined in which the Rosacean metadyne operates not only as a transformer but also as a member of the Subservient group.

For this purpose, the metadyne is equipped with a speed-moderator device as described in Sections 3 and 4 of Chapter 6.

Figure 303 gives a simplified scheme. Rosacean metadyne 1 has its brushes a and c connected to terminals P and Q of a network and its brushes b and d connected to a consumer, say two dynamos 2 and 2′, forming the Capital group. The shunt-excited regulator dynamo, 3, has its field winding 4 connected to resistor 11, the active segment of which is determined by the position of a movable finger driven by the small dynamo, 5, through a worm gear. Dynamo 5, called the governor dynamo, is assumed to be fed by a constant-voltage source with a current of practically constant intensity because of the ballast resistor, 12, and because the speed of this dynamo is either zero or very low. The torque of the governor dynamo is controlled by the resultant ampere-turns due to the currents x, y, and z flowing through field coils 6, 7, and 8, respectively.

First, assume that the network terminating at P and Q is a shunt network at a constant voltage, V; that winding 9 is a variator winding carrying current I_α; and that 10 is a regulator winding carrying current I_ρ. The fundamental metadyne equations are

$$\frac{1}{n} E_{ca} = KI_b + K_{ca}^\alpha I_\alpha$$

$$\frac{1}{n} E_{bd} = KI_a + K_{bd}^\rho I_\rho$$

(234)

where n is now a variable. This variable changes very slowly compared with the transient electric phenomena of the currents in the metadyne, and therefore Equations 234 are valid practically. The variator current, I_α, controls the intensity of the current, I_b, flowing through the dynamos of the Capital group; and the regulator current, I_ρ, sets the current, I_a, supplied or absorbed by the constant-voltage network.

Suppose, now, that it is desired to keep the intensity of current I_a constant at an arbitrarily determined value. Then, cause this current (or a current proportional to it) to pass through field winding 7; let field winding 6 create a constant number of ampere-turns. The torque t of the speed-variator dynamo 5 may be expressed as follows:

$$t = hx + kI_a$$

(235)

the constants h and k having opposite signs, say h positive and k negative. Choose the connections of the specified field windings in such a way as to decrease speed n when t is positive. Then the current, I_a, supplied or absorbed by the network will be kept constant at an arbitrarily defined value by setting the corresponding value for current x; the Rosacean metadyne will decelerate and as a generator will supply the necessary energy to the consumers when they are absorbing more power than VI_a, and it will accelerate if the absorbed power is smaller than VI_a, the metadyne losses being neglected.

For the particular case in which I_a is caused to be zero, and x is also made zero, the transfer of energy occurs only between the Capital group and the rotating masses of the metadyne. A flywheel, 13, may be added to increase the total energy stored.

If it is desired to have I_a decrease with the voltage E_{bd}, i.e., approximately with the speed of the dynamos of the Capital group, the action of field winding 8 shunt-excited across brushes b and d may be added to the action already considered above, in which field winding 6 creates a constant number of ampere-turns and field winding 7 creates ampere-turns proportional to current I_a.

As another particular case, consider a resistor of fixed resistance R substituted for the network. This resistor will dissipate a constant power RI_a^2, and the variation of the kinetic energy of the metadyne will compensate for the difference of power supplied by the dynamos of the Capital group above or below the value RI_a^2.

Again, assume that the Capital group is generating electric energy and that most of it is to be stored as kinetic energy in the rotating parts of the metadyne, the acceleration being kept constant at its maximum safe value: resistor 11 is graduated to give constant variations of the critical speed for constant angular displacements of the contact finger, and the speed-variator motor is caused to rotate at constant speed with only one of its field windings energized with a constant current creating constant ampere-turns. This current, set by the operator, controls the acceleration of the rotating masses of the metadyne.

The analysis and the discussion of the case for which the network terminating at P and Q is a series network supplying constant current may be made in a similar way that leads to similar results. More cases can be considered after the dynamic properties of the speed moderator have been examined.

22 · Pliodynes

1. DEFINITION—GENERAL RULES—AN EXAMPLE

The author defines a pliodyne as a set of dynamos or metadynes, each unit having at least one stator winding excited by a current proportional at any moment to the current of another unit. All these rotating machines, dynamos or metadynes, may rotate at speeds proportional to one another at any moment, and then the pliodyne is rigid; or the machines may rotate at speeds independent of one another, and then the pliodyne is loose. In this chapter only rigid pliodynes will be considered, and these will be made up of dynamos exclusively.

For any reactive metadyne, there is at least one pliodyne having the same fundamental operation. For determining such equivalence, resolve the m brushes of the metadyne under consideration into, say, h pairs of brushes, and construct a pliodyne having h dynamos, each dynamo corresponding to a pair of brushes. Further, let each dynamo have as many field coils as there are terms in the second member of the fundamental metadyne equation corresponding to the relative brush pair, with such connections as to cause the pliodyne to satisfy the same equations as the metadyne.

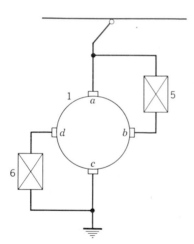

Fig. 304. The basic Eight transformer metadyne.

The metadyne and pliodyne thus obtained are said to be equivalent. Many pliodynes equivalent to a given metadyne may be found. The converse occurs less frequently.

For a metadyne of degree m, there are $m(m-1)/2$ different fundamental equations; therefore, one may synthesize an equivalent pliodyne comprising $m(m-1)/2$ different dynamos. Generally, of the $m(m-1)/2$ fundamental equations there are only $m-1$ independent ones; therefore, one can generally synthesize at least one equivalent pliodyne comprising only $m-1$ different dynamos. In many cases the fundamental equations are reduced to, say, g equations, where g is an integer smaller than $m-1$. In these cases at least one equivalent pliodyne can be synthesized comprising only g dynamos.

As an example, consider the Eight transformer metadyne, the simplified scheme of which is repeated in Fig. 304 for the reader's convenience. Resolve its set of four brushes, a, b, c, and d, into the following pairs: a and b; b and c; c and d; d and a. From these pairs, synthesize the pliodyne shown by Fig. 305, comprising four dynamos, 1, 2, 3, 4, having the homonymous brushes connected together, and further connected to

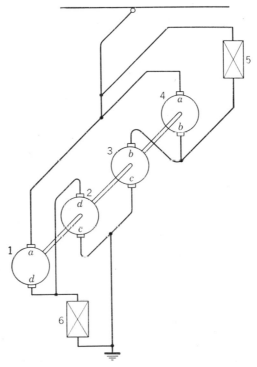

Fig. 305.   An equivalent pliodyne for the Eight transformer metadyne.

the overhead line and to the two consumers, 5 and 6, in imitation of the corresponding connections of the metadyne of Fig. 304. Since the four fundamental equations corresponding to the electromotive forces, E_{ba}, E_{cb}, E_{dc}, and E_{da}, comprise at least one group of a complete system of independent equations, the pliodyne of Fig. 305 may be made equivalent to the metadyne of Fig. 304 by a suitable choice of stator windings. But, as the scheme of Fig. 305, representing the dynamos coupled on a single shaft, is somewhat cumbersome, it is preferable to use instead the scheme of Fig. 306, in which the little square indicated in the center of each dynamo is a reminder that these units rotate at a speed propor-

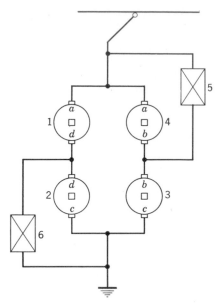

Fig. 306. A conventional representation for a more general pliodyne equivalent to the Eight transformer metadyne.

tional to one another at any moment. Thus the scheme of Fig. 306 is not only easier to read but also more general than the scheme of Fig. 305, in which the speed is the same for all dynamos.

Now consider the three pairs a and b, b and d, d and c. The fundamental equations corresponding to E_{ba}, E_{bd}, and E_{cd} comprise a complete system of independent equations; therefore, the corresponding pliodyne indicated by Fig. 307 can be made an equivalent pliodyne for the Eight transformer metadyne by an appropriate choice of field windings.

Because of the symmetrical location of the brushes of the Eight transformer metadyne, the system of independent fundamental equations comprises only two equations; for instance, the equations corresponding to the voltages E_{ca} and E_{bd} constitute such a system. Therefore, the pliodyne of the scheme of Fig. 308, comprising only two dynamos, may be arranged to become

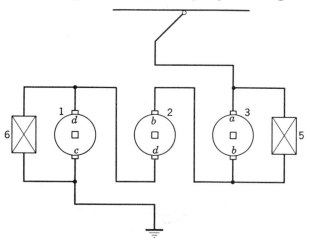

Fig. 307.   A simpler pliodyne for the Eight metadyne.

an equivalent pliodyne for the Eight transformer metadyne by a suitable choice of stator windings.

Suppose, for example, that the Eight transformer metadyne has the following stator windings: a primary stabilizing winding, a secondary variator winding independently excited, and a regulator winding having its magnetic axis along the primary commutating axis. Then the stator windings of the pliodyne of Fig. 308 may be arranged as Fig. 309 shows:

the series winding, 8, corresponds to the primary stabilizing winding; the independently excited winding, 10, corresponds to the secondary variator winding; winding 12 corresponds to the regulator winding, and it is indicated carrying the regulator current due to the regulator dynamo, 7, shunt-excited by the field winding, 13, and connected to the overhead line; windings 11 and 9 correspond to the action of the primary armature ampere-turns on voltage E_{bd} and to the action of the secondary armature ampere-turns on voltage E_{ca}, respectively.

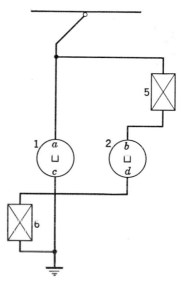

Fig. 308. A further simplification of the pliodyne equivalent to the Eight transformer.

If the two fundamental equations are written for the pliodyne of Fig. 309, there results exactly the system of independent fundamental equations of the Eight transformer metadyne equipped with the three above-mentioned stator windings. Therefore, the operation will be the same. For instance, resistor 13 will control the intensity of the current flowing in dynamo 2; and consumers 5 and 6 and the regulator current will set the value of the current flowing in dynamo 1 so as to keep the speed practically constant around the critical speed of regulator dynamo 7, and so as to absorb from the overhead line the current just necessary for the transformation of power.

In order to complete the investigation of the possible equivalent pliodynes, consider Fig. 310. The fundamental equations corresponding to the voltages E_{da}, E_{bd}, and E_{bc} comprise a system of independent fundamental equations, and therefore the scheme of Fig. 310 shows an equivalent pliodyne, on the assumption that the proper field windings are used.

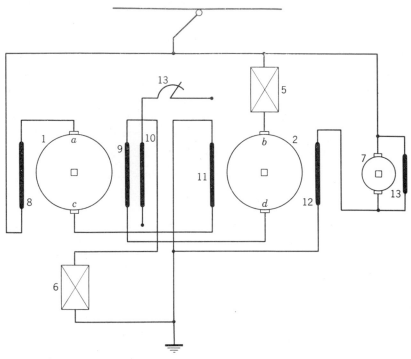

Fig. 309.   A specific pliodyne based on the general form shown in Fig. 308.

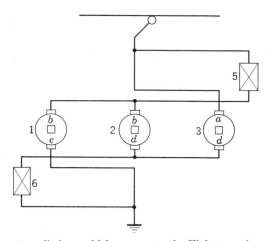

Fig 310.   Another pliodyne which represents the Eight transformer metadyne

One may think that dynamo 1 of the scheme of Fig. 308 can be eliminated, leaving only dynamo 2. This would permit supplying consumers 5 and 6 with the variable voltage necessary, for instance, for starting and accelerating a locomotive; but the line current, instead of being practically zero at starting, will necessarily be very large for the acceleration at the starting point. In fact, the system of fundamental independent equations has two equations, and two dynamos are required and at least two dynamos are necessary for an equivalent pliodyne.

With only one dynamo, as the scheme of Fig. 311 shows, it is necessary to provide a driving machine, 14, able to supply some times an accelerating and sometimes a decelerating torque. The operation becomes quite different from the operation of the Eight transformer metadyne.

Finally, mention will be made of a further

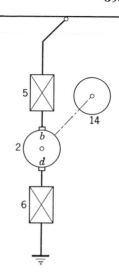

Fig. 311. An arrangement with one dynamo and a drive motor does not duplicate the behavior of the Eight transformer.

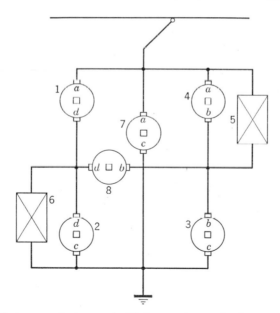

Fig. 312. A pliodyne, equivalent to the Eight transformer, having all possible voltage pairs represented.

equivalent pliodyne comprising 6 dynamos and represented by Fig. 312. Thus, all possible combinations of four brushes, taken two by two, have been indicated, as pliodynes equivalent to the Eight transformer metadyne of Fig. 304.

2. COMPARISON OF THE METADYNE AND ITS EQUIVALENT PLIODYNE

Subdividing a single machine into many others having the same overall capacity involves an increase in weight and in overall size. Thus a pliodyne is heavier and more cumbersome than the equivalent metadyne.

Furthermore, a pliodyne loses many advantages compared with its equivalent metadyne:

1. The superposition of currents in the armature of a metadyne permits an important reduction of the total armature copper losses; in the pliodyne, every armature carries a single current.

2. In a metadyne the field inductor is common to two or more systems of armature currents; in the pliodyne there is a special field inductor for each armature current.

3. In a metadyne the magnetizing ampere-turns are generally supplied by the armature. Therefore, if F is the useful flux passing through the armature, the field inductor has to convey only the flux $F(1/k)$, where k is the coefficient of flux leakage, say about 1.1. In a dynamo of the pliodyne, the field inductor creates the magnetizing ampere-turns and therefore it must be dimensioned to convey the flux kF. This results in a cross section of the iron of the field inductor of a metadyne k^2 smaller than in a dynamo for the same useful flux.

4. In a dynamo the armature reaction is an inescapable inconvenience, and, in order to minimize its action, a large air gap is used; in a metadyne the armature reaction is a fundamental factor of the operation, and the air-gap depth is reduced as much as possible, say to one-third or to one-fifth of the depth of the air gap of the corresponding dynamo. Therefore, the magnetizing ampere-turns are much smaller for a metadyne than for a corresponding dynamo, and, if the magnetizing ampere-turns must be created by the field winding, the copper of the field winding is smaller for a metadyne than for a corresponding dynamo. The comparison is even more favorable for the metadyne when its stator windings must demagnetize the magnetic circuit in opposing action with respect to the armature.

5. The end connections of the metadyne armature react upon one another exactly as in the part of the conductors embedded in the slots

of the laminations. Therefore, in a metadyne the useful flux is the sum of the flux passing through the laminations and of that surrounding the end connections, whereas in a dynamo the latter flux is inoperative.

6. The local armature reaction on the polar segments, saturating one pole tip and unsaturating the other, results in an overall reduction of the flux. This action is larger in a dynamo where the polar segments cover a large arc of the diametrical pitch of the armature, and it is smaller in a metadyne where the polar segment generally covers half of the above-mentioned arc.

On the other hand, there are other features not in favor of the metadyne:

7. The number of slots per cycle in a metadyne is larger than in a corresponding dynamo, thus reducing the good utilization of the area of the slot. However, one may point out as a compensation that the large number of slots causes easier dissipation of the heat and better commutation.

8. The pliodyne, unlike the metadyne, lends itself to construction in the shape of a long cylinder. This shape may facilitate certain applications where space is scarce.

So far dynamic operation has not been considered, which is more satisfactory with a metadyne because of two reasons:

1. The magnetizing ampere-turns are due, generally, to the armature ampere-turns, and therefore their action is quicker.

2. The flux created by the armature end connections passes only through air. Therefore, it is not damped at all, and its action during the transient current variations is quicker than the flux action when enclosed in iron.

The conclusion is that, generally, a metadyne is lighter and has smaller overall size than the best equivalent pliodyne. It follows that the efficiency is higher, since the losses are roughly proportional to the weight.

3. A CASE OF PRACTICAL APPLICATION OF A PLIODYNE

In accordance with the reservation made in the final statement of the previous section, there are rare cases in which a pliodyne is used instead of the equivalent metadyne. One of these cases is considered here.

The scheme of Fig. 313 corresponds to a special motor metadyne. The motor metadyne, 1, has four equidistant brushes, a, b, c, and d, brushes a and c being connected to the terminals P and Q of a series network supplying constant current, and brushes b and d being connected to a dynamo, 2. Current I_b, due to the difference of the electromotive forces, E_{bd}, induced between brushes b and d, and V, induced by the auxiliary dynamo, 2, flows through a secondary amplifying winding, 5. Further, special motor metadyne 1 is provided with a primary variator winding, 7, excited by a current I_α, the intensity of which may

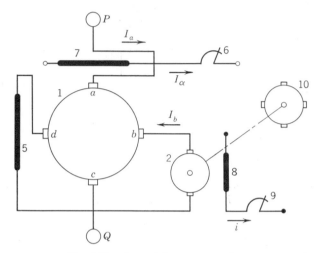

Fig. 313.   A special motor metadyne.

be set by a resistor, 6. Finally, auxiliary dynamo 2 is driven by a motor, 10, preferably at constant speed, and it is excited by a field winding, 8, excited by a current, i, controlled by resistor 9.

The following equations hold:

$$\frac{1}{n} E_{ca} = (K + K_{ca}^\beta) I_b$$
$$\frac{1}{n} E_{bd} = K I_a + K_{bd}^\alpha I_\alpha \tag{236}$$

where $K_{ca}^\beta > 0$. Further, there is

$$E_{bd} = V + R_b I_b = ki + R_b I_b \tag{237}$$

where R_b is the resistance of the circuit carrying I_b, and where k is a constant.

The torque T may be expressed as follows, if the losses are neglected:

$$2\pi T = K_{ca}^\beta I_b I_a - K_{bd}^\alpha I_\alpha I_b \tag{238}$$

Eliminating I_b and E_{bd} between these equations yields

$$2\pi T = (K_{ca}^{\beta} I_a - K_{bd}^{\alpha} I_\alpha)\frac{1}{R_b}[(K I_a + K_{bd}^{\alpha} I_\alpha)n - ki] \equiv A(Bn - C) \quad (239)$$

where A, B, and C are constants determined by the parameters I_α and i.
Equation 239 shows that around the speed n_0,

$$n_0 = \frac{C}{B} = \frac{ki}{K I_a + K_{bd}^{\alpha} I_\alpha} \quad (240)$$

the motor metadyne is very stable, for it is able to develop a torque
positive when $n < n_0$ and negative when $n > n_0$, of any magnitude
within the capacity of the machine. This speed, n_0, is called the no-
load speed.

The derivative of torque T with respect to speed n is

$$2\pi\frac{dT}{dn} = AB = (K_{ca}^{\beta} I_a - K_{bd}^{\alpha} I_\alpha)(K I_a + K_{bd}^{\alpha} I_\alpha)\frac{1}{R_b} \quad (241)$$

It is controlled by the arbitary current I_α, whereas the value of n_0 is
controlled mainly by the arbitrary current i.

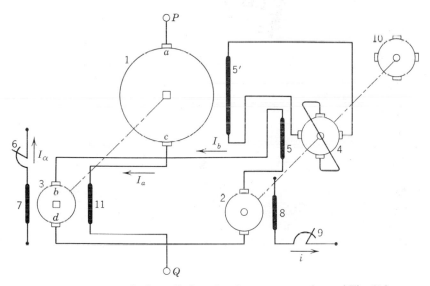

Fig. 314. An equivalent pliodyne for the motor metadyne of Fig. 313.

Figure 314 gives the scheme of an equivalent pliodyne, the corresponding elements being indicated by the same numerals. The amplifier metadyne, 4, is now interposed between winding 5 and winding 5'.

Let a be the amplification factor of the amplifier metadyne, 4, and let b and c be two constant coefficients. Then

$$\left. \begin{array}{c} \dfrac{1}{n} E_{ca} = aI_b \\[2mm] \dfrac{1}{n} E_{bd} = bI_a + cI_\alpha \\[2mm] E_{bd} = V + R_b I_b = ki + R_b I_b \end{array} \right\} \qquad (242)$$

$$2\pi T = aI_b I_a - (bI_a + cI_\alpha)I_b$$

$$= \frac{1}{R_b}[(a - b)I_a - cI_\alpha][(bI_a + cI_\alpha)n - ki] \qquad (243)$$

These are the same equations as for the motor metadyne. Constant a is positive and very large compared with constant b.

Since current I_b is very small compared with I_a, dynamo 1 is practically as large as the motor metadyne and dynamo 3 is a relatively small

Fig. 315. The pliodyne of Fig. 314 comprises these machine groups. (*Courtesy of the San Giorgio Co., Genoa.*)

machine. Thus the pliodyne and the equivalent motor metadyne differ very little as far as size and weight are concerned, but this difference is in favor of the metadyne and confirms the conclusion of the preceding section. Amplifier metadyne 4 is not considered in this comparison because it could be added as well to the scheme of Fig. 313. Dynamo 3 operates independently of the saturation of dynamo 1, permitting a

Fig. 316. The constant-current set for the motor pliodyne. (*Courtesy of the San Giorgio Co., Genoa.*)

more accurate control of the no-load speed, n_0, for wider limits of speed variation and for higher values of the derivative dT/dn.

The photograph of Fig. 315 shows such a pliodyne, the two horizontal machines forming a set of twin motors and the vertical machine comprising the auxiliary dynamo, the amplifier metadyne, and their driving motor.

Figure 316 shows a group of machines comprising a 240-volt dynamo driving an S generator metadyne, which feeds the main circuit of the pliodyne.

The construction of the auxiliary dynamo is a special one, represented schematically by Fig. 317. The set of brushes of the arma-

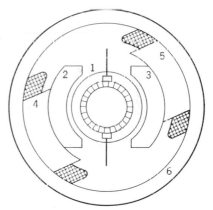

Fig. 317. Form of the auxiliary dynamo for the motor pliodyne.

ture, 1, and the pole shoes, 2 and 3, are fixed with respect to one another and rotatable with respect to the magnetic yoke, 6, and the pole bodies, 4 and 5, interlinked with the field winding.

The voltage, V, is then a function of the angular displacement between elements 2, 3 and elements 4, 5, 6, and it may vary from its maximum positive value to its maximum negative value with continuity. The twin motors represented in the photograph show great stability of operation over a range of no-load speed values varying from one to eighty.

4. CONSIDERATIONS ON THE WEIGHT, SIZE, AND EFFICIENCY OF A METADYNE

In the early days of the applications of electricity, the efficiency of the machines used was rapidly improving and their weight and size were decreasing, and these improvements drew general attention. So it became traditional to judge the quality of a machine from these points of view.

Now the construction of electric machines dealing with generation and utilization of high power is greatly improved, and every detail is accurately finished. The efficiency has reached values very close to unity for all kinds of electric machines; weight and size are also reduced to low values. Only minor improvements can be expected unless the magnetic material, the conductive material, the insulating material, and the cooling medium show some basic changes. Such changes, however, will affect all machines equally and leave them practically at the same mutual position as far as efficiency, weight, and size are concerned.

When a large generator must operate 24 hours per day over a period of years at a load not very different from full-load, even a fraction of 1% of its efficiency is important. But when the operation of a plant is periodic, or quasi-periodic, with frequent modifications of the speed, of the power, and of the accelerating or braking rate—modifications often controlled through rheostats—then a slight difference in the efficiency of each machine, considered separately, loses its importance compared with the overall efficiency of the cycle of operation.

When the purpose of the operation is the performance of given movements in a given sequence in the shortest time possible, maintaining the proper rate of acceleration or deceleration of the entire system is by far more important than the efficiency of the single machines. When precision, flexibility, and safety are of capital importance, slight differences in the efficiency of the separate electric machines do not matter practically, compared with the working characteristics of these machines, which must be especially suitable for the particular purpose considered. The merit of the system is then measured rather by the number of seconds in which the operation is performed, or by the maximum angular error that the system allows, or by the time lag between a pilot movement and the movement of the final, heavy tools. Thus, for judging a system, the efficiency of a single machine is just one of the many factors to be considered, the importance of which may be large, small, or negligible, depending on the nature of the particular application.

In comparing the efficiency of two systems, operations as identical as possible are required. Thus, in comparing a metadyne with a set of dynamos, the equivalent pliodyne must be considered. In this case, the conclusion of the second section of this chapter holds; and this conclusion is more favorable to the metadyne the more complex is the operation considered, as, for instance, the operation of a transformer metadyne.

Departing from this rule, let us compare the simplest generator metadyne, an S generator metadyne, with a dynamo generator, although the operation is different, the S generator metadyne being supposed to supply constant current and the dynamo generator constant voltage. In this case, the basic advantage of the metadyne disappears, i.e., the advantage of being a single main unit operating as many main dynamos working together toward the same result.

First consider a small unit of, say, 20 kilowatts, at 2200 revolutions per minute. The dynamo generator is shunt-excited, and the S generator metadyne is provided with: a primary variator winding shunt-excited across the secondary brushes, a primary stabilizing winding, and a secondary variator winding. No auxiliary apparatus is used. The useful segment of the dynamo generator may be represented by the straight segment de of diagram I of Fig. 318, voltage being taken as the abscissa and current as the ordinate.

Let the dynamo and the metadyne have the same magnetic circuit. The characteristic of the secondary current as a function of the secondary voltage may be represented by the curve abc. The maximum voltage oc obtained takes into account the voltage due to the flux of the end connections and the fact that the dynamo, always working around the same point of the magnetic curve of the machine, must operate at a magnetic induction in the iron lower than the maximum magnetic induction attained by the S generator metadyne.

The maximum output of the dynamo and of the metadyne are represented by the product of the coordinates of the points e and b, respectively. Thus, the maximum output of the metadyne is a few per cent lower.

Now consider a medium unit of, say, 200 kilowatts, at 1600 revolutions per minute. The dynamo generator has its exciter, and the S generator has its auxiliary amplifier metadynes. Then the respective characteristics may be represented by diagram II of Fig. 318, the maximum output being slightly higher for the metadyne. The stator of the metadyne is now lighter than the stator of the dynamo. This also causes a slight increase in the efficiency.

Finally, consider a large unit of, say, 2000 kilowatts, at 800 revolutions per minute. The characteristics are still represented by diagram II, showing a small advantage for the metadyne; but, for large meta-

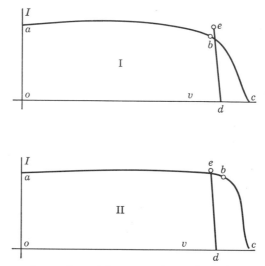

Fig. 318.   Comparison of dynamo and metadyne characteristics.

dynes, a fundamental factor in its favor is added to the factors listed in Section 2 of this chapter. With the aid of dynamic analysis, it can be shown that for large reactive metadynes the commutation becomes easier than for the corresponding dynamos; under the same conditions of operation, a reactive metadyne may satisfactorily commutate 10% to 25% more current.

As commutation is the limiting feature for the length of the laminated core, this property of the metadyne may be used by leaving the armature diameter untouched and by increasing the length of the core 10% to 25%. This will result in a characteristic having the same ordinates but with the abscissas extended 10% to 25%; the maximum output becomes proportionally higher, and the efficiency is slightly improved.

The case considered above is one of the most unfavorable to the metadyne. Now compare the simplest motor metadyne, the Alpha motor metadyne, with a shunt- or with a series-excited dynamo motor. Again the rule for a fair comparison is violated because the operation of the motors being compared is different.

For a small output, the weight, the sizes, and the efficiency are practically the same. For a medium output, an advantage is found for the motor metadyne because of smaller copper weight on the stator. For a large output, a larger advantage is obtained for the motor metadyne, because the stator is lighter and commutation easier for the same reasons as for the generator metadyne.

Near the rotating machine itself, the switchgear for its control and its starting must be considered, resulting in a further advantage for the motor metadyne. Thus even with consideration of cases most unfavorable to the metadyne, the weight and size of the metadyne are larger only for a small output and become smaller for a large output.

It is understood that for some very simple operations, such as operation at roughly constant speed, the employment of the metadyne is out of the question. The metadyne must be taken into consideration when the operation has special requirements and then compared with a dynamo set somehow having similar operation. If the equivalent pliodyne is avoided in order to simplify the dynamo set, the advantage of the metadyne becomes conspicuous immediately when the dynamo set comprises two or more main dynamos. Further comparison, based on dynamic analysis, can be made for whole systems of metadynes and dynamos, not limited just to single machines.

There are a large number of United States and foreign patents covering the metadynes described in this volume. Since many of the metadyne patents concern dynamic behavior, a list of the patent numbers has not been presented here.

GLOSSARY OF NOMENCLATURE

Since a metadyne is by definition a multiterminal device, both description and analysis demand close attention to an intricate notation. Although a conceptual understanding of the theory is to be preferred to a deftness at formally manipulating symbols, this glossary has been assembled to present important nomenclature concisely as an aid in acquiring the desired understanding.

In general, the nomenclature can be divided into three classes.

1. Names for important metadynes.
2. Symbols for enumeration.
3. Descriptive symbols.

Class 1 embraces designations such as K generator, Beta motor, Cross transformer. The form of these designations has been chosen to identify the type of metadyne.

Transformer	Descriptive name, as Clover
Motor	Orthographic form of Greek letter, as Theta
Generator	Capital roman letter, as S

Class 2 contains numeric and alphabetic sequences needed to identify individual elements within groups. Numeric sequences are obvious; the alphabetic sequences carry with them some additional information.

Letters standing alone	
Lower case roman	Brushes, as brush c
Capital roman	Stator parts associated with a brush, as commutating pole C
Indices	
Lower case roman	General alphabetic sequence, distinguishes armature quantities
Capital roman	Generally designates terminal quantities
Lower case Greek	Distinguishes stator quantities
Double subscripts	
Current	First subscript denotes brush at which current enters armature.
Voltage	Second subscript denotes positive terminal.

407

Class 3 comprises the usual algebraic and electric symbols as well as those that appear in the following list. Some standard symbols have been listed when the same notations were employed in another sense. Page references have been chosen to provide typical context.

Symbol and Description		*Appears on page*
a	Air gap depth under a commutating pole	110
A	Ampere-turns on a commutating pole	152
B	Flux density	97
$\bar{B}$	Vector magnetic induction	152
C	Compensating winding	190
C	Contactor	134
C	Copper losses	167
e	Always a sequence symbol	
e	General instantaneous voltage	3
$\mathbf{e}$	Speed-moderator equations	62
E	Direct voltage	9
ε	Kinetic energy	61
F	Field winding	137
H	Hypercompensating winding	202
H	Magnetic field intensity	152
i	Instantaneous current	51
I	Direct current	6
I_ρ	Regulator current	46
J	Moment of inertia	56
K	Voltage constant	17
L	Self-inductance	46
L	Relay	141
m	Degree of a metadyne	119
M	Consumer	181
M	Mutual inductance	91
n	Speed of a metadyne	17
N	Number of armature conductors	3
p	Electric potential	26
P	Electric power	23
P	Potentiometer	137
r	Resistance of an armature-winding segment	10
R	Armature resistance between diametrical points	153
R	Resistor	134
s	Speed of connected apparatus	61
S	Locomotive speed	136
S	Series amplifying winding	180
t	Instantaneous time	47
T	Torque	27
T_c	Time for commutation	89
v	Characteristic voltage	117
V	Terminal voltage	180
w	As a subscript, load component	188
W	Geometric variety or manifold	32

INDEX